W9-BGL-482

WITHDRAWN

Fundamentals
of Vacuum Science
and Technology

Gerhard Lewin, Ph.D.
Plasma Physics Laboratory
Princeton University

McGraw-Hill Book Company
New York   St. Louis   San Francisco   Toronto   London   Sydney

To my wife

Preface

High vacuum is required in many scientific studies such as mass-spectroscopic analyses, preparation of solid-state devices by evaporation of thin films, the investigation of gas discharges, and electron physics. In all these cases, high-vacuum technique is a tool used by the experimenter to provide the proper environment. The purpose of this book is to aid the research worker who is not a vacuum expert and is faced with the need for this tool. It discusses the basic phenomena occurring in vacuum, so that he can appraise whether and how they will affect his investigation. It will help him to decide what experimental setup he should use and to select the right equipment among the many types commercially available. It should also guide him in the design of special equipment, if the need arises.

To give some illustrations, it must be decided whether the vacuum system must be baked; this greatly influences the type of hardware selected. This decision, based on an analysis, must be made before a system is assembled, in order to avoid later delays by its failure to meet the necessary requirements. Vacuum gages have a limited range and may give false readings if not properly used. There are many different types of pumps available, and it is difficult for the novice to decide what kind of pump, or combination of pumps, is most suitable.

To limit the size of the book, references are given to more detailed treatments and general textbooks. Preferably, recent publications which in turn mention previous work are listed. Although this book is primarily intended to serve those who have a general background in physics or engineering but are not familiar with vacuum technique, it is hoped that it may also be helpful to workers in the field in special cases.

The first four chapters give the theoretical background of vacuum technique. Chapter 1 discusses the kinetic theory of gases to the extent that it applies to this subject. To limit the scope, the pertinent equations are given without detailed derivation. One special application of the theory important in vacuum technique is the flow of gases through orifices and tubes treated in Chap. 2. After some pumping all the gas comes from the wall of the container and the other surfaces inside the vacuum. Hence, the interaction of gases with surfaces and release of gas from a surface are important phenomena; these are dealt with in Chap. 3. The next chapter gives the theory of the pumping process without reference to any specific pumping system. Chapter 5 deals with vacuum measurements. There exist two types of diagnostics to determine the behavior of a vacuum system: total-pressure gages and partial-pressure gages or mass spectrometers. The most important gages, their advantages, and their limitations are discussed. One special application of the mass spectrometer is leak detection. Other important vacuum measurements are determination of pumping speed and conductances, and gage calibrations. Chapters 6 and 7 deal with the various hardware, such as pumps, valves, and detachable joints. It is most important not just to enumerate all reported items but to appraise their merits and reliability. This is difficult to do for the more recent equipment. Therefore, the author has emphasized the experience accumulated at the Plasma Physics Laboratory of Princeton University (abbreviated PPL in the text). Chapters 8 and 9 discuss materials for and the joining and preparation of components. The last chapter outlines how to approach the design of a vacuum system and gives some examples.

The author wants to thank F. Blau, D. Mullaney, and S. Steinitz for reading part of the manuscript and making valuable comments. He is especially indebted to P. A. Redhead and H. A. Steinherz who critically read the whole manuscript and suggested many improvements. He also thanks Mrs. A. Antony and Mrs. B. Rye for their patient and efficient secretarial work.

Gerhard Lewin

Contents

Symbols

A area

A_m Avogadro's number (number of molecules in mole)

B magnetic induction

C conductance for gases
C_k conductance for transitional flow
C_m conductance for molecular flow
C_v conductance for viscous flow
c conductivity (conductance of tube of unit length); concentration of gas in solid
c_p specific heat at constant pressure
c_v specific heat at constant volume

D tube diameter; diffusion coefficient; energy of dissociation
d thickness of a slab

E energy; Young's modulus; electric field intensity
E_A activation energy of chemisorption
E_D energy of desorption
E_m activation energy for surface migration
E_P energy of physical adsorption
e electron charge

H_A heat of nonactivated adsorption
H_B heat of evaporation
H_C heat of chemisorption

i electric current

K permeation constant
k Boltzmann constant

L length of tube

M molecular mass of molecule; $M = mA_m$
m mass of molecule (gram); slope of curve

N total number of molecules
N_0 number of molecules in a monolayer on unit area (1 cm^2)
n number of molecules in unit volume

n_A number of molecules adsorbed at unit area (1 cm^2)

n_M number of moles

P pressure

P_0 initial pressure

P_u ultimate pressure

P_v vapor pressure

Q flow rate (torr liters/sec)

Q_L gassing rate of leaks

Q_P gassing rate of pumping system

Q_T total flow (torr liters)

Q_W gassing rate of wall

q specific gassing rate of wall (torr liters/sec cm^2)

R gas constant

r pressure ratio

S pumping speed

s solubility of gas in solid; gage sensitivity; sticking coefficient

T temperature

T_S temperature of surface

T_v temperature of cryogenic surface

t time; wall thickness

t_s sojourn time

V volume; volt

v volume of tube of unit length; velocity

v_a arithmetic average velocity

v_{rms} root-mean-square velocity

W rate of evaporation

α thermal accommodation coefficient

γ ratio of specific heats c_p/c_v

δ gas kinetic diameter of molecule; differential expansion of glass between freezing and room temperature

η coefficient of viscosity

Θ fraction of surface covered with monolayer

κ thermal conductivity

λ mean free path

ν number of molecules incident on unit area (1 cm^2) in 1 sec

τ e folding time

τ_0 period of oscillation of a molecule normal to the surface

Introduction

High-vacuum technique was limited to the laboratories of a few scientists until the beginning of the twentieth century. The modern age of vacuum technique began only when efficient high-vacuum pumps—in particular, the diffusion pump—were invented. In this regard, most credit is due to Gaede, who is really the foremost inventor of modern vacuum equipment. This technological progress made possible the large-scale manufacture of incandescent lamps and electron tubes. Other applications, such as vacuum metallurgy and freeze drying, followed. More recently, large vacuum installations also became important for scientific investigations, in conjunction with the development of particle accelerators, the design of thermonuclear machines, and the construction of environmental test chambers for the testing of satellites. Also, the requirement for the degree of vacuum increased in connection with the study and preparation of surfaces, especially for solid-state devices where contamination by gas adsorption must be minimized.

To convey a feeling for vacuum conditions, Table I lists some gas kinetic data for nitrogen. Column 1 gives typical pressures for the different vacuum regions. These pressures are expressed in torr, now the most commonly used unit. One torr is equal to the pressure of a mercury column of 1 mm height. (It is to be regretted that this unit has been generally accepted since a unit such as dynes per square centimeter would certainly be more feasible from a physicist's viewpoint.) High vacuum is generally considered to be the pressure range from 10^{-3} to 10^{-8} torr. At pressures below the high-vacuum region the vacuum is called ultrahigh-vacuum. Pressures of 10^{-13} torr and lower have been reached.

Column 2 gives the number of molecules in the unit volume (cm^3). Column 3 shows the mean free path of a nitrogen molecule between collisions. This path is very large at low pressures since the cross section of a molecule is small (approximately 10^{-15} cm^2). At 10^{-13} torr, the mean free path equals about the distance between the

1

Table I   Gas Kinetic Data for Nitrogen at Room Temperature

	1	2	3	4	5
	Pressure, torr	Molecules in cubic centimeter	Mean free path, cm	Molecules incident on a square centimeter per second	Time to form monolayer, sec
Atmospheric pressure	760	2.5×10^{19}	6.3×10^{-6}	2.9×10^{23}	2.6×10^{-9}
Vacuum	1	3.3×10^{16}	4.8×10^{-3}	3.9×10^{20}	2×10^{-6}
High vacuum	10^{-6}	3.3×10^{10}	4800	3.9×10^{14}	2
Ultrahigh vacuum	10^{-10}	3.3×10^{6}	4.8×10^{7}	3.9×10^{10}	2×10^{4}

earth and the moon.   Column 4 gives the number of nitrogen molecules incident on each square centimeter of wall area per second.

Finally, column 5 shows the time required to form a monomolecular layer of nitrogen if it is assumed that all incident molecules stick.   In ultrahigh vacuum only, this time can be long compared with the average time spent in conducting an experiment.   This is the reason that ultrahigh vacuum is required whenever clean surfaces are needed.   But even in ultrahigh vacuum, a surface is often covered with gas unless the gas is removed by a cleaning process.   At low pressures, the amount of gas adsorbed on the wall is large compared with the gas contained in the volume.   If a monomolecular layer were suddenly released from the wall of a tube of 1-cm diameter, the pressure would rise 10^{-1} torr; in a sphere of 1-liter volume the pressure would increase 10^{-2} torr.

Pertinent Equations of the Kinetic Theory of Gases

1

The kinetic theory of gases describes the behavior of gases in a volume. Its basic assumption is that the molecules of which the gas consists are in constant random motion, colliding elastically with each other and the container wall. We shall limit the discussion to those aspects of the theory that are of importance in vacuum work. The texts (1) to (4)† treat this theory in detail.

1-1 Equation of State

The three main parameters characterizing the condition of a gas are the pressure P, the volume V, and the temperature T. Among them exists the well-known relation called the equation of state, namely,

$$PV = NkT \qquad (1\text{-}1)$$

where N is the total number of molecules. It is the same for all gases for fixed values of P, V, and T. The symbol k is the Boltzmann constant. Its value is usually given as 1.38×10^{-16} erg/°K. For the purpose of vacuum calculations, this is better expressed

† Numbers in parentheses in the text refer to the numbered list of references at the end of the chapter.

3

as $k = 1.03 \times 10^{-22}$ torr liter/°K. It follows from Eq. (1-1) that the number of molecules in a liter at 1 torr and 293°K is

$$N = \frac{PV}{kT} = \frac{1}{1.03 \times 10^{-22} \times 293} = 3.3 \times 10^{19}$$

Equation (1-1) can also be written

$$P = nkT \tag{1-2a}$$

where n is the number of molecules in unit volume or molecular density, and

$$PV = n_M RT \tag{1-2b}$$

where n_M is the number of moles and R is the so-called gas constant

$$R = kA_m \tag{1-3}$$

Here A_m is the number of molecules per mole or Avogadro's number; $A_m = 6.023 \times 10^{23}$ and $R = 62$ torr liters/°K mole $= 2$ g cal/°K mole. At 760 torr and 0°C, 1 mole of any gas occupies a volume of 22.4 liters.

Equation (1-1) applies strictly to an ideal gas only. This is a gas in which the molecules repulse each other like elastic bodies. In vacuum, all real gases behave like ideal gases as long as the gas does not approach the condition of a saturated vapor, i.e., as long as the pressure is somewhat lower than the pressure of the vapor in equilibrium with the solid or liquid phase at the operating temperature.

PV is the translational kinetic energy of the gas. This energy is a function of the temperature only. k or R is the proportionality constant. The energy of gas at 293°K is 0.6 kcal/mole [see Eq. (1-2b)] or 0.026 eV, since 1 eV = 23 kcal/mole. If a molecule consists of more than one atom, the molecule also possesses other temperature-dependent energy such as rotational energy. This increases the specific heat but does not concern us here.

1-2   Energy and Velocity of the Molecules

The continual collisions of molecules result in a specific velocity distribution first calculated by J. C. Maxwell. This distribution is a function of the mass of the molecules and the temperature only. The pressure P is produced by the impulse of the molecules hitting the wall. It can easily be shown that

$$P = \tfrac{1}{3} n m v_{rms}^2 \tag{1-4}$$

where m is the mass of a molecule and v_{rms} is the root-mean-square velocity. It follows that the translatory kinetic energy of a molecule is

$$\frac{m}{2} v_{rms}^2 = \frac{3}{2} kT \qquad (1\text{-}4a)$$

and

$$v_{rms} = \left(\frac{3kT}{m}\right)^{\frac{1}{2}} = 15{,}800 \left(\frac{T}{M}\right)^{\frac{1}{2}} \qquad \text{cm/sec} \qquad (1\text{-}5)$$

where M is the molecular mass, $M = mA_m$. The arithmetic average velocity is

$$v_a = \left(\frac{8kT}{\pi m}\right)^{\frac{1}{2}} = 14{,}551 \left(\frac{T}{M}\right)^{\frac{1}{2}} \qquad \text{cm/sec} \qquad (1\text{-}6)$$

1-3   Molecules Incident on a Surface

For many calculations, it is necessary to know ν, the number of molecules incident on the unit area per second.

$$\nu = \frac{1}{4} n v_a = \frac{n}{4}\left(\frac{8kT}{\pi m}\right)^{\frac{1}{2}} = P(2\pi mkT)^{-\frac{1}{2}}$$

$$\nu = \frac{14{,}551}{4} n \left(\frac{T}{M}\right)^{\frac{1}{2}} = 3.5 \times 10^{22} P_{torr}(M T_{\circ K})^{-\frac{1}{2}} \qquad \text{cm}^{-2}\text{sec}^{-1}$$
$$(1\text{-}7)$$

from Eqs. (1-2a) and (1-6).

1-4   Mean Free Path

Another important parameter is λ, the mean free path of a molecule between collisions. Two limiting cases must be distinguished. If the pressure is low and collisions between the molecules and the wall predominate, there is so-called molecular flow. If most collisions are between molecules, there is viscous flow. The laws for heat transfer and flow through pipes are very different in the two cases. If λ is known, one can decide what condition applies.

$$\lambda = \frac{1}{\pi n \delta^2 \sqrt{2}} \qquad (1\text{-}8)$$

or, from (1-2a),

$$\lambda = \frac{kT}{\pi P \delta^2 \sqrt{2}} \qquad (1\text{-}9)$$

where δ is the gas kinetic diameter of the molecule.   This is the diameter defined by Eqs. (1-8) and (1-9), which are based on the assumption that the molecules are smooth, rigid, elastic spheres.   Its value can be found experimentally from measurements of the viscosity or heat conductivity; see Eqs. (1-10) and (1-11) below.

1-5   Viscosity

The viscosity of a gas affects the flow in the viscous flow range. If two adjacent gas layers move with different velocities, molecules that cross the boundary between the layers have different momenta. The ensuing momentum transfer causes the gas to exhibit viscosity. The coefficient of viscosity is defined as the tangential force exerted per unit area at unit velocity gradient.   Its value is

$$\eta = 0.5\lambda \, nmv_a \tag{1-10}$$

The cgs unit is 1 poise.   One poise = 1 dyne sec/cm².   The viscosities of some gases are listed in Table 2-1.

1-6   Heat Transfer

Heat can propagate through a gas in several ways.   At high pressure and low temperature, the density is high and the viscosity low, and macroscopic upward flow of the gas occurs if a temperature gradient exists in the direction of the force of gravity.   Under these conditions, heat is carried away by convection, because of the difference in density.

When the density is reduced and/or when the temperature and therefore η is increased, heat conduction takes place.   Heat conduction is the transfer of kinetic energy from one molecule to another by collisions on a microscopic scale.   The thermal conductivity κ is proportional to η and c_v, the specific heat of the gas at constant volume. The theory predicts, in good agreement with experiment, that

$$\kappa = 2.5\eta c_v \tag{1-11}$$

for monatomic gases.   For polyatomic molecules the proportionality constant is less than 2.5, because of the rotational and vibrational energy. κ is the heat flux per second across an area of unit cross section, for unit temperature gradient.   It is usually expressed in watts per square centimeter for a temperature gradient of 1°C per centi-

meter.   Hence its dimension is W/cm °C.   It is interesting to note
that the viscosity and heat conductivity are independent of pressure
in the viscous flow range as long as the density is not excessively high
and attractive forces between molecules do not come into play, i.e.,
as long as the gas behaves as an ideal gas.   The η and κ are functions
only of temperature; this follows from Eqs. (1-6) and (1-8).   These
predictions were early triumphs of the kinetic theory of gases.

At still lower pressures the molecules collide predominantly
with the wall.   This is the region of molecular heat conduction.   If a
wall of temperature T_w is hit by molecules of temperature T_i ($T_w > T_i$),
the cooling rate is proportional to the number of incident molecules per
second and the temperature difference $T_w - T_i$.   But molecules may
leave the wall without having attained temperature equilibrium.
Hence it is important to know to what extent a molecule hitting a wall
of different temperature transfers its energy to the wall, or vice versa.
In the ideal case, the molecule will not be specularly reflected but will
remain at the wall for some time.   Upon its leaving, all directions have
equal probability, and the energy of the molecule will correspond to
the temperature of the wall.

When studying the gas flow through pipes, it was found that it
can usually be assumed with good approximation that, at least at
temperature equilibrium, the reflection of common surfaces is diffuse.
But the heat transfer is not always perfect.   Hence, the accommodation coefficient α has been introduced by Knudsen to give the efficiency
of heat transfer in a single wall collision.   If T is the temperature of
the leaving molecules,

$$\alpha = \frac{T - T_i}{T_w - T_i} \tag{1-12}$$

Here the assumption is made that the velocity distribution of the
reflected molecules remains maxwellian.   Therefore, it follows from
Eqs. (1-4a) and (1-7) that the cooling rate is

$$W = \frac{3}{2} vk\alpha(T_w - T_i) = \frac{\alpha b P(T_w - T_i)}{(T_i M)^{\frac{1}{2}}} \tag{1-13}$$

where b is a constant.   Its value depends on the choice of units.
Hence W is proportional to the pressure, a fact utilized in pressure
gages based on molecular heat conduction.

The coefficient α is strongly dependent on the surface condition,
as was demonstrated by Roberts (5).   He investigated the adsorption
of hydrogen on tungsten by observing the change in α for neon.

Therefore, measurements should be conducted in ultrahigh vacuum and with very pure gases. Among the smallest values reported is 0.017 for He on clean tungsten (6). A value of 0.9 was found by Thomas and Brown (7) for Kr on Pt. In general, "dirty" surfaces have larger coefficients. The literature has recently been reviewed by Wachman (8) and Hartnett (9).

Finally, not enough gas remains to transfer appreciable heat. Heat can be transferred only by radiation. The total radiated power of a surface of unit area is given by Stefan-Boltzmann's law,

$$W = \sigma \varepsilon T^4 \tag{1-14}$$

where σ is the Stefan-Boltzmann constant and ε the ratio of the emissivity of the surface to the emissivity of the black body ($0 \le \varepsilon \le 1$). $\sigma = 5.67 \times 10^{-12}\,\text{W/cm}^2\,{}^\circ\text{K}^4$. At high temperatures, heat transfer by radiation predominates even at higher pressures, on account of the fourth power dependence on temperature.

1-7 Thermal Transpiration

If the molecules collide only with the wall and the wall temperature is not uniform, a pressure gradient will exist in the gas. This is called thermal transpiration. Let us assume that two chambers are maintained at different temperatures and are connected by a tube. If the pressure is low enough, there is molecular flow in the tube, and thermal transpiration takes place. Equilibrium requires that the same number of molecules flow through the connecting tube in either direction. Therefore, by Eq. (1-7),

$$\frac{P_2}{P_1} = \left(\frac{T_2}{T_1}\right)^{\frac{1}{2}} \tag{1-15}$$

The pressures are proportional to the square root of the temperatures.

Unless all parts are at room temperature, it is often more meaningful to consider the gas densities rather than the pressures. To mention an extreme case, in thermonuclear reactions the pressure is of the order of atmospheric pressure, while the density is about 10^{14} atoms/cm^3, corresponding to a pressure of 3×10^{-3} torr at room temperature. This constitutes a "high-pressure vacuum." Also, most gages indicate the gas density and not the pressure. For thermal transpiration, it follows that

$$\frac{n_2}{n_1} = \left(\frac{T_1}{T_2}\right)^{\frac{1}{2}} \tag{1-16}$$

Thermal transpiration must be taken into consideration when the gas density is measured in a volume whose temperature differs from the gage temperature; e.g., in a vacuum furnace with a gage at room temperature the pressure in the furnace is higher and the density lower than in the gage.

If two chambers of different temperatures are connected by a

Table 1-1   Values of Gas Kinetic Constants for Some Common Gases

Gas	Mass of a molecule, $g \times 10^{24}$	Diameter of a molecule, $cm \times 10^8$	Mean free path at 1 torr and 0°C, $cm \times 10^3$	Arithmetic average velocity at 15°C, $cm/sec \times 10^5$	Heat conductivity at 0°C, W/cm °K $\times 10^3$
H_2	3.35	2.7	8.8	1.74	1.74
He	6.64	2.2	13	1.23	1.43
H_2O	29.9	4.6	3.0	0.582	0.229*
N_2	46.5	3.7	4.5	0.467	0.237
O_2	53.1	3.6	4.8	0.437	0.237
A	66.2	3.6	4.7	0.391	0.163
CO	46.5	3.8	4.5	0.467	0.221
CO_2	73.0	4.6	3.0	0.372	0.142
Hg	334	5.1	2.2	0.174	0.050

* At 100°C.

Table 1-2   Some Constants for Vacuum Calculations

Boltzmann constant k: 1.38×10^{-16} erg/°K
1.03×10^{-22} torr liter/°K

Gas constant R: 62 torr liters/°K mole
2 g cal/°K mole

Molecules in liter at 1 torr, 293°K: 3.3×10^{19}

Molecules in mole (Avogadro's number): 6.023×10^{23}

Volume of mole at 760 torr, 273°K: 22.4 liters

Energy of gas at 293°K: 0.6 kcal/mole
0.026 eV

1 eV = 23 kcal/mole

Monomolecular layer: approximately 5×10^{14} molecules/cm²
1.5×10^{-5} torr liter/cm² at 293°K

tube of such large diameter and/or the pressure is so high that the flow is viscous, the pressure in both chambers must be the same in equilibrium. It follows from Eq. (1-2a) that the densities will be inversely proportional to the temperature.

Thermal transpiration in the transition range was investigated by Liang (10).

REFERENCES

(1) L. B. Loeb, "Kinetic Theory of Gases," 2d ed., McGraw-Hill Book Company, New York, 1934.

(2) E. H. Kennard, "Kinetic Theory of Gases," McGraw-Hill Book Company, New York, 1938.

(3) J. H. Jeans, "Introduction to the Kinetic Theory of Gases," Cambridge University Press, London, 1960.

(4) S. Dushman and J. M. Lafferty, "Scientific Foundation of Vacuum Technique," 2d ed., chap. 1, John Wiley & Sons, Inc., New York, 1962.

(5) J. K. Roberts, *Proc. Roy. Soc. (London)*, *Ser. A*, vol. 152, p. 445, 1935.

(6) L. B. Thomas and E. B. Shofield, *J. Chem. Phys.*, vol. 23, p. 861, 1955.

(7) L. B. Thomas and R. E. Brown, *J. Chem. Phys.*, vol. 18, p. 1367, 1950.

(8) H. Y. Wachman, *Am. Rocket Soc. J.*, vol. 32, p. 2, 1962.

(9) J. P. Hartnett, "Rarefied Gas Dynamics," p. 1, Academic Press Inc., New York, 1961.

(10) S. C. Liang, *J. Appl. Phys.*, vol. 22, p. 148, 1951.

Flow of Gas through Orifices and Tubes

2

In this chapter we treat the gas flow through orifices and tubes as a function of the pressure difference. Obviously, this is important for the calculation of the pressure distribution in a dynamic vacuum system with local pressure variations. As mentioned in Sec. 1-4, the flow pattern changes when the mean free path becomes larger than the orifice or tube diameter. This transition from viscous to molecular flow is gradual. We discuss only tubes of circular cross section. For the conductance of tubes of other cross sections and further references, see Dushman-Lafferty (1). If a configuration does not lend itself to an easy calculation of the flow, it is often feasible just to measure it. Such measurements are discussed in Sec. 5-16.

2-1 Mass Flow and Conductance

The flow Q of gas across an area is the volumetric flow rate multiplied by the pressure, or

$$Q = P \frac{dV}{dt} \qquad (2\text{-}1)$$

As mentioned in Sec. 1-1, PV is an energy.

Hence, Q constitutes an energy flow or power. But we are not concerned with the energy flow. We wish to know the mass flow, i.e., the number of molecules moving across the area which is proportional to Q. Since $P = nkT$, the mass flow is

$$n \frac{dV}{dt} = Q(kT)^{-1} \tag{2-1a}$$

The dimension of Q is torr liters per second. In general, Q is used rather than Q/kT, since most calculations refer to room temperature.

We now define the conductance C of a member connecting two parts of a vacuum system as the ratio of flow to pressure difference. It has the dimension of liters per second.

$$C = \frac{Q}{\Delta P} \tag{2-2}$$

Its reciprocal is the flow resistance or impedance. A pipe or orifice is characterized by its conductance, and this chapter deals exclusively with the calculation of conductances. The analogy between the flow of gas and an electrical current is obvious; C corresponds to the electrical conductance and ΔP to the potential difference. As in the electrical circuit, the rules for parallel and series connection of conductances apply, namely:

$$C = C_1 + C_2 \qquad \text{for parallel connection} \tag{2-3}$$

$$\frac{1}{C} = \frac{1}{C_1} + \frac{1}{C_2} \qquad \text{for series connection} \tag{2-4}$$

2-2 *Conductance of an Orifice for Molecular Flow*

Let us consider the stationary flow between two chambers at different pressures and connected by a pipe or an orifice. The chambers are assumed to be large compared with the diameter of the pipe or the size of the orifice. We postulate molecular flow; i.e., the molecules do not collide with each other but hit the wall only. The walls are rough on a molecular scale and reflect the molecules diffusely. It follows from Lambert's law that the probability that a reflected molecule will be in an elementary solid angle is proportional to the cosine of the angle that is formed by the solid angle and the normal to the surface. Also, the molecules do not stay at the wall, or, what amounts to the same, equilibrium exists between the adsorbed molecules and the gas phase; equal numbers of molecules arrive at and stick to the wall and leave the wall.

We now compute the conductance of an orifice of area A.   Gas streams across the orifice in both directions without mutual interference.   It follows from Eqs. (2-1) and (1-7) that the flow in one direction is

$$Q = P\frac{dV}{dt} = kT\frac{dN}{dt} = kT(\tfrac{1}{4}nv_aA) = PA\left(\frac{kT}{2\pi m}\right)^{\frac{1}{2}} \qquad (2\text{-}5)$$

The net flow downstream is $A\,\Delta P\,(kT/2\pi m)^{\frac{1}{2}}$.   From Eq. (2-2),

$$C = \left(\frac{kT}{2\pi m}\right)^{\frac{1}{2}} A$$

or,

$$C = 3.64\left(\frac{T}{M}\right)^{\frac{1}{2}} A \qquad \text{liters/sec} \qquad (2\text{-}6)$$

where A is expressed in square centimeters.   This is the volumetric flow Av/n across the aperture.   [The factor is 3.64 instead of 3640 since n in Eq. (1-7) is the number of molecules in a cubic centimeter and C is given in liters per second.]   There is no limitation on the shape of the aperture other than that the largest dimension must still be small enough to ensure molecular flow.   The conductance for nitrogen at 293°K is

$$C_{N_2} = 11.8A \qquad \text{liters/sec} \qquad (2\text{-}7)$$

where A is expressed in square centimeters.

If the vessel dimensions are not large compared with area A, the conductance is higher.   Loevinger (2) showed that, for an aperture of cross section A at the end of a tube of cross section A_0, the value of the conductance calculated from Eq. (2-6) must be multiplied by the factor $A_0/(A_0 - A)$ to obtain the effective conductance.

An aperture is often a convenient means to provide a conductance of known size for the measurement of pumping speeds or calibration of gages.

2-3   *Conductance of Pipes for Molecular Flow*

We consider a long tube of length L and diameter D.   Momentum is transferred from the gas to the tube wall in the downstream motion.   The force necessary to overcome this external friction equals

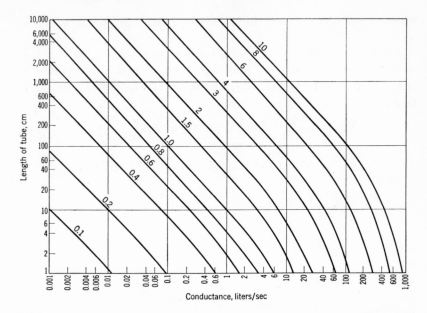

Fig. 2-1 The conductance, in liters per second, for air in the case of cylindrical tubes. (Parameter is diameter of tube in centimeters.) Calculated from Eq. (2-14). (From S. Dushman-J. M. Lafferty, "Scientific Foundations of Vacuum Technique," chap. 2, John Wiley & Sons, Inc., New York, 1962.)

the force required to push the gas through the tube. From Eq. (1-7),

$$\frac{\pi}{4} D^2 \, \Delta P = \frac{1}{4} n v_a \pi D L m u \tag{2-8}$$

where u is the net gas velocity in axial direction. From Eqs. (1-2a) and (2-2),

$$\frac{\pi}{4} D^2 n k T u = Q = C \, \Delta P \tag{2-9}$$

Combining Eqs. (1-6), (2-8), and (2-9)

$$C = \frac{\pi}{16} \left(\frac{2\pi k T}{m} \right)^{\frac{1}{2}} \frac{D^3}{L} \tag{2-10}$$

A more rigorous derivation gives

$$C_m = \frac{1}{6} \left(\frac{2\pi k T}{m} \right)^{\frac{1}{2}} \frac{D^3}{L} \tag{2-11}$$

$$C_m = 3.8 \left(\frac{T}{M} \right)^{\frac{1}{2}} \frac{D^3}{L} \qquad \text{liters/sec}$$

where D and L are expressed in centimeters. For nitrogen at 293°K,

$$C_{N_2} = 12.3 \frac{D^3}{L} \quad \text{liters/sec} \tag{2-12}$$

If the tube is short, the conductance of the entrance aperture cannot be neglected. As proposed by Dushman, we assume

$$\frac{1}{C} = \frac{1}{C_m} + \frac{1}{C_{\text{aperture}}} \tag{2-13}$$

It follows from Eqs. (2-6) and (2-11) that

$$C = C_m \left(1 + \frac{4}{3} \frac{D}{L} \right)^{-1} \tag{2-14}$$

Figure 2-1 from Ref. (1) is a plot of conductances of cylindrical tubes for air at 20°C, calculated from Eq. (2-14). Equation (2-14) gives values that are slightly too high. The approximation is good near the limiting cases of an orifice and of long tubes. Figure 2-2 shows the percentage error according to another calculation by Clausing which

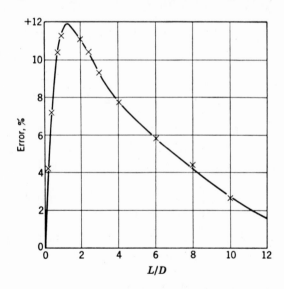

Fig. 2-2 Plot of L/D against the percentage error involved in using Eq. (2-14). (From M. Pirani-J. Yarwood, "Principles of Vacuum Engineering," p. 15, Reinhold Publishing Corporation, New York, 1961.)

is known to be accurate for $L/D < 5$ and $L/D = \infty$. The maximum deviation of 12 percent occurs at an intermediate ratio of $L/D = 1.3$.

If the chamber is not large compared with the tube diameter, the correction term for the entrance aperture is smaller. A similar situation exists if two short tubes of different diameters are joined. These complications are usually disregarded. As stated previously, if high accuracy is required and/or the geometry is complex, it is more feasible to measure the conductance than to rely on calculations.

Right-angle bends do not materially change the flow rate. Davis (3) calculated the conductance of short elbows of total length L and $L/D \leq 5$. The maximum difference compared with a straight tube of the same L/D was 8 percent. Short elbows had a slightly higher conductance and longer ones a slightly lower one. Davis used a Monte Carlo calculation. Measurements by Milleron and Levenson (4) confirmed his results. They applied this method also to other shapes. Adsorption in a tube may reduce the flow. This can cause erroneous gage readings at low pressures; see Sec. 3-4.

2-4   *Conductance of an Orifice in the Viscous Flow Range*

In viscous flow the mean free path is small compared with the dimensions of the container, and the properties of the gas do not change markedly within one mean free path. The gas can, therefore, be treated as a fluid, i.e., a continuum. We make the same assumptions as before, with the exception that collisions between molecules now dominate. The orifice is assumed to be thin and sharp-edged. Hence, wall effects due to viscosity can be neglected. The flow depends on the pressure ratio $r = P_2/P_1$ of downstream to upstream pressure. The equation adapted from Prandtl by Loevinger (2) follows:

$$Q = \left[\frac{2\gamma k T_1}{m(\gamma - 1)} \right]^{\frac{1}{2}} r^{1/\gamma} [1 - r^{(\gamma-1)/\gamma}]^{\frac{1}{2}} P_1 A \qquad (2\text{-}15)$$

$\gamma = c_p/c_v$ is the ratio of the specific heats of the gas. The flow becomes a maximum for

$$r = \left(\frac{2}{\gamma + 1} \right)^{\gamma/(\gamma-1)} \qquad (2\text{-}16)$$

Below a critical value of r, Eq. (2-15) is invalid. At low pressure ratios, the gas streams with the velocity of sound, and the flow is independent of P_2. For air at 20°C, the following three regions exist:

$$C = 76.6r^{0.712} \sqrt{1 - r^{0.288}} \frac{A}{1-r} \qquad \text{liters/sec}$$
$$r \geq 0.52 \qquad (2\text{-}17a)$$

$$\approx 20 \frac{A}{1-r} \qquad \text{liters/sec} \qquad r \leq 0.52 \qquad (2\text{-}17b)$$

$$\approx 20A \qquad \text{liters/sec} \qquad r \leq 0.1 \qquad A \text{ area in cm}^2 \qquad (2\text{-}17c)$$

The transition region for a circular orifice and small r has been investigated by Liepmann (5). He used A, He, and N_2. The conductance began to increase from the value of Eq. (2-6) at $D/\lambda \approx 0.1$ and reached a 50 percent higher value at $D/\lambda \approx 20$ (λ, mean free path; D, diameter). The conductance remained constant at further increase of D/λ. Hence, Eq. (2-6) is valid for $D/\lambda < 0.1$, and Eq. (2-17c) for $D/\lambda > 20$.

If the orifice is not thin and sharp-edged, e.g., if there is a nozzle, the above statements and equations do not apply.

2-5   Conductance of Pipes in the Viscous Flow Range

If the flow is laminar, i.e., the flow lines are substantially parallel, the viscosity of the gas reduces the velocity near the wall. In the derivation of the so-called Poiseuille equation for viscous flow in a circular pipe, the further assumption is made that the gas is incompressible. This condition is sufficiently complied with if

$$Q < \frac{10^{-3}}{12} \pi D^2 P v_s \qquad \text{torr liters/sec} \qquad (2\text{-}18)$$

where v_s is the velocity of sound in centimeters per second, 3.44×10^4 cm/sec for air at 20°C; D is the diameter in centimeters; and P is the pressure in torr. The conductance of a long pipe in the viscous flow range is

$$C_v = \frac{\pi}{128} \frac{D^4}{\eta L} \bar{P} \qquad (2\text{-}19)$$

where D and L are diameter and length, η is the viscosity, and $\bar{P}$ is the average pressure in the pipe. Here the conductance is proportional to the average pressure. For N_2 at 20°C, D and L in centimeters, and P in torr,

$$C_{N_2} = 188 \frac{D^4 \bar{P}}{L} \qquad \text{liters/sec} \qquad (2\text{-}20)$$

Table 2-1 lists the viscosities of some common gases at 20°C and the ratio of their conductance to the conductance of N_2.

Table 2-1   Viscosity η in
Micropoises at 20°C and
Relative Viscous Conductance
of Some Common Gases

Gas	η	C_{gas}/C_{N_2}
N_2	175	1
O_2	203	0.86
Air	182	0.96
H_2	88	2
He	196	0.89
A	222	0.79
CO_2	147	1.2
H_2O	94	1.9
Hg	235	0.75

Equations (2-19) and (2-20) are not applicable to short tubes since a length $l = 0.227 \ mQ/\pi\eta kT$ from the entrance of the tube is required to develop the flow fully.   For a short tube, Eq. (2-19) becomes

$$C_v = \frac{\pi}{128} \frac{D^4 \bar{P}}{\eta L} \left(1 + 1.14 \frac{m}{8\pi\eta kT} \frac{Q}{L}\right)^{-1} \tag{2-21}$$

Equation (2-21) is valid for

$$L > 0.304 \ \frac{mQ}{\pi\eta kT} \tag{2-22}$$

For air at 25°C,

$$C_{air} = 184 D^4 \frac{\bar{P}}{L} \left(1 + 0.38 \frac{Q}{L}\right)^{-1} \qquad \text{liters/sec} \tag{2-23}$$

for $L > 0.818Q$ $\tag{2-24}$

where $\bar{P}$ is expressed in torr, Q in torr liters per second, and D and L in centimeters.

2-6   Conductance of Pipes in the Transition Range

Knudsen gave the following semiempirical equation for the conductance of a long circular pipe and proved its accuracy for a wide range of $D\bar{P}$.

$$C_k = C_v + ZC_m \tag{2-25}$$

where

$$Z = \frac{1 + (m/kT)^{\frac{1}{2}} D\bar{P}/\eta}{1 + 1.24(m/kT)^{\frac{1}{2}} D\bar{P}/\eta} \qquad (2\text{-}26)$$

or

$$C_k = \frac{\pi}{128} \frac{D^4 \bar{P}}{\eta L} + \frac{1}{6} \left(\frac{2\pi k T}{m} \right)^{\frac{1}{2}} \frac{D^3}{L} \frac{1 + (m/kT)^{\frac{1}{2}} D\bar{P}/\eta}{1 + 1.24(m/kT)^{\frac{1}{2}} D\bar{P}/\eta} \qquad (2\text{-}27)$$

Here $\bar{P}$ is the average pressure in the pipe, η is the viscosity, and m the mass of a molecule. Equation (2-27) is valid in the molecular, transitional, and viscous-flow range. For very small and very large pressures, C_k becomes C_m [Eq. (2-11)] and C_v [Eq. (2-19)], respectively. It follows from Equations (1-2a), (1-6), and (1-10) that

$$\eta = \lambda P \left(\frac{2m}{\pi k T} \right)^{\frac{1}{2}} \qquad (2\text{-}28)$$

If we substitute this value of η in Eq. (2-26), we obtain

$$Z = \frac{1 + 1.25 D/\bar{\lambda}}{1 + 1.55 D/\bar{\lambda}} \qquad (2\text{-}29)$$

where $\bar{\lambda}$ is the mean free path at the average pressure $\bar{P}$. Also it follows from Equations (2-10), (2-19), and (2-27) that

$$C_v = 0.0736 \frac{D}{\bar{\lambda}} C_m \qquad (2\text{-}30)$$

Hence we can write Eq. (2-27) in the form

$$C_k = C_m \left(0.0736 \frac{D}{\bar{\lambda}} + \frac{1 + 1.25 D/\bar{\lambda}}{1 + 1.55 D/\bar{\lambda}} \right)$$
$$\approx C_m \left(0.0736 \frac{D}{\bar{\lambda}} + 1 \right) \qquad (2\text{-}31)$$

The approximation $Z = 1$ is good for large and small $D/\bar{\lambda}$. The maximum error is about 15 percent at $D/\bar{\lambda} = 3$. The values for C_k near the molecular and viscous flow range are given in Table 2-2. The value of C_k has an experimentally confirmed minimum of 95 percent of C_m for $D/\bar{\lambda} = 0.646$. For $D/\bar{\lambda} = 2$, C_k/C_m again becomes unity. For $D/\bar{\lambda}$ equal to 3 and 4, C_k is 6 and 13 percent larger than C_m. For large $D/\bar{\lambda}$, C_k approaches C_v of Eq. (2-30). For $D/\bar{\lambda}$ equal to 100 and 200, C_k is 11 and 5.5 percent larger than C_v. The flow is molecular for $D/\bar{\lambda} < 3$ and viscous for $D/\bar{\lambda} > 200$. In both cases, the error is not more than 6 percent. For odd shapes, it is sometimes

Table 2-2   Conductance C_k in Transition
Range Near Molecular and Viscous Flow

$D/\bar{\lambda}$	C_k/C_m	$D/\bar{\lambda}$	C_k/C_v
0.02	0.997	50	1.22
0.10	0.981	100	1.11
0.20	0.970	200	1.055
0.40	0.962	300	1.037
0.646	0.952 min	400	1.028
1.0	0.959	500	1.022
2.0	1.004	1000	1.011
3.0	1.061		
4.0	1.128		
5.0	1.197		

difficult to calculate the conductance and to appraise whether the flow is still molecular. In such cases, C has to be determined experimentally. The flow range is found by varying the pressure. In the molecular range only, the conductance is independent of pressure.

2-7   *Temperature Dependence of Conductance*

The temperature dependence of C is important in the case of cold traps. When a trap is filled with liquid nitrogen of 77°K temperature, its molecular conductance drops 50 percent since $C \propto v_a$. But the author experienced one incident where the conductance actually increased. In this case the thermal transpiration [Eq. (1-16)] reduced the mean free path to such an extent that the flow was no longer molecular.

2-8   *Turbulent Flow Through Pipes*

At high velocities and pressures, the viscous flow changes to turbulent flow. For air at 25°C, the flow is turbulent when

$$Q > 200D_{cm} \qquad \text{torr liters/sec} \tag{2-32}$$

This does not happen in vacuum systems.

REFERENCES

(1) S. Dushman and J. M. Lafferty, "Scientific Foundations of Vacuum Technique," chap. 2, John Wiley & Sons, Inc., New York, 1962.

(2) A. Guthrie and R. K. Wakerling, "Vacuum Equipment and Techniques," chap. 1, McGraw-Hill Book Company, New York, 1949.
(3) D. H. Davis, *J. Appl. Phys.*, vol. 31, p. 1169, 1960.
(4) L. L. Levenson, N. Milleron, and D. H. Davis, *Le Vide*, no. 103, p. 42, 1963, and 1960 *Vacuum Symp. Trans.*, p. 372, 1961.
(5) H. W. Liepmann, *J. Fluid Mech.*, Pt. 1, vol. 10, p. 65, 1961.

Surface Effects 3

In this chapter we discuss the effects of walls
and surfaces on gas composition. The lower
the pressure, the more important these effects
are. They determine the pressure and the
composition of the residual gas. Gas is
normally adsorbed on all surfaces. This gas
may desorb. The necessary energy can be
supplied thermally or by particle or photon
bombardment. This gas can be replenished
by gas dissolved in the solid which diffuses to
the surface. Such diffusion may produce
permeation, i.e., gas transfer from the
outside through the wall into the vacuum
space.

We shall first discuss permeation and
diffusion and then adsorption and thermal desorption from surfaces. This includes
evaporation and thermal dissociation on the
surface. Gas desorption and other effects
caused by impinging ions and electrons and by
photons will be treated next. Then we shall
consider chemical reactions between gas and
surface that result in the release of a new
gaseous compound. Finally we shall change
to a more practical rather than fundamental
approach and survey what is known about
gassing of typical materials in vacuum and
how it can be minimized.

3-1   Gas Permeation

For small concentrations, gases usually dissolve in solids according to Henry's law.

$$c = sP^n \tag{3-1}$$

where c is the concentration, s is the solubility, and P the gas pressure; n is unity for nonmetals. In metals diatomic molecules dissociate upon dissolving. It follows from the law of mass action that the concentration is proportional to the square root of the pressure, or $n = \frac{1}{2}$. The concentration is measured in torr or atmospheres. It is the amount of gas in torr cm^3 or atm cm^3 at 293°K that is dissolved in 1 cm^3 of the substance. s is the quantity of gas in cubic centimeters at standard temperature and pressure (STP, 293°K and 1 atm) that is dissolved in 1 cm^3 of the material at a pressure of 1 atm. It is dimensionless for $n = 1$. For $n = \frac{1}{2}$ it has the dimension atm$^{\frac{1}{2}}$.

If a pressure difference exists, gas diffuses in the stationary state according to Fick's first law of diffusion.

$$Q = -D\frac{dc}{dx} \tag{3-2}$$

where Q is the gas flow across an area of unit cross section in unit time, and D is the diffusion coefficient. Its unit is square centimeters per second. The minus sign is used because the flow is opposite to the concentration gradient. The diffusion constant changes exponentially with temperature.

$$D = D_0 \exp\left(-\frac{E}{RT}\right) \tag{3-3}$$

The exponential term is the Boltzmann factor; E is the activation energy for diffusion, usually expressed in kilocalories per mole; R is the gas constant; and D_0 is the proportionality constant.

Let us consider an area of unit cross section inside a slab of very large area and thickness d with the pressures P_1 and P_2 on the two faces. The concentrations at the surfaces are, as given in Eq. (3-1), $c_1 = sP_1^n$ and $c_2 = sP_2^n$. It follows from Eq. (3-2) that

$$Q\int_0^d dx = -D\int_{c_1}^{c_2} dc \tag{3-4}$$

$$Q = Ds\frac{P_1^n - P_2^n}{d} \tag{3-5}$$

Table 3-1   Gas Permeation Through:

Glasses	Metals	Semiconductors	Polymers
He, H_2, D_2, Ne, A, O_2 measurable through SiO_2	No rare gas through any metal.	He and H_2 through Ge and Si.	All gases permeate all polymers.
	H_2 permeates most, especially Pd.	Ne, A not measurable.	Water rate apt to be high.
Vitreous silica (fastest)	O_2 permeates Ag. H_2 through Fe by corrosion, electrolysis, etc.		Many specificities.
All rates vary directly as pressure	Rates vary as (pressure)$^{\frac{1}{2}}$	H_2 rate varies as (pressure)$^{\frac{1}{2}}$	All rates vary as pressure.

SOURCE: F. J. Norton, 1961 *Vacuum Symp. Trans.*, p. 8, 1962.

where $n = 1$ for nonmetals and $n = \frac{1}{2}$ for diatomic molecules in metals. Ds is called the permeation constant K. It is commonly expressed as the amount of gas, in cubic centimeters (STP), diffusing through a 1-cm^2 cross section of a slab of 1-cm thickness for a pressure difference of 1 atm.

Norton (1) gives a review of permeation. Table 3-1 is taken from his article. For the effect of permeation on gassing, see Secs. 3-10 and 7-3.

In most cases, equilibrium is reached only after a long time or not at all, since D is small. Hence, the transient case has to be considered. Fick's second law states that

$$D \frac{\partial^2 c}{\partial x^2} = \frac{\partial c}{\partial t} \tag{3-6}$$

We shall discuss solutions for some typical cases encountered in vacuum work.

Let us first consider the initial phase of gas permeation, preceding the steady state of Eq. (3-5). In this case, c and P are initially zero. At time $t = 0$, one face is exposed to a constant pressure P_1 which produces a concentration c_1 at this surface while vacuum is maintained at the other face. Hence we must solve Eq. (3-6) for the following initial and boundary conditions:

$$c = 0 \quad\quad 0 \leq x \leq d \quad\quad t = 0$$
$$c = 0 \quad\quad x = 0 \quad\quad\quad t > 0$$
$$c = c_1 \quad\quad x = d \quad\quad\quad t > 0$$

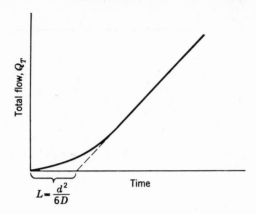

Fig. 3-1 Flow out of an initially empty slab with constant pressure on upstream face.

The solution is

$$c(x,t) = \frac{c_1 x}{d} + \frac{2c_1}{\pi} \sum_{1}^{\infty} \frac{(-1)^n}{n} \sin \frac{n\pi x}{d} \exp\left[-\left(\frac{n\pi}{d}\right)^2 Dt\right] \quad (3\text{-}7)$$

The instantaneous gassing rate at time t is

$$Q = D\left(\frac{\partial c}{\partial x}\right)_{x=0} = \frac{Dc_1}{d} + \frac{2c_1 D}{d} \sum_{1}^{\infty} (-1)^n \exp\left[-\left(\frac{n\pi}{d}\right)^2 Dt\right] \quad (3\text{-}8)$$

The total amount of gas permeated into the vacuum is

$$Q_T = \int_0^t D\left(\frac{\partial c}{\partial x}\right)_{x=0} dt$$

$$= \frac{c_1 Dt}{d} - \frac{c_1 d}{6} - \frac{2c_1 d}{\pi^2} \sum_{1}^{\infty} \frac{(-1)^n}{n^2} \exp\left[-\left(\frac{n\pi}{d}\right)^2 Dt\right] \quad (3\text{-}9)$$

since $\displaystyle\sum_{1}^{\infty} \frac{(-1)^n}{n^2} = \frac{\pi^2}{12}$

This reduces for large t to

$$Q_T = \frac{c_1 D}{d}\left(t - \frac{d^2}{6D}\right) \quad (3\text{-}10)$$

If we plot Q_T against t (Fig. 3-1), we can find the "time lag" $L = d^2/6D$ and calculate D. For an application to the determination of the permeation and diffusion coefficient of some gases and their activation energy for some plastic and metal foils, see Klumb and Schroeter (2). The time t has to be very long if D is small. Rogers

Fig. 3-2 Permeation constants for various gas-nonmetal combinations as a function of temperature. Units are square centimeters per second. [Quantity of gas in cubic centimeters (STP) passing per second through a wall of 1-cm² area and 1-cm thickness, when a pressure difference of 1 atm exists across the wall.] (Numbers 2 to 12 and 14 from P. A. Redhead, J. P. Hobson, and E. V. Kornelsen, *Adv. Electron. Electron Phys.*, vol. 17, p. 323, 1962; Nos. 1, 13, and 15 from V. O. Altemose, *J. Appl. Phys.*, vol. 32, p. 1309, 1961; and 16 to 19 from B. B. Dayton, 1959 *Vacuum Symp. Trans.*, p. 101, 1960.)

1. He-fused silica
2. Air-Pyroceram
3. Air-97% alumina ceramic
4. Air-Pyrex
5. He-lead borate glass G
6. He-97% alumina ceramic
7. Ne-Vycor
8. N_2-SiO_2
9. He-1720 glass
10. He-Pyroceram 9606
11. H_2-SiO_2
12. He-Pyrex 7740
13. He-Vycor 7900
14. H_2-Pyrex
15. He-Pyrex 7052
16. He-Neoprene
17. H_2-Neoprene
18. N_2-Neoprene
19. A-Neoprene

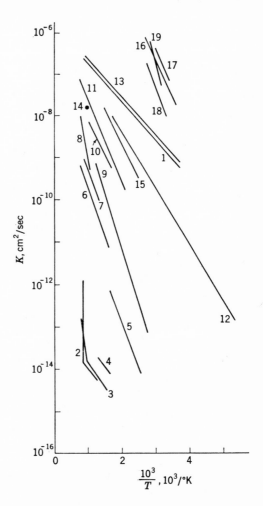

et al. (3) used another series solution which converges rapidly for small t to determine the diffusion coefficient and solubility of helium in pyrex glass. For permeabilities and solubilities, see Figs. 3-2 to 3-6 and Refs. (13) and (57). See Ref. (3b) for more data on permeability of Corning glasses and Table 7-1 for permeability of some gasket materials. The permeation increases rapidly with temperature because of the Boltzmann term in Eq. (3-3) for the diffusion coefficient.

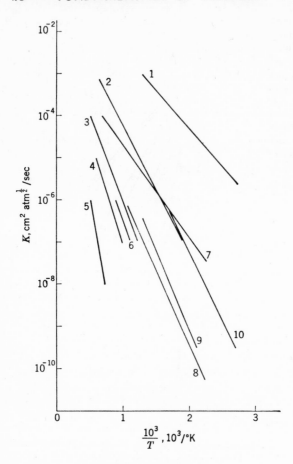

Fig. 3-3 Permeation constants for various diatomic gas-metal combinations as a function of temperature. Units are cm² atm$^{1/2}$/sec. [Quantity of gas in cubic centimeters (STP) passing per second through a wall of 1-cm² area and 1-cm thickness, when a pressure difference of 1 atm exists across the wall.] (Numbers 1 to 8 from P. A. Redhead, J. P. Hobson, and E. V. Kornelsen, *Adv. Electron. Electron Phys.*, vol. 17, p. 323, 1962; Nos. 9 and 10 from H. L. Eschbach, F. Gross, and S. Schulien, *Vacuum*, vol. 13, p. 543, 1963.)

1. H_2-Pd	6. CO-Fe
2. H_2-Ni	7. H_2-Fe
3. H_2-Mo	8. H_2-Cu
4. N_2-Fe	9. H_2-300 series stainless steel
5. N_2-Mo	10. H_2-400 series stainless steel

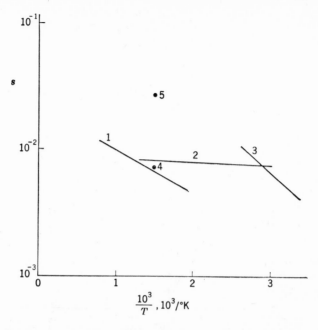

Fig. 3-4 Solubilities s for various gas-nonmetal combinations as a function of temperature. s is dimensionless. [Quantity of gas in cubic centimeters (STP) in 1 cm^3 of material at 1 atm pressure.] (Numbers 1 to 4 from P. A. Redhead, J. P. Hobson, and E. V. Kornelsen, *Adv. Electron. Electron Phys.*, vol. 17, p. 323, 1962, and No. 5 from V. O. Altemose, *J. Appl. Phys.*, vol. 32, p. 1309, 1961.)

1. H_2-SiO_2	4. H_2-Vycor
2. He-Pyrex 7740	5. He-Pyrex 7052
3. He-Vycor	

This is even more pronounced when the solubility also increases with temperature.

Here, as in other solutions of Eq. (3-6), c and Q_T are functions of the product Dt only and not of t alone. Hence the same gas distribution in the solid and the same total flow Q_T can be obtained in shorter time by raising the temperature and thereby increasing D.

3-2 *Gas Diffusing from a Semi-infinite Slab*

Another important case is the degassing of a semi-infinite slab of unit cross section. It has initially a uniform concentration c_0 throughout. At $t = 0$, one face is exposed to a vacuum. The residual

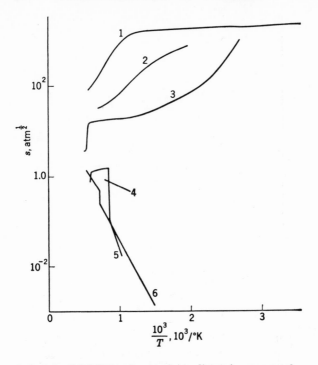

Fig. 3-5 Solubilities for various diatomic gas-metal combinations as a function of temperature. Unit is atm$^{\frac{1}{2}}$. [Quantity of gas in cubic centimeters (STP) in 1 cm^3 of material at 1 atm pressure.] (From P. A. Redhead, J. P. Hobson, and E. V. Kornelsen, *Adv. Electron. Electron Phys.*, vol. 17, p. 323, 1962.)

1. H_2-Ti	4. O_2-Cu
2. H_2-Ta	5. N_2-Fe
3. H_2-Pd	6. H_2-Cu

gas pressure in the vacuum is assumed to remain negligible. The container wall often represents such a slab. We must solve Eq. (3-6) for the following initial and boundary conditions:

$$c = c_0 \quad x \geq 0 \quad t = 0$$
$$c = 0 \quad x = 0 \quad t > 0$$

The solution is

$$c(x,t) = 2c_0(\pi)^{-\frac{1}{2}} \int_0^{x/2(Dt)^{\frac{1}{2}}} \exp\left(-y^2\right) dy = c_0 \operatorname{erf} \frac{x}{2(Dt)^{\frac{1}{2}}} \quad (3\text{-}11)$$

The instantaneous gassing rate at time t is

$$Q = D\left(\frac{\partial c}{\partial x}\right)_{x=0} = c_0 D^{\frac{1}{2}}(\pi t)^{-\frac{1}{2}} \quad (3\text{-}12)$$

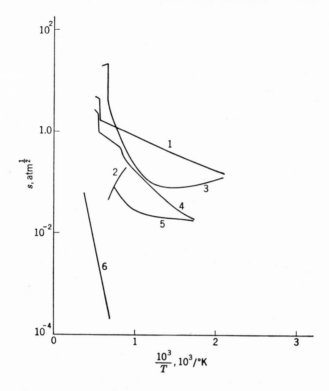

Fig. 3-6 Solubilities for various diatomic gas-metal combinations as a function of temperature. Unit is atm$^{\frac{1}{2}}$. [Quantity of gas in cubic centimeters (STP) in 1 cm^3 of material at 1 atm pressure.] (From P. A. Redhead, J. P. Hobson, and E. V. Kornelsen, *Adv. Electron. Electron Phys.*, vol. 17, p. 324, 1962.)

1. H_2-Ni	3. O_2-Ag	5. H_2-Mo
2. N_2-Mo	4. H_2-Fe	6. N_2-W

If the vacuum space is connected to a pump of speed S, $Q = PS$ [see Eq. (4-2)] and

$$P = c_0 D^{\frac{1}{2}} S^{-1}(\pi t)^{-\frac{1}{2}} \tag{3-13}$$

This relation is characteristic for such a diffusion process. During the degassing, the pressure is inversely proportional to the square root of time. The total amount of gas removed from the slab is

$$Q_T = \int_0^t D\left(\frac{\partial c}{\partial x}\right)_{x=0} dt = 2\pi^{-\frac{1}{2}}c_0(Dt)^{\frac{1}{2}} \tag{3-14}$$

The same amount would diffuse into a thoroughly degassed slab from an atmosphere, c_0 being the equilibrium concentration. If we plot

Q_T as a function of $t^{\frac{1}{2}}$, the slope will be, in accordance with Eqs. (3-14) and (3-3),

$$m = 1.13c_0 D_0^{\frac{1}{2}} \exp\left(\frac{-E}{2RT}\right) \tag{3-15}$$

$$\log m = \log (1.13c_0 D_0^{\frac{1}{2}}) - \frac{0.434E}{2RT} \tag{3-16}$$

After determining m for several temperatures, $\log m$ can be plotted as a function of $1/T$. We can then calculate the activation energy of diffusion E from the slope of this plot. Such a representation of a process involving an activation energy is called an Arrhenius plot.

This approach has been used by Todd (4) to investigate the removal of water from glass by bakeout. To obtain D_0, he had to know c_0. He found c_0 by measuring the amount of water evolved when the glass was remelted in vacuum at 1300°C for $\frac{1}{2}$ hr.

Todd demonstrated that degassing at high temperatures is more effective, in agreement with theory. Two glass tubes were baked at 530 and 465°C for 1 hr each. The one baked at the lower temperature gave off 3.2 times as much water vapor during a subsequent bake of $2\frac{1}{2}$ hr at 400°C. The observed amounts of desorbed gas were 24 and 33 percent less than the calculated ones. See Sec. 3-10 for sample calculations of gassing.

3-3 Diffusion of Gas from a Finite Slab

We solve Eq. (3-6) for a slab of unit cross section and thickness d. Initially the concentration is c_0 and constant throughout. At time $t = 0$, vacuum is applied to both faces. The initial and boundary conditions are

$$c = c_0 \qquad 0 \le x \le d \qquad\qquad t = 0$$
$$c = 0 \qquad x = 0 \text{ and } x = d \qquad t > 0$$

The solution is

$$c = c_0 \frac{4}{\pi} \sum_0^\infty (2n + 1)^{-1} \sin \frac{\pi(2n + 1)}{d} x$$
$$\exp\left\{-\left[\frac{\pi(2n + 1)}{d}\right]^2 Dt\right\} \tag{3-17}$$

Figure 3-7 shows $c = f(x,t)$.

The instantaneous gas flow from the two faces of the slab is

$$Q = 2D\left(\frac{\partial c}{\partial x}\right)_{x=0} = \frac{8c_0 D}{d} \sum_0^\infty \exp\left\{-\left[\frac{\pi(2n + 1)}{d}\right]^2 Dt\right\} \tag{3-18}$$

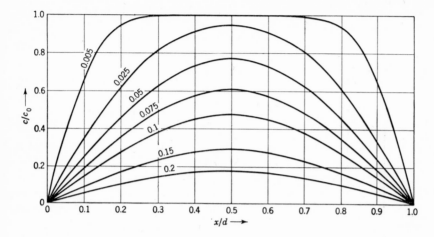

Fig. 3-7 Relative concentration in a finite slab of thickness d for various (dimensionless) times Dt/d^2 as parameter.

The total amount of gas removed from the slab is

$$Q_T = 2D \int_0^t \left(\frac{\partial c}{\partial x}\right)_{x=0} dt = c_0 d \left(1 - \frac{8}{\pi^2} \sum_0^\infty (2n+1)^{-2}\right.$$

$$\left. \exp\left\{-\left[\frac{\pi(2n+1)}{d}\right]^2 Dt\right\}\right) \quad (3\text{-}19)$$

since $\sum_0^\infty (2n+1)^{-2} = \frac{\pi^2}{8}$

This is also the amount of gas absorbed by a degassed plate at a pressure that produces an equilibrium concentration c_0.

Initially, when the concentration is still nearly c_0 in the center of the slab (see Fig. 3-7), Eq. (3-14) is an approximation of Eq. (3-19). Using either equation, $Q_T/c_0 d$, the fraction of gas removed, is a function of Dt/d^2. Both equations are compared in Table 3-2. Even after two-thirds of the gas has been removed, the error is only 1.6 percent. Todd plots $Q_T/c_0 d$ versus $(Dt)^{\frac{1}{2}}/d$ for a slab, sphere, and cylinder to show when departure from linearity occurs. Diffusion constants are given in Figs. 3-8 and 3-9 and Ref. (57). Like the permeation, the diffusion increases rapidly with temperature because of the Boltzmann term [Eq. (3-3)].

For application of these calculations to degassing problems, see Sec. 3-10. For a treatise on diffusion, see Jost (5).

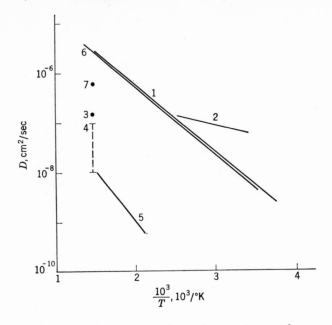

Fig. 3-8 Diffusion constants for various gas-nonmetal combinations. Units are square centimeters per second. (Numbers 1 to 6 from P. A. Redhead, J. P. Hobson, and E. V. Kornelsen, *Adv. Electron. Electron Phys.*, vol. 17, p. 323, 1962, and No. 7 from V. O. Altemose, *J. Appl. Phys.*, vol. 32, p. 1309, 1961.)

1. He-Pyrex 7740
2. He-Vycor
3. H_2-Vycor
4. N_2-Vycor

5. H_2-SiO$_2$
6. He-Duran glass
7. He-Pyrex 7052

Table 3-2 Degassing of a Finite Slab. Error of Approximation [Eq. (3-14)] and fraction of gas removed

Dt/d^2	$\dfrac{[2Q_T/c_0 d]_{\text{Eq. (3-14)}} - [Q_T/c_0 d]_{\text{Eq. (3-19)}}}{[Q_T/c_0 d]_{\text{Eq. (3-19)}}}$	$[Q_T/c_0 d]_{\text{Eq. (3-19)}}$
0.06	0.0029	0.55
0.07	0.0057	0.59
0.08	0.014	0.63
0.09	0.016	0.67
0.10	0.023	0.70
0.15	0.072	0.82
0.20	0.14	0.89
0.25	0.21	0.93
0.30	0.29	0.96

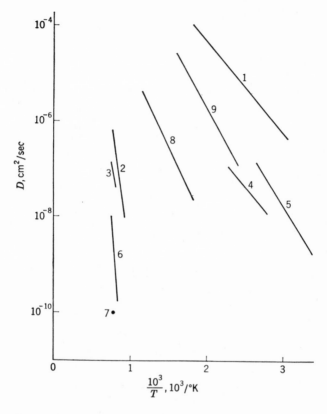

Fig. 3-9 Diffusion constants for various gas-metal combinations. Units are square centimeters per second. (Numbers 1 to 7 from P. A. Redhead, J. P. Hobson, and E. V. Kornelsen, *Adv. Electron. Electron Phys.*, vol. 17, p. 323, 1962; Nos. 8 and 9 from H. L. Eschbach, F. Gross, and S. Schulien, *Vacuum*, vol. 13, p. 543, 1963.)

1. H_2-Pd	6. O_2-Ni
2. N_2-Fe	7. O_2-Fe
3. CO-Ni	8. H_2-300 series stainless steel
4. H_2-Ni	9. H_2-400 series stainless steel
5. H_2-Fe	

3-4   Adsorption and Thermal Desorption

Any surface of a solid or liquid exhibits forces of attraction normal to the surface. Hence gas molecules impinging on the surface are adsorbed. This gas is desorbed, under certain conditions of temperature and pressure, and constitutes the main source of gas in high

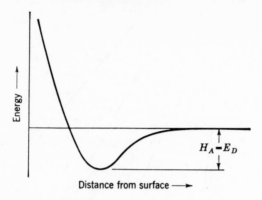

Fig. 3-10 Potential energy of a molecule in non-activated adsorption. H_A is heat of adsorption; E_D is energy of desorption.

vacuum, as was mentioned in the introduction. The molecules adsorbed at the wall exceed those in the volume by orders of magnitude. Conversely, gas can be removed from the volume by adsorption, a process utilized in the so-called sorption pumps (Sec. 6-4).

Figure 3-10 shows schematically the potential energy of a molecule as a function of its distance from the surface for nonactivated adsorption. It is attracted and will assume an equilibrium position at minimum potential energy. This energy is the heat of adsorption H_A. It is equal to the energy of desorption E_D and can be measured with a calorimeter. Depending on the type of force or bond, there is a distinction between physical adsorption and chemical adsorption, or chemisorption. Physical adsorption involves van der Waal, intermolecular forces, like the ones causing liquefaction of gases. H_A is similar to, though of course larger than, the heat of liquefaction. Additional layers may be adsorbed with decreasing H_A until the two-dimensional liquid becomes a regular three-dimensional one. E_D is small, not over 8 kcal/mole. In physical adsorption, the free energy F and the entropy S decrease, since adsorption occurs spontaneously and the molecule loses one degree of freedom. The change in energy is $\Delta U = \Delta F + T \Delta S$. Therefore ΔU is also negative, and the adsorption is exothermic.

In chemisorption, the adsorption is similar to the formation of a chemical compound with transfer of electrons. After a strongly bonded monomolecular layer has been formed, further chemisorption can take place at surface singularities; also, a second layer can be adsorbed. The situation is often complicated by simultaneous adsorp-

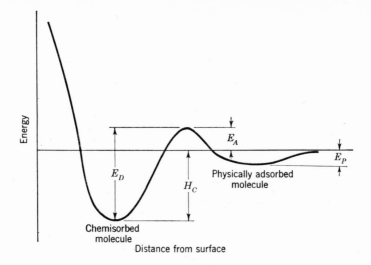

Fig. 3-11a Potential energy for activated chemisorption. Molecular adsorption. (For explanation of symbols in Figs. 3-11a and 3-11b see Fig. 3-11c, page 39.)

tion with different energies. The heat of chemisorption is higher than in physical adsorption, in extreme cases over 200 kcal/mole (236 kcal/mole for initial adsorption of oxygen on titanium). Often an activation energy is required, as shown in Fig. 3-11a. There the molecule is first physically adsorbed. If energy is supplied, this changes to activated chemisorption with further approach. The energy of desorption $E_D = E_A + H_C$, where H_C is the heat and E_A the activation energy of chemisorption. In activated chemisorption, more gas may be adsorbed when the temperature is raised; e.g., a pumpdown experiment of Hayashi (6) suggested that more water vapor was adsorbed at a hot steel surface than at room temperature. The chemisorption of molecules is also exothermic. The inert gases undergo physical adsorption only.

Molecules may dissociate and be chemisorbed as atoms. This is shown in Fig. 3-11b and c. There D is the energy of dissociation and E_D the activation energy for desorption of an atom. If $2E_D < D$, the sorption is endothermic (Fig. 3-11b); if $2E_D > D$, the reaction is exothermic (Fig. 3-11c). In either case, the surface atomizes the molecular gas. Hydrogen adsorbs on tungsten as atoms. The dissociation of H_2 at an incandescent tungsten filament is an example of atomic desorption. D_{H_2} is 105 kcal/mole; the heat of adsorption of hydrogen on tungsten is 46 kcal/mole. Hence it follows from Fig.

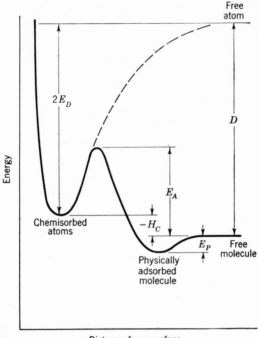

Fig. 3-11*b* Potential energy for activated chemi-sorption. Endothermic atomic adsorption of diatomic molecule: $2E_D < D$. (From G. Ehrlich, *J. Chem. Phys.*, vol. 31, p. 1111, 1959.)

3-11*c* that $2E_D = D + H_c = 151$ kcal/mole. The measured value of E_D is 74 kcal/mole.

The atoms have a certain mobility on the surface. They may migrate over the surface, like a two-dimensional gas, as the necessary activation energy E_m is relatively small. When two adsorbed atoms collide, they may recombine and desorb as a molecule. This process is indicated when there is a second-order desorption, i.e., when the rate of desorption is proportional to the square of the surface coverage. Below 1000°K, hydrogen desorbs from tungsten as H_2 in second order. Whether atomic or molecular desorption predominates depends on a number of factors such as pressure and temperature; see Ref. (6a) or (8a).

Tables 3-3 to 3-5 list chemisorption on metals at room temperature, activation energies of surface migration, and heats of adsorption. References (9) and (7) are texts on physical and chemical adsorption.

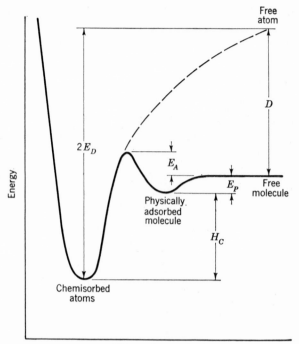

Fig. 3-11c Potential energy for activated chemisorption. Exothermic atomic adsorption of diatomic molecule: $2E_D > D$. (From G. Ehrlich, *J. Chem. Phys.*, vol. 31, p. 1111, 1959.)

E_D is energy of desorption as molecule (*a*) or atom (*b,c*); E_P is energy of physical adsorption; E_A, activation energy of adsorption; H_C, heat of chemisorption; *D*, energy of dissociation.

We shall now discuss the kinetics of adsorption and consider the interaction between the gas and a surface of unit area (1 cm²). The rate at which molecules are adsorbed is

$$\frac{dn_A}{dt} = s\nu = sP(2\pi mkT)^{-\frac{1}{2}} = 3.5 \times 10^{22}sP(MT)^{-\frac{1}{2}} \text{ sec}^{-1} \text{ cm}^{-2}$$

$$(3\text{-}20)$$

where ν is the number of impinging molecules, from Eq. (1-7), and *s* is the sticking coefficient, defined as the probability that an incident molecule be adsorbed. When both sides are multiplied by kT, the amount of gas is expressed in torr liters at the temperature T:

$$\frac{d(PV)_A}{dt} = 3.64sP\left(\frac{T}{M}\right)^{\frac{1}{2}} \qquad \text{torr liters/sec cm}^2 \qquad (3\text{-}21)$$

Here T is the temperature of the impinging molecules. At pressure P and temperature T, n_A molecules occupy a volume V. The temperature of the surface may be different.

Table 3-3   Chemical Adsorption of Gases on Metals at Room Temperature

Metal	Gas							
	N_2	H_2	CO	C_2H_4	C_2H_2	O_2	CO_2	CH_4
Ag	N	N	N, Y^*					
Al	N	N	Y	Y	Y	Y		
Au	N	N	N, Y^*	Y	Y	N		
Ba	Y	Y	Y	Y	Y	Y	Y	Y
Ca	Y	Y	Y	Y	Y	Y		
Cd	N	N	N	N	N	Y		
Co	N	Y	Y			Y		N
Cu	N	N	Y	Y	Y	Y		
Cr	N	Y	Y	Y		Y		Y
Fe	Y	Y	Y	Y	Y	Y		N
Hg	N	N	N					
In	N	N	N	N	N	Y		
Mg		Y						
Mn						Y		
Mo	Y	Y	Y	Y	Y	Y		Y
Nb	Y	Y	Y			Y		
Ni	N	Y	Y	Y	Y	Y		N
Pb	N	N	N	N	N	Y		
Pd	N	Y	Y	Y	Y	Y		Y
Pt	N	Y	Y	Y	Y	Y		
Rh	N	Y	Y	Y	Y	Y		Y
Sn	N	N	N	N	N	Y		
Sr		Y						
Ta	Y	Y	Y	Y	Y	Y		Y
Ti	Y	Y	Y	Y	Y	Y	Y	Y
W	Y	Y	Y	Y	Y	Y		Y
Zn	N	N	N	N	N	Y		
Zr	Y	Y	Y	Y	Y	Y		

N = No, Y = Yes.
* Two different investigators.
SOURCE: J. P. Hobson, *Brit. J. Appl. Phys.*, vol. 14, p. 544, 1963.

Table 3-4 Activation Energy for Surface Migration E_m and Energy of Desorption E_D in Dilute Adlayers

	E_m kcal/mole	E_D kcal/mole	E_m/E_D
Cs on W	14	64	0.22
W on W (110)	30	134	0.22
Ba on W (100)	15	87	0.17
O on W	30	147	0.22
H on W	16	74	0.22
N on W	35	155	0.23
CO on W	65	~100	0.7
Xe on W	3.8	9	0.4
Kr on W	>1.1	4.5	>0.25
A on W	0.6	1.9	0.3
H on Ni	7	67	0.11

SOURCE: G. Ehrlich, *Ann. N.Y. Acad. Sci.*, vol. 101, art. 3, p. 722, 1963.

Table 3-5 Heats of Adsorption in Kilocalories per mole for Dilute Layers

Chemisorption:			
Rb on W	60	O_2 on Ni	115
Cs on W	64	H_2 on Fe	32
B on W	140	N_2 on Fe	40
Ni on Mo	48	H_2 on Ir	26
Ag on Mo	35	H_2 on Rh	26
H_2 on W	46	H_2 on Co	~24
O_2 on W	194	H_2 on Pt	27
CO on W	~100	O_2 on Pt	67
N_2 on W	85	H_2 on Pd	27
CO_2 on W	122	H_2 on Ni	30
NH_3 on W	70	NH_3 on Ni	36
H_2 on Mo	~40	CO on Ni	35
H_2 on Ta	46	H_2 on Cu	8
Physical adsorption:			
Xe on W	8–9	Xe on Mo	~8
Kr on W	~4.5	Xe on Ta	~5.3
A on W	~1.9		

SOURCE: G. Ehrlich, *Ann. N.Y. Acad. Sci.*, vol. 101, art. 3, p. 722, 1963, and 1961 *Vacuum Symp. Trans.*, p. 126, 1962.

For nitrogen at room temperature and 10^{-6} torr,

$$\nu = 3.9 \times 10^{14} \sec^{-1} \mathrm{cm}^{-2}$$

The gas kinetic diameter of the N_2 molecule is 3.7×10^{-8} cm (Table 1-1). We assume for simplicity that, in a monomolecular layer, the distance between the centers of the N_2 molecules is the gas kinetic diameter. Therefore a monolayer contains $N_0 = 7.3 \times 10^{14}$ molecules. If $s = 1$, the monolayer will form in 2 sec at 10^{-6} torr. N_0 depends on the surface structure, e.g., the lattice constant of the adsorbent and the size of the molecule. For the following, $N_0 = 5 \times 10^{14}/\mathrm{cm}^2$ is used as an average value. This corresponds to 1.5×10^{-5} torr liter at room temperature. s is some function of the number of sites available for adsorption. s and H_A change after the first monolayer has been formed.

Consider less than a monolayer coverage and desorption without recombination. We assume first-order desorption. The desorption rate is proportional to the number of molecules on the surface and inversely proportional to their average sojourn time t_s on the surface, or

$$\frac{dn_D}{dt} = \frac{N_0\Theta}{t_s} \tag{3-22}$$

or, at room temperature,

$$\frac{d(PV)_D}{dt} \approx \frac{1.5 \times 10^{-5}\Theta}{t_s} \qquad \text{torr liter/sec cm}^2 \tag{3-23}$$

where Θ is the fractional coverage. Frenkel (10) showed that

$$t_s = \tau_0 \exp\left(\frac{E_D}{RT}\right) \tag{3-24}$$

where τ_0 is the period of oscillation of the molecule normal to the surface, approximately 10^{-13} sec. Hence

$$\frac{dn_D}{dt} = N_0\Theta\tau_0^{-1} \exp\left(-\frac{E_D}{RT}\right) \tag{3-25}$$

Equation (3-25) applies to less than a monolayer of physically adsorbed and first-order chemisorbed gas. For second-order molecular desorption of adsorbed atoms, mentioned above,

$$\frac{dn_D}{dt} = r_2(N_0\Theta)^2 \exp\left(-\frac{E}{RT}\right) \tag{3-26}$$

where r_2 is the rate constant.

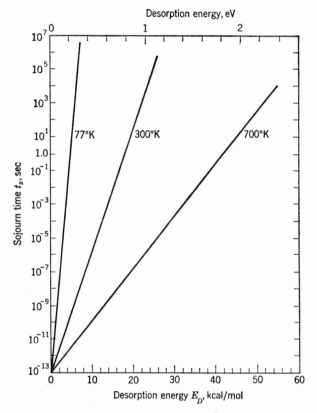

Fig. 3-12 Dependence of sojourn time on desorption energy at various temperatures. (From E. Apgar, Plasma Physics Summer Institute, 1962, Princeton University.)

Because of the exponential dependence, t_s and dn_D/dt vary over a wide range. Figure 3-12 shows $t_S = f(E_D)$ with T as parameter calculated from Eq. (3-24).

To appraise the effect of desorption on the gassing of an ultra-high-vacuum system, Hobson (11) calculated the gassing of an idealized system, due to a first-order desorption of a monolayer on the wall. He assumed $V = 1$ liter, $A = 100$ cm², $s = 0.5$, $T = 295°$K, and pumping speed $S = 1$ liter/sec. Figure 3-13 shows the pumpdown speed as a function of E_D. If $E_D < 15$ kcal/mole, the gas is readily removed. This includes all physically adsorbed gas. If $E_D > 25$ kcal/mole, the gassing is negligibly small. Gas with a desorption energy between 15 and 25 kcal/mole is only slowly removed and causes protracted gassing. The determining parameter is E_D/T; it

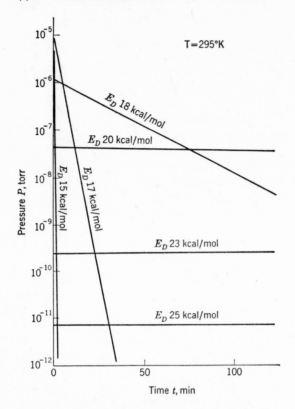

Fig. 3-13 Evacuation of system; $V = 1$ liter, $S_P = 1$ liter/sec, $T = 295°K$, $A = 100$ cm² covered initially with a monolayer. (From J. P. Hobson, 1961 *Vacuum Symp. Trans.*, p. 26, 1962.)

must be larger than 0.083 or smaller than 0.05. Hence the slowly desorbing gas ($15 < E_D < 25$) can be removed by a bake at 300°C. At this temperature all gas with $E_D = 30$ kcal/mole is as easily desorbed as a gas with $E_D = 15$ kcal/mole at room temperature. Experience shows that a bake at 300 to 400°C reduces gassing effectively. (See also Table 3-11.)

We shall now consider equilibrium between adsorption and desorption for nonactivated first-order adsorption of less than one monolayer. Equating Eqs. (3-20) and (3-25), we find the number of molecules on a surface of 1 cm² area:

$$N_0 \Theta = 3.5 \times 10^{22} s P (MT)^{-\frac{1}{2}} \tau_0 \exp\left(\frac{E_D}{RT_s}\right) \tag{3-27}$$

or $$\Theta = 7 \times 10^7 s P (MT)^{-\frac{1}{2}} \tau_0 \exp\left(\frac{E_D}{RT_s}\right) \tag{3-28}$$

where T is the temperature of the gas and T_S is the temperature of the surface.

Equation (3-28) gives an upper limit for the amount of gas that can be physically adsorbed at room temperature. For $E_D = 8$ kcal/mole, the sojourn time is 10^{-7} sec (Fig. 3-12). Assuming $s = 1$ and $M = 131$ (Xe), we find $\Theta = 0.036P$. In high vacuum very little gas is adsorbed, less than 10^{-7} monolayer at 10^{-6} torr. Hence physical adsorption, such as the adsorption of rare gases, is negligible at room temperature.

If the temperature is raised, gas of higher E_D will desorb. This fact is used in cleaning a tungsten filament by flashing at a high temperature in a good vacuum. If $T_S = 2400°K$, $s = 0.5$, $M > 2$, and $P = 10^{-7}$ torr, $\Theta < 10^{-3}$ for $E_D < 120$ kcal/mole. The flash-filament technique is also used to study desorption. If the temperature of a filament is gradually increased, gas with a desorption energy E_D will be released in a sudden burst when a specific temperature T_S is reached, on account of the exponential dependence of Θ on T_S.

At low temperatures the coverage becomes large even if E_D is small, as in physical adsorption. Hobson (12) pointed out that the adsorption of He on glass at 4.2°K is large enough to predict a pressure of 10^{-33} torr in a $\frac{1}{2}$-liter Pyrex flask when starting with 5×10^{-10} torr of He, despite the low heat of adsorption of 0.68 kcal/mole. Low-temperature adsorption is utilized in cryogenic sorption pumps; see Sec. 6-4. A surface alternately adsorbs and desorbs gas of appropriate E_D when the temperature is cycled, a procedure used in cryogenic sorption forepumps (see Sec. 6-1).

Equation (3-27) permits, in principle, calculation of the amount adsorbed as a function of pressure or temperature, i.e., plotting the three characteristic relations: $N_0\Theta = f(P)$ for constant T, the adsorption isotherm; $N_0\Theta = f(T)$ for constant P, the adsorption isobar; and $P = f(T)$ for constant coverage $N_0\Theta$, the adsorption isostere. The difficulty is that s and E_D are not constant. On a polycrystalline surface, s and E_D depend on the crystal face, s is also a function of Θ, etc. To explain the observations, many adsorption equations have been proposed making various assumptions with regard to $s(\Theta)$ and $E_D(\Theta)$. We shall mention only three of them.

Langmuir assumed for less than monolayer adsorption that a constant fraction of molecules striking an empty site is reflected and that all molecules striking an occupied site are reflected [see (9) or (13)]. Although his isotherm does not always agree with the measurements, it marked the beginning of a new theoretical approach. Brunauer et al. [(9) or (13)] extended Langmuir's equation to multilayer adsorption by assuming that the heat of adsorption is equal to the heat of condensation of the bulk substance for all subsequent layers after the first monolayer. Although subject to criticism, the "BET" equation is a convenient method to calculate the true surface area from the adsorption isotherm. Schram (14) found the following ratios of actual to geometric surface: 3 for stainless steel, 1.2 for pyrex glass, 5 for OFHC copper, and about 90 for alumina.

One of the oldest theories is the potential theory introduced by Polanyi in 1914 [see (13)]. This theory is thermodynamic and does not give a detailed physical picture, but it yields a semiempirical equation that fits many isotherms. Polanyi assumed that the attractive forces of adsorption create a potential distribution near the surface of the absorbent. A functional relation exists between the potential at any distance and the gas volume per unit area that is inside the boundaries formed by the equipotential surface and the surface of the adsorbent. The gas is compressed or even liquefied by the attractive forces and the weight of gas above it. This relation is called the characteristic curve and is postulated to be independent of the temperature. If its constants are calculated from one measured isotherm, all other isotherms can be predicted.

At temperatures well below the critical temperature the isotherm can be given in the form proposed by Dubinin and Radushkevish (14a):

$$\ln n_A = A - B\left(RT \ln \frac{P}{P_0}\right)^2$$

where n_A is the number of adsorbed molecules per unit area, A and B are constants, and P_0 is the vapor pressure of the liquid adsorbate at the temperature T. Hobson and Armstrong (14b) showed that this equation fitted their data for N_2 and A on 7740 glass for pressures from 5×10^{-10} to 10^{-3} torr, coverages from 10^{-6} to 0.3, and temperatures from 63 to 90°K. Manes and Grant (14c) used the potential theory to predict adsorption isotherms for N_2, H_2, and He on activated carbon at low temperatures. But the physical interpretation of a liquidlike adsorbate is doubtful.

The sticking probability s has been the subject of many investigations. It is often determined by measuring the sorption or pumping speed S of a surface and comparing it with that of an orifice of equal size that is a perfect pump S_P. Then $s = S/S_P$. Since only the difference between adsorption and desorption is observed, desorption must be small compared with adsorption. It follows from Eqs. (3-20)

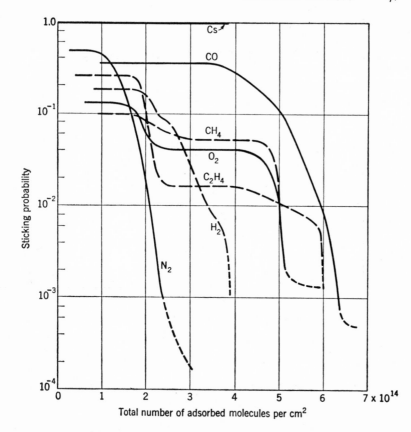

Fig. 3-14 Sticking probability versus number of adsorbed molecules on the 411 plane of tungsten at 300°K. (After J. Becker, "Solid State Physics," vol. 7, p. 379, Academic Press Inc., New York, 1958.)

and (3-22) that

$$t_s \gg 1.4 \times 10^{-8}\Theta(sP)^{-1}(MT)^{\frac{1}{2}} \tag{3-29}$$

For 293°K, $P = 10^{-5}$ torr, $\Theta = 1$, $s = 0.5$, and $M = 20$, this requires that $t_s \gg 0.2$ sec or $E_D > 19$ kcal/mole. It is also important to use high-purity gas in sorption experiments. Otherwise, impurities that are not sorbed may accumulate and give the impression of a reduced sorption rate. A mass spectrometer prevents such misinterpretations. Typically, sticking probabilities at room temperature lie between 0.1 and 1 and decline when monolayer coverage is approached. Tungsten has often been used as an adsorbent, since it can be cleaned by flashing.

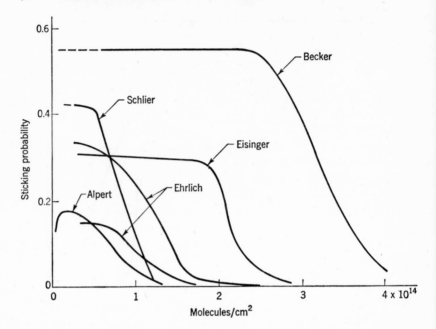

Fig. 3-15 Comparison of the results of various investigators for the sticking probability of nitrogen on tungsten. The two curves given for Ehrlich are for surface temperatures of 290 and 373°K. All others are nominally at room temperature. (After D. Lee, H. Tomaschke, and D. Alpert, 1961 *Vacuum Symp. Trans.*, p. 153, 1962.)

Figure 3-14 shows s for various gases. Figure 3-15 shows the results of a number of determinations of the sticking coefficient of nitrogen on tungsten at room temperature. The considerable variation can be explained, in part, by different crystal surfaces. Measurements on different samples of the same filament can differ by a factor of 2. The initial probability is between 0.15 and 0.55 and drops to a very low value as a monolayer is approached. Contrary to other investigations, it was found by Alpert (15) that the initial probability is low. The explanation has been suggested that this can be attributed to the need for nucleation centers. s usually decreases with increasing temperature. The values are typical for metals. Semiconductors are different. The Sb(111) face of GaSb has maximum sticking coefficients of 10^{-5} and 10^{-6} for oxygen and CO_2 (16).

Hydrogen, oxygen, and nitrogen are chemisorbed as atoms on tungsten surfaces, while CO is adsorbed without dissociation. Their adsorption is nonactivated. Hickmott (17) found that, at 77°K, hydrogen is adsorbed on tungsten primarily as atoms, with molecular hydrogen adsorbed on top of the atomically chemisorbed layer.   But Simonov et al. (17a) observed that the initial sticking coefficient of 0.1 for H_2 on a titanium film increases four to five times when the metal is cooled below $-170°C$ and chemical reactions such as methane formation cease.   (See also Figs. 6-12 and 6-14.)   They propose the explanation that the hydrogen is adsorbed in molecular form at low temperatures since only one active site is required for molecular adsorption whereas two are needed for atomic adsorption.

Another effect that has had little attention, so far, is the replacement of one adsorbed gas by another.   Robins (18) showed that CO partially replaces H_2 on polycrystalline tungsten wire at room temperature.   Pasternak and Wiesendanger (19) found that H_2 was gradually replaced by N_2 on Mo.   Surfaces can also cause the recombination of atoms.   Wood and Wise (20) measured the recombination coefficient for hydrogen, nitrogen, and oxygen atoms at some metal surfaces at different temperatures.   It varied between 10^{-3} for oxygen on platinum at 380°K and 0.4 for hydrogen on titanium between 300 and 600°K.

Adsorption can cause erroneous readings, if a gage is connected to a system through a tube.   A typical case is the vapor of pump oil. Blears (21) was the first to demonstrate that a gage connected to a vacuum system through a tube does not register the vapor of pump oil, because of the trapping effect of the connecting tube.   A nude gage (see Sec. 5-6) located in the vacuum vessel must be used.   For a more recent investigation, see Ref. (21a).   If gage pumping is negligible, the pressure in the tubulated gage will be the equilibrium pressure of the adsorbed oil for the existing coverage of the surface.   As more oil is adsorbed, the coverage increases until, after a long time, the pressure becomes equal to the pressure of the oil in the nude gage.

Apgar (22) reports that nude gages indicate much higher pressures than tubulated gages in ultrahigh vacuum.   In the case of CO, at a nude-gage pressure of 10^{-7} torr, the tubulated gage indicated 10^{-9} torr (tubulation 7 in. long, $\frac{1}{2}$-in. diameter, half glass, half stainless steel) for a number of minutes.   The difference persists longer at lower pressures and disappears at higher pressures.   The effect was less pronounced with H_2 and N_2 and absent with He.   Raising the pressure above 10^{-6} torr or heating the tubulation to 300°C eliminated the effect.

It has been believed that the conductance of a tube is reduced by adsorption because of an increased transit time of the molecules. They are not immediately reflected but stick to the wall.   This has been clarified by Clausing (23).   If the surface is in equilibrium with

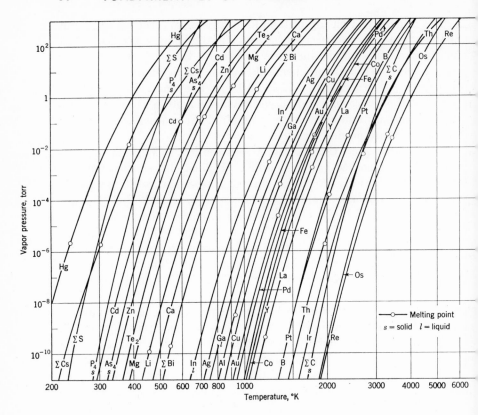

Fig. 3-16 Vapor-pressure curves for solid and liquid elements. (From R. E. Honig, *RCA Rev.*, vol. 23, p. 567, 1962.)

the gas, the same number of molecules, though not necessarily the same ones, leave and arrive at the surface.

If Cs, Rb, or K vapor impinges on a hot tungsten surface, all atoms are adsorbed, and most of them are desorbed as ions. These and other surface ionizations have been studied extensively and were reviewed by Zandberg and Ionov (24). The ionization is appreciable whenever the work function ϕ of the surface is higher than the ionization potential I of the vapor and the temperature of the surface is high enough to avoid complete coverage with condensed vapor. The ratio of ions to atoms evaporating from unit area in unit time in equilibrium is

$$R = \frac{s_+}{s_a} \frac{w_+}{w_a} \exp\left[- \frac{(I - \phi)e}{kT} \right] \tag{3-30}$$

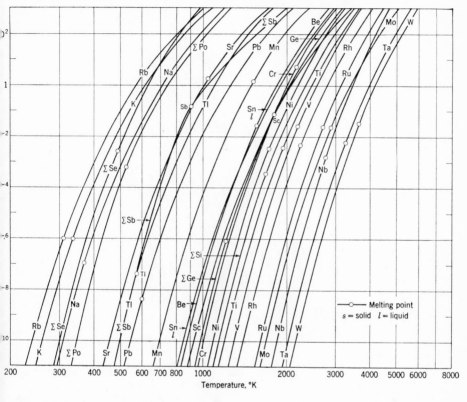

Fig. 3-17 Vapor-pressure curves for solid and liquid elements. (From R. E. Honig, *RCA Rev.*, vol. 23, p. 567, 1962.)

where s_+ and s_a are the sticking coefficients of ions and atoms, w_+ and w_a the statistical weights of the ionic and atomic states of an adsorbed atom, and e is the ionic charge.

3-5 Evaporation and Dissociation

The vapor pressure P_v of a substance is derived thermodynamically from the Clausius-Clapeyron equation:

$$\frac{dP_v}{dT} = \frac{H_B}{T(v_G - v_B)} \tag{3-31}$$

where H_B is the latent heat of evaporation and v is the specific volume, the reciprocal of the density. The subscript G refers to the gas and

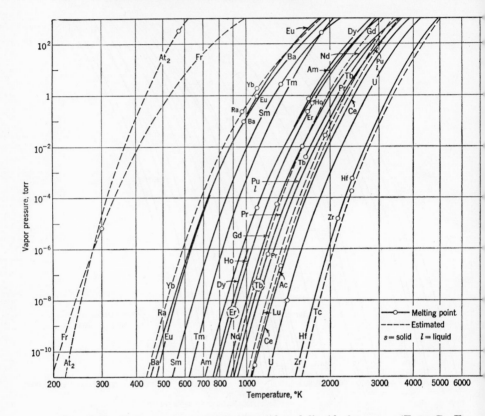

Fig. 3-18 Vapor-pressure curves for solid and liquid elements. (From R. E. Honig, *RCA Rev.*, vol. 23, p. 567, 1962.)

the subscript B to the bulk substance, solid or liquid. In vacuum, $v_G \gg v_B$, and the specific molar volume $v_G = RT/P_v$, from Eq. (1-2b). We assume that H_B is a constant. Then

$$P_v = C \exp\left(-\frac{H_B}{RT}\right) \qquad (3\text{-}32)$$

or $$\log P_v = A - \frac{B}{T} \qquad (3\text{-}33)$$

Equation (3-33) is a convenient form for calculations. Figures (3-16) to (3-20) show vapor pressures of some elements. Nesmeyanov (26a) wrote a monograph on the vapor pressure of the elements.

Evaporation of a bulk substance is similar to a physical desorption with the same exponential dependence on H/RT. When equilibrium exists between the solid or liquid and gaseous phases, the rate

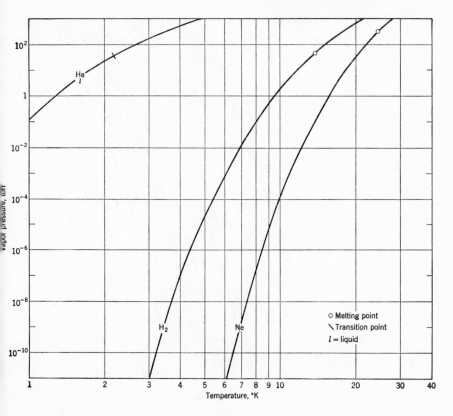

Fig. 3-19 Vapor-pressure curves of common gases. (From R. E. Honig and H. O. Hook, *RCA Rev.*, vol. 21, p. 360, 1960.)

of evaporation W equals the rate of condensation, or, by Eq. (3-20),

$$W = ms_v P_v (2\pi mkT)^{-\frac{1}{2}} = 0.058 s_v P_{v,\text{torr}} \left(\frac{M}{T^{\circ}{}_K}\right)^{\frac{1}{2}}$$

$$\text{g/cm}^2 \text{ sec} \quad (3\text{-}34)$$

The sticking probability s_v is unity for metals in equilibrium with their own vapor. The evaporation rate W remains the same if no equilibrium exists and more substance evaporates than condenses, since the supply is not limited.

The vapor pressure P_v changes rapidly with temperature. This influence determines the dependence of evaporation rate on temperature rather than the $T^{-\frac{1}{2}}$ term. Equation (3-34) permits one to predict the growth rate of evaporated films. It can also be used as Langmuir

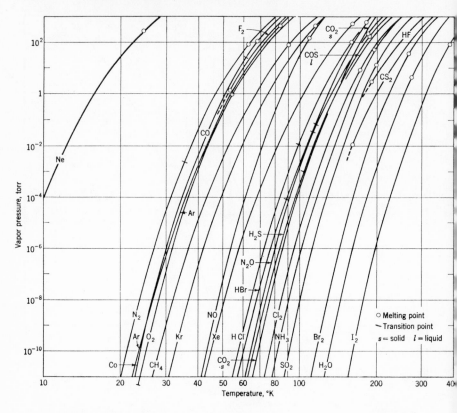

Fig. 3-20 Vapor-pressure curves of common gases. (From R. E. Honig and H. O. Hook, *RCA Rev.*, vol. 21, p. 360, 1960.)

did to determine small vapor pressures from the loss of substance. Evaporation in vacuum has many industrial applications. Reference (27) is a comprehensive text on the subject.

If a particle is in poor thermal contact with a wall, rapid evaporation by application of vacuum can cause considerable cooling, with subsequent reduction of evaporation until an equilibrium is reached between the rather poor heat transfer to the particle and evaporation cooling. If water is present in a system, this effect can delay the removal of the water by pumping, unless the water is heated by radiation from a hot surface. Otherwise, the water might freeze.

At any given temperature a compound is in equilibrium with its decomposition products, in accordance with the law of mass action. If the partial pressures of the gaseous decomposition products are reduced below the equilibrium value, the compound dissociates. This can occur in vacuum. For example, the equilibrium pressure of oxygen over Ag_2O is 0.164 torr at room temperature. Hence Ag_2O dissociates in vacuum.

3-6   Ion-Surface Interactions

In the preceding two sections we dealt with neutral atoms and molecules. Their average thermal energy is 0.026 eV at room temperature. We shall now discuss the effects of surface bombardment by ions of about 10^1 to 10^4 eV. Fast neutral atoms can be generated by charge exchange. They are expected to behave similarly in many cases since ions of higher ionization energy are neutralized when approaching the surface. The only difference is that they cannot produce Auger electrons (see below). When hitting a surface, some ions are reflected either as ions, metastables, or neutrals. The others penetrate and are trapped. Some are spontaneously emitted, and some are released by the sputtering of the parent metal or by more specific interaction with the bombarding particle. Most experiments have been conducted with noble gases to avoid chemical reactions. Metal (and some semiconductor) surfaces were preferably used in order to establish easily a definite surface potential. Ion bombardment of metal surfaces was reviewed by Colligon (28).

When an ion of moderate energy (< 2 keV) and sufficiently high ionization energy approaches a metal surface, an electron from the conduction band can combine with the ion into an excited state. The energy emitted when it drops to the ground state causes the emission of an Auger or secondary electron from the surface. The ionization energy must be higher than the sum of the energies of the work function of the metal and the excited state. The secondary-electron yield is around 10 per cent and decreases when the surface is not clean. This electron emission may affect the wall potential in a glass bulb and the collector current of ion gages and mass spectrometers. But any such effect will be included in the calibration.

The momentum has to be conserved in an atom-electron collision. It follows that a maximum fraction $4m_a m_e/(m_a + m_e)^2 \approx 4m_e/m_a$ of kinetic energy can be transferred from the atom to an electron. The effective mass of the electrons in a metal can differ greatly from the mass of the free electrons. On account of the small mass ratio, electrons are ejected by this process at higher energies only, e.g., above 500 eV for neutral A on Mo [Ref. (29)].

Hagstrum (30) studied the reflection of noble-gas ions of 100 to

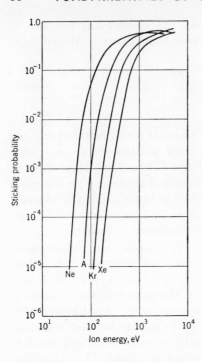

Fig. 3-21a Sticking probability of noble gas on tungsten as a function of ion energy for low concentration. (From E. V. Kornelsen, *Can. J. Phys.*, vol. 42, p. 364, 1964.)

1000 eV from metals, Si and Ge, and found a very low reflection coefficient $(1 - s)$ for reflection as ions; reflection of ions as metastables was equally small for low energies but increased up to 0.04 for 1000 eV. He determined the number of metastables by the yield of secondary electrons produced by the impact of the metastables on a metallic collector. Kornelsen (31) found initial trapping or sticking probabilities of less than 10 percent at 100 eV (see Fig. 3-21a) for noble gases on tungsten. Apparently the ions are reflected as neutrals which do not generate secondary electrons. At low energies the trapping probability was greater for lighter atoms. Kornelsen investigated also the ion trapping at larger concentrations for argon on tungsten, as shown in Fig. 3-21b. The trapping probability is independent of the number of trapped ions for low gas concentrations in the metal. At higher concentrations the concentration increases more slowly until saturation is reached. At higher ion energies, the trapping probability and the saturation concentration are larger. The amount of trapped gas was determined by thermal desorption. Such desorption patterns reveal activation energies ranging from 33 to 105 kcal/mole for noble gases of 40 to 5000 eV energy in tungsten. The highest energy could be associated with normal impurity diffusion of the gas.

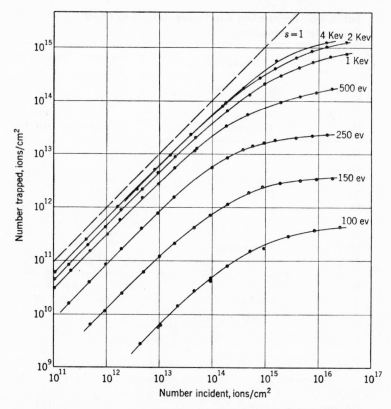

Fig. 3-21*b* Number of ions trapped versus number of incident ions for argon on tungsten at various ion energies. (From E. V. Kornelsen, *Can. J. Phys.*, vol. 42, p. 364, 1964.)

In penetrating, the ions transfer their energy to the lattice in nuclear collisions. Table 3-6 lists some penetration depths (a linear relation between depth and energy is assumed). Accurate determinations were made by trapping radioactive gases and measuring the activity while the metal was gradually removed by an accurately controlled etching process. Such a curve for krypton in tungsten is shown in Fig. 3-22.

Gas is reemitted spontaneously. The Westinghouse group studied the reemission of gas from Mo and Ni after the bombardment ceased and found that the rate of reemission of N_0 trapped ions at a time t after bombardment ceased could be represented by

$$\frac{dN}{dt} = N_0 k t^{-1} \tag{3-35}$$

Table 3-6   Penetration depths normalized to 1 keV for Various Gas-metal Combinations

Bombarding ion	Target material	Energy used, keV	Depth/keV, Å units
Ne	Silver	60	1.7
H or H_2	Aluminum	1–25	200
He	Aluminum	1–25	150
H			80
H_2			40
He	ZnS:Ag powder	20	90
Ne	Phosphor		50
N_2			25
A			25
Ce^{134} + Ce	Germanium	4	250
N_2	Ilford C-2 emulsion film	20,000	6.5
He			10
A	Cu_3Au alloy	4	10
Xe			10
Rb^{86}			37
Na^{24}	Aluminum	30	61.7
Cs^{137}			61.7
H_2			117
He	Quartz	5–60	121
Ne			19
A			18
Kr			15
Li	Aluminum	1–2	10
	Molybdenum		4.1
A	Tungsten	1.7	5.0
	Platinum		3.2
He	Single-crystal silicon	30	300

SOURCE: J. S. Colligon, *Vacuum*, vol. 11, p. 272, 1961.

for moderate gas concentrations in the metal.   The ion energy was about 150 eV. k ranges from 3.2×10^{-3} for Kr in Ni to 0.15 for A in Mo [Ref. (32)].   The target temperature was 250 to 300°C.

Obviously Eq. (3-35) can apply only for a limited time interval when t is neither very small nor very large.   Equation (3-35) was con-

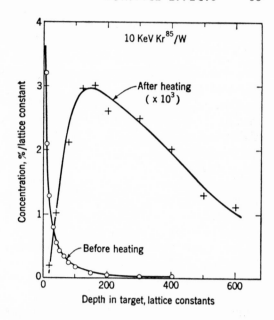

Fig. 3-22 Depth distributions of radioactive krypton in tungsten after bombardment with 10^{12} ions/cm² and heating to 2400°K. (From E. V. Kornelsen, *Can. J. Phys.*, vol. 42, p. 364, 1964.)

firmed by measurements from 1 to 1000 min for Kr in Ni [Ref. (32)] and from 0.03 to 10 min for He in Ni ($k = 7.2 \times 10^{-2}$) [Ref. (32a)]. In the latter case, the gas concentration was very low and the ion energy was about 100 eV. During these intervals 2 and 42 percent of the previously trapped gas was released. When the target is cooled, the trapping probability increases and k decreases. For He in Mo, it dropped from 6.5×10^{-2} to 3.4×10^{-2} when the temperature was reduced from 330 to 190°K and was less than 10^{-3} at 77°K [Ref. (32a)].

Similarly, Hobson and Edmonds (32b) found enhanced ion pumping on a cold glass surface when pumping He and Ne ionically into the glass wall of an ion gage covered with a thin conducting film of tin oxide. When it was cooled to 77°K, the pumping speed for He increased ninefold. All additionally pumped gas was spontaneously desorbed when the gage was warmed to room temperature, indicating low activation energy of desorption. It was possible that some nonionic pumping occurred. Simonov et al. (17a) mention the high trapping efficiency of a titanium film at 77°K for hydrogen and nitrogen ions of energies of less than a few hundred electron volts.

Smeaton et al. (33) investigated the desorption of ionically pumped argon of 250 eV maximum energy from glass at temperatures ranging from -75 to $+300°C$. For $1 < t < 100$ min, the rates were proportional to t^{-x}, where x depended on the pumping condition. If the same total amount of gas was pumped at a slower rate, x was smaller. Apparently more ions with low desorption energies were reemitted during the pumping, and more ions were trapped at sites of higher desorption energies. Again the reemission rate decreased when the temperature was lowered.

Gas is also released by the sputtering of the target. Spontaneous reemission and gas release by sputtering produce saturation with an equilibrium gas distribution in the target. This has been calculated for a simplified model by Kuchai and Rodin (34). They make the following assumptions: An ion current of constant density Q_0 hits the surface. All ions penetrate to the same depth l. From there they diffuse, and the diffusion coefficient is independent of concentration and coordinates. The concentration is zero at the surface. The surface recedes with a velocity v on account of the sputtering. Under these conditions, saturation will occur and an amount of $Q_0 l/v$ of gas will accumulate in the metal per unit surface area.

Carter et al. (35) treated the sorption with sputtering but without diffusion. They deduced the form of the penetration function from observable data. For 1-keV argon ions on molybdenum, they found a distinct, most probable range, with a considerable tail of higher penetration. Actual values of saturation sorption are listed in Tables 3-7 and 6-4. In Table 3-7, the ion energy is normalized to 1 keV, since it was found that the saturation is proportional to the energy between 300 and 3000 eV.

Under ion bombardment, gas can be released either by sputtering of the target or by a more specific process of "gas sputtering," where the gas is removed without removal of a corresponding amount of target material. Carmichael and Trendelenburg (35a) bombarded a Ni target with one noble gas and measured the amount released when the surface was sputtered afterward with another noble gas (krypton bombardment of He, Ne, A, and vice versa). The energy was about 100 eV for both gases. Their data can be satisfactorily explained by target sputtering. Carmichael and Waters (36) released He^3 by bombarding with He^4, and vice versa. They found that their data are consistent with gas release by gas sputtering where a trapped particle is released when a bombarding particle replaces it in the trapping site.

Similar experiments were conducted by James and Carter (37)

Table 3-7 Maximum Number of Ions Sorbed per cm^2/keV Energy

	Helium	Neon	Argon	Krypton	Actual voltage, keV	Ion bombardment
Uranium			1.00×10^{15}	0.72×10^{13}	40	8×10^{17} ions
Germanium			3.56×10^{14}		0.4	2×10^{16}
Nickel ⎫*		6.23×10^{15}		6.22×10^{13}	0.10	4.45×10^{15}
Nickel ⎭				6.12×10^{13}	0.18	4.5×10^{15}
Molybdenum ⎫*	1.71×10^{17}	1.5×10^{16}	3.0×10^{15}	1.8×10^{15}	1.1	2×10^{17}
Molybdenum ⎭			3.8×10^{15}		1	2×10^{17}
Tungsten ⎫*	1.7×10^{16}	6.7×10^{15}	1.6×10^{15}	2.8×10^{14}	2	3×10^{16}
Tungsten ⎭		7.2×10^{15}		6.3×10^{14}	1	4×10^{16}
Platinum					1	3×10^{17}
Silver		5×10^{14}	3.5×10^{15}	1.0×10^{15}	60	6×10^{16}

* Two different investigators.

SOURCE: J. S. Colligon, *Vacuum*, vol. 11, p. 272, 1961.

Table 3-8   Threshold Energies (eV) for Sputtering

	Ne	A	Kr	Xe	Hg		Ne	A	Kr	Xe	Hg
Be	12	15	15	15		Mo	24	24	28	27	32
Al	13	13	15	18	18	Rh	25	24	25	25	
Ti	22	20	17	18	25	Pd	20	20	20	15	20
V	21	23	25	28	25	Ag	12	15	15	17	
Cr	22	22	18	20	23	Ta	25	26	30	30	30
Fe	22	20	25	23	25	W	35	33	30	30	30
Co	20	25	22	22		Re	35	35	25	30	35
Ni	23	21	25	20		Pt	27	25	22	22	25
Cu	17	17	16	15	20	Au	20	20	20	18	
Ge	23	25	22	18	25	Th	20	24	25	25	
Zr	23	22	18	25	30	U	20	23	25	22	27
Nb	27	25	26	32							

SOURCE: R. V. Stuart and G. K. Wehner, *J. Appl. Phys.*, vol. 33, p. 2345, 1962.

with glass as the target.   They conclude that gas sputtering occurs. The bombarding ion transfers energy to the glass which in turn transfers the desorption energy (< 2 eV) to the trapped atom.   One indication of this process is the very high yield of the gas release, many times higher than the sputtering yield for glass.

Several theories of sputtering have been advanced, but a detailed quantitative understanding of the process is still lacking. The older literature was reviewed by Wehner (38).   Wolsky (38a) published a shorter review article more recently.   In single crystals the energy given to a lattice atom can cause sputtering by a chain mechanism of momentum transfer, with a preferred direction of sputtering along closely packed lines of atoms terminating at the surface.   This causes characteristic patterns of sputtered atoms which have been observed.   But not all chains reach the surface, and displaced atoms also diffuse to the surface.   Table 3-8 shows threshold energies for noble gases and Hg.   Figure 3-23 gives typical yields near threshold for argon.   Sputtering starts around 20 eV and increases very steeply in the beginning.   Some sputtering coefficients are given in Table 3-9.

In general, heavier ions have larger yields, as is to be expected. Metal targets that amalgamate exhibit increased sputtering for mercury.   The yield becomes constant for higher energy.   It is 6 for copper bombarded by argon between 10 and 60 keV.   The maximum yield for helium ions on copper is only 0.2 at 16 keV because of the smaller mass.   Figure 3-24 tabulates the sputtering yield of 45-keV

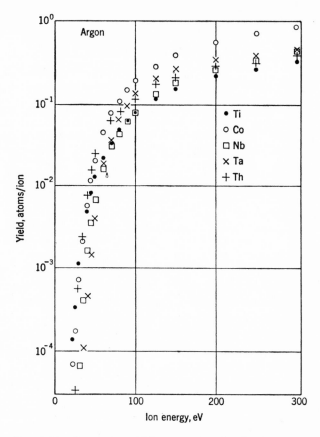

Fig. 3-23 Sputtering-yield curves for bombardment of metals with argon ions of low energy. Ion current not corrected for secondary electrons. (From R. V. Stuart and G. K. Wehner, *J. Appl. Phys.*, vol. 3, p. 2345, 1962.)

ions of many elements on Ag, Cu, and Ta targets. Zero sputtering means that the ions build up in a layer which protects the target underneath. Although the ion energy is higher than the range under discussion, the figure is reproduced in view of the large amount of elements investigated. A correlation with the periodic table is obvious.

Sputtering is an effective means for cleaning surfaces. Hagstrum and D'Amico (41) cleaned tungsten by bombardment with helium and neon of 100-eV energy. The cleanliness of the surface was judged by the emissivity for Auger (secondary) electrons. To clean a surface with a minimum of gas adsorption, a low voltage, perhaps 70

Table 3-9 Sputtering Coefficients for Various Gas-metal Combinations

Ion energy, keV / Ion	0.4 He	2 He	5 He	0.4 Ne	0.6 Ne	1 Ne	5 Ne	0.4 A	0.6 A	1 A	3 A	5 A	0.4 Kr	0.8 Xe	0.2 Hg	0.4 Hg	0.8 Hg	2 Hg	3 Hg	10 Hg
Tungsten				0.34	0.32				0.62						0.3	0.54	1.3	2.0	2.75	3.0
Molybdenum				0.44	0.54				0.93						0.1	0.44	1.0	2.0	2.75	5.0
Platinum					0.7				1.56						0.5					10.0
Aluminum				0.68	0.83				1.24						0.14	0.45		1.5		
Silver		0.36	0.48	1.6	1.98	2.3* 2.4*	5.5* 5.5*		3.4	5.1* 4.6*	7.0	9.2			0.85					22.5
Germanium	0.08			0.63	0.82			0.92	1.27				0.91	1.41	0.21	0.63	1.23			
Nickel					1.34				1.52						0.5		1.4		3.6	7.0
Iron				0.76	0.97				1.26						0.13	0.5	1.1	2.0	2.75	4.5
Copper				1.53											0.54					12.0
Gold				1.0											1.0			8.0		21.0

* Two different investigators.

SOURCE: J. S. Colligon, *Vacuum*, vol. 11, p. 272, 1961.

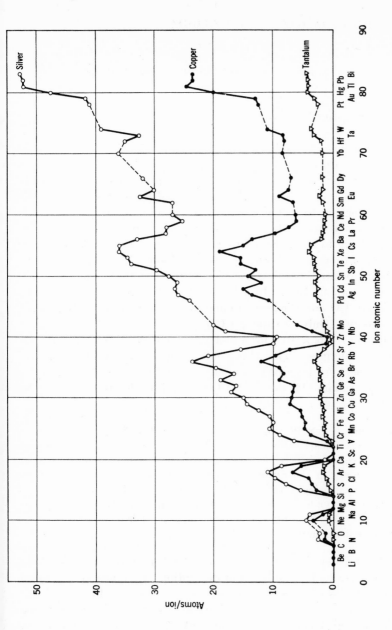

Fig. 3-24 Sputtering ratios S for different ions of 45-keV energy. Experimental errors are ± 10 percent. (In order to get comparable values, $S - 1$ is plotted instead of the three self-sputtering ratios.) (From O. Almen and G. Bruce, 1961 *Vacuum Symp. Trans.*, p. 245, 1962; or *Nucl. Instr. Methods*, vol. 11, p. 279, 1961.)

to 100 V, should be used, since the sticking coefficient drops more rapidly than the sputtering coefficient as the ion energy is lowered.

3-7 Desorption by Electrons

A surface can be heated by electron bombardment. This may cause gas desorption and surface evaporation. Here we are not concerned with such thermal effects but with specific electron reactions. The maximum energy fraction that can be transferred by collision from an electron to a free atom of molecular mass M is only $2.2 \times 10^{-3}/M$, on account of the small mass ratio. Hence the effects of slow electrons have to be explained by electronic excitation A number of such interactions have been reported. Moore (42) found that solid SrO is dissociated by slow electrons (up to 400-eV energy). The efficiency is about 10^{-7}. In a later paper (43), he described the dissociation of CO adsorbed on Mo and W by electrons of 300-eV maximum energy. Only O^+ and no CO^+, C^+, O_2^+, or CO_2^+ was found. The efficiency is 6×10^{-5} for a monolayer and 85 eV, and slightly less at higher energies. The threshold energy is about 18 eV. His detector was very insensitive to neutrals, and none were found.

Petermann (44) desorbed CO from Ni by electron impact. He states:

The efficiency is 8×10^{-8} molecules/electron at 270 eV for strongly bound surface layers (nickel oxide containing carbon); the desorption mechanism probably involves dissociation. Gas yield is proportional to electron bombardment power in the range investigated [160–270 V, 1–10 mA]. On the other hand, a much higher efficiency of 1.9×10^{-2} molecules/electron at 270 eV is observed for an adsorbed layer of CO on pure nickel. Gas yield is proportional to electron bombardment current and independent of electron energy in the range investigated [100–300 V, 1–10 mA].

He did not determine what fraction was released as ions or neutrals.

Redhead (45) studied the desorption of oxygen from molybdenum. At 90-eV electron energy, the ionization efficiency has a maximum of 10^{-5} ions/electron. Fifty atoms are released for each ion. The ion energy has a maximum at 6 eV. He presents a theoretical model that explains the observed facts. Many more atoms than ions are released, because of the high probability of Auger neutralization of the ions near the surface. Ions desorbed from the grid of an ion gage increase the collector current [Ref. (46)]. (See Sec. 5-6.)

Todd et al. (47) studied the gassing of baked glasses covered with a 1000-Å-thick layer of aluminum when bombarded with 20-keV electrons. They found that, for Pyrex 7740, the initial rate is about 10^{-3} torr liter/sec cm^2 amp. At least 95 percent was oxygen. Quartz had the smallest gassing rate. Since the temperature rose to 250°C, heat was at least a contributing factor. In a second paper Lineweaver (47a) proposed the following oxygen-release mechanism. The high-energy electrons come to rest at some depth inside the glass. Their charge produces a field in the glass between the electrons and the grounded aluminum layer. Positive (e.g., Na) ions move toward the electron layer and oxygen ions drift toward the surface.

Organic molecules adsorbed at a surface are cross-linked by electron bombardment and form a solid polymer film. Christy (48) investigated the formation of a thin insulating film by bombarding adsorbed molecules of silicone diffusion-pump oil DC 704 with electrons of 225-V energy. At 25°C he found a deposition rate of 0.3 Å/sec for a beam current of 0.4 ma/cm^2. Saturation was approached at this current density. The deposition rate decreases with increasing temperature of the substrate because of the reduced sojourn of the molecules on the surface.

Garbe (48a) found in a similar experiment with the same oil that mainly H$_2$ was given off. The yield increased with increasing electron energy. The evolution reached a value of 2×10^{-3} torr l /amp sec at 150 eV and remained constant at higher energies up to 600 eV. The coverage, though not known, was more than a mono-layer. A similar effect may exist under ion bombardment and could account for the reported formation of an insulated layer on the collector of an ion gage in the presence of silicone oil.

3-8   Photon Desorption

Few papers have been published on this subject, although this phenomenon is of increasing interest in thermonuclear investigations. Terenin and Solonitzin (49) gave a review of some older Russian work. Carbon monoxide was desorbed from nickel at wavelengths below 2400 Å and water from cadmium and zinc ($\lambda < 2500$ Å), the latter under partial dissociation.

Lange and Riemersma (50) studied the desorption of CO from a monolayer on nickel and found a maximum yield of about 2×10^{-8}/ photon for an energy of about 3.7 eV (3350 Å). About the same yield was found for CO on W by Lange (51) for 3.9 to 5.9 eV. But two peculiarities were noted:

1. Immediately after a bake no desorption was noticeable.

2. The tungsten ribbon was flashed and CO was usually adsorbed for 20 min at 1.6×10^{-9} torr. After 165 min of adsorption, up to 10 times as much CO can be desorbed, either by irradiation or by heating the tungsten ribbon to a temperature about equal to the temperature attained under irradiation. Such heating had a negligible effect after the 20-min adsorption. This indicates that CO, which was adsorbed later, had a smaller desorption energy.

Medved (51a) observed a pressure rise, presumably due to desorbed oxygen, when he illuminated ZnO with the visible light from an incandescent lamp.

3-9 Production of Gaseous Compounds by Surface Reactions

Gas not only is chemisorbed or forms a nonvolatile compound at a surface but also can combine and form a volatile one. Such a reaction is the production of methane when hydrogen ions bombard a surface containing carbon. Chemical reactions that occur at the surface of hot filaments are most important, since they change the gas composition in ion gages and mass spectrometers. Pump oil is cracked. Oxygen in contact with a hot tungsten filament forms CO_2 and CO with the carbon in the tungsten. This has been thoroughly investigated by Becker et al. (52). The carbon can be removed by heating the filament in O_2 of 10^{-6} torr pressure at 2200°K for 10 to 60 hr. Schissel (53) found that CO and O_2 are formed in a CO_2 atmosphere at a tungsten filament. A thoria-coated iridium filament acts probably similarly. Hence the sensitivity of an ion gage for CO_2 is affected by the filament temperature.

Hydrogen is dissociated at a hot tungsten surface, and CO, H_2O, and CH_4 are produced in a glass envelope [(54), (55)]. Probably the carbon comes from the filament and the oxygen from the glass wall. Table 3-10 shows the amount of H_2O, CO, and CH_4 produced in hydrogen by a tungsten and thoria-coated iridium filament in a glass envelope. The approximate temperatures of the filaments were 2070 and 1680°K, respectively. The amount was proportional to the hydrogen pressure from 10^{-7} to 10^{-5} torr, the range covered by this investigation. Therefore, it is given in torr of hydrogen. The values are poorly reproduced and are only an order-of-magnitude indication.

If a temperature differential exists in a vacuum, a substance may form, at one temperature, a gaseous compound that is decomposed elsewhere in the system at another temperature, because of a

Table 3-10   Amount of Gas in Torr
Liters/cm^2 Torr Sec Produced in H$_2$ of
10^{-7} to 10^{-5} Torr Pressure by a Hot
Filament in a Glass Envelope

	W	$ThO_2\ on\ Ir$
H$_2$O	6×10^{-3}	1.5×10^{-4}
CO	1.5×10^{-3}	3×10^{-3}
CH$_4$	5×10^{-4}	6×10^{-4}

SOURCE: G. Martin, private communication.

shift of the equilibrium.   Tungsten reacts with water vapor in such a
manner.   A volatile tungsten oxide is formed at a hot filament.   This
oxide sublimes and deposits on the wall.   There it is reduced by the
hydrogen liberated in the first reaction, and the newly formed water
vapor reacts again with the filament.   Hence the water is not used up
in this "water cycle," and the tungsten gives the impression of an
excessive evaporation rate.

It is generally advisable to operate filaments at low tempera-
tures and, therefore, to use a filament with a low work function, such as
ThO$_2$-coated tungsten or iridium.   Practical filaments are discussed in
Sec. 5-10.

3-10   Gassing and Degassing of Surfaces

Gassing can be caused by surface desorption and diffusion of
gas from the inside of the solid to the vacuum surface, possibly with
replenishing of the gas by diffusion into the solid from the outside.
The latter case constitutes permeation.

Permeation constants were given in Figs. 3-2 and 3-3.   Permeation is generally small in metals, glasses, and ceramics at room temperature.   Hydrogen permeates Pd and, to a lesser but still appreciable
extent, Fe and Ni.   This becomes noticeable only if hydrogen is
present in large concentration, e.g., by the corrosion of a steel container in water.

Helium permeation through glass and quartz is not negligible in
ultrahigh vacuum.   The equilibrium pressure of helium in the atmosphere is 4×10^{-3} torr (Table 6-1).   The helium pressure in a bulb of
5-cm diameter, 8-cm length, and 1-mm wall thickness, made of pyrex
7740 glass, will rise to 10^{-6} torr in 2 months under steady-state condi-

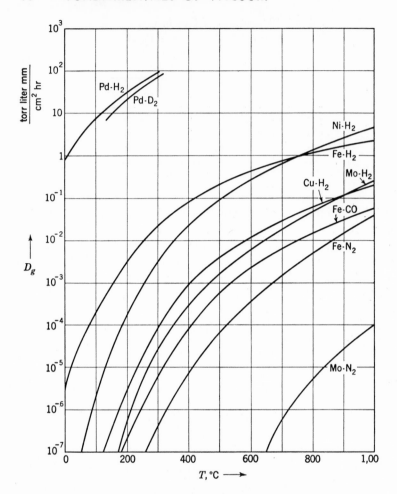

Fig. 3-25 Gas permeation of metal walls versus temperature. Permeation rate D_g is the pressure rise per hour in a vessel of 1-liter volume for a wall area of 1 cm², a wall thickness of 1 mm, and a gas pressure of 760 torr on the outside. T is the temperature of the wall. (From M. von Ardenne, Tabellen Elektronenphysik Ionenphysik und Übermikroskopie, vol. 2, VEB Deutscher Verlag der Wissenschaften, Berlin, 1956.)

tions, because of the helium permeating from the atmosphere. If this flask is a sealed-off ion gage with a pumping speed of 3×10^{-3} liter/sec for helium, the equilibrium pressure will be 10^{-11} torr. The permeation can be avoided by a neutral atmosphere or vacuum on the outside, or the use of special glasses, e.g., Corning 1720.

Figure 3-25 shows the permeation of gases through metals as a

function of temperature.   Nitrogen begins to permeate steel at bakeout temperature.   Around 800°C, a wall temperature reached in the
processing of some electronic tubes, permeation is appreciable.   The
permeation of H_2 through Pd, O_2 through Ag, and He through quartz
at elevated temperatures is utilized for the purification of these gases
(see Sec. 7-7).   The permeation of plastics is quite high.   This is the
cause of high gassing rates of some gaskets.   It is discussed in Sec. 7-3.
Figure 3-2, Table 7-1, and Refs. (2) and (57) give data on permeation
and diffusion for some plastics.

Like permeation, desorption of absorbed gas depends on the
value of the diffusion coefficient.   Let us calculate the gassing of a
semi-infinite iron slab saturated with hydrogen at STP, owing to
diffusion at room temperature.   It follows from Figs. 3-25 and 3-9
that the permeation constant K is 3.7×10^{-10} cm^3 (STP)/sec at
760 torr for 1-cm thickness, and the diffusion coefficient is

$$D = 2.5 \times 10^{-9} \text{ cm}^2/\text{sec}$$

hence $s = K/D = 0.15$ at 760 torr.   The initial concentration is
$c_0 = 0.15$ cm^3 (STP) of hydrogen in each cubic centimeter of iron or
0.11 torr liter.   This value appears to be somewhat high when compared with the data of Fig. 3-6 for higher temperatures.   From Eq.
(3-12), the gassing rate after 3 hr is

$$Q = c_0 \left(\frac{D}{\pi t}\right)^{\frac{1}{2}} = 0.11 \left(\frac{2.5 \times 10^{-9}}{3.14 \times 3 \times 3600}\right)^{\frac{1}{2}}$$
$$= 3 \times 10^{-8} \qquad \text{torr liter/sec cm}^2$$

All other gases have much lower diffusion coefficients.   Hence desorption of adsorbed rather than absorbed gas causes the gassing of metals
at room temperature.   Plastics desorb large amounts of absorbed
water.   Schram (62a) found that gassing rates of plastics were proportional to $t^{-\frac{1}{2}}$ as typical for diffusion whereas those of many unbaked
metals were approximately proportional to t^{-1}.

The surface reactions that we have discussed are too complicated to permit an accurate calculation of the gassing of surfaces in
vacuum.   Therefore, the practical approach has been to measure the
gassing rates of the various materials under conditions comparable to
customary vacuum operations.   A comprehensive list of outgassing
rates can be found in Dayton's article (57) on degassing.   Typical
gassing rates at room temperature are listed in Table 3-11.   The
values apply for reasonably clean materials, washed or degreased and/
or baked in air or in vacuum.   In metal and glass systems, mostly

Table 3-11   Gassing Rates at Room Temperature in Torr Liters/cm² sec

Material	After a few hours of pumping	After a 24-hr bake	Bakeout temp., °C	Ref.
Nylon 51	2×10^{-8} (51 hr)	4×10^{-11}	120	(59)
Araldite CT200 + HT901	5×10^{-8} (51 hr)	10^{-10}	100	(59)
Neoprene	10^{-6}			(57)
Viton A	7×10^{-8} (52 hr)	1.3×10^{-9}	200	(60)
Teflon	10^{-8}–10^{-7}	Low	250	(57),(61)
Glass	10^{-9}–10^{-8}	10^{-15}–10^{-14}	400	(62)
Ceramic	10^{-9}–10^{-8}	10^{-15}–10^{-14}	400	(57),(62)
Metal	10^{-9}–10^{-8} (10^{-10} after 50–100 hr)	10^{-15}–10^{-14}	400	(62),(63)

H_2O, with some CO and H_2, desorbs from the surface in the beginning. As the pressure drops, about the same amount of H_2O and CO is present with some H_2. Hence, adsorbed water vapor and CO are mainly desorbed.

It would be interesting to know how the pumping speed S (see Sec. 4-1) affects the degassing rate PS. It follows from Eqs. (3-21), (3-23), and (4-1) that, at temperature T,

$$-V \frac{dP}{dt} = SP - \left[\frac{5 \times 10^{-8} T\Theta}{t_s} + 3.64 sP \left(\frac{T}{M} \right)^{\frac{1}{2}} \right] A \qquad (3\text{-}36)$$

After the initial pumpdown, P changes slowly with time. Therefore $V \, dP/dt \approx 0$.

$$PS \approx \left[\frac{5 \times 10^{-8} T\Theta}{t_s} - 3.64 Ps \left(\frac{T}{M} \right)^{\frac{1}{2}} \right] A \qquad (3\text{-}37)$$

To maximize degassing,

$$\frac{5 \times 10^{-8} T\Theta}{t_s} \gg 3.64 sP \left(\frac{T}{M} \right)^{\frac{1}{2}} \quad \text{or}$$

$$P \ll 1.4 \times 10^{-8} \Theta (st_s)^{-1} (MT)^{\frac{1}{2}}$$

This is the opposite situation to Eq. (3-29). Most published data state the gassing rate as a function of time and do not give P, S, or the total amount of gas removed from the sample. Measurements of $PS = f(P)$ for typical materials would yield valuable information about the necessary pumping speed and help in understanding the desorption process.

Surfaces are cleaned effectively by a gas discharge. (See Sec. 10-2.) For efficient cleaning, a substantial fraction of the desorbed surface gas must be removed before it is readsorbed by the clean, highly active surface. This requires high pumping speed with continuous gas flow. If the power input and the rate of desorption are too high, a runaway condition can develop, as in sputter-ion pumps at high pressures (see Sec. 6-6). The discharge parameters can be optimized by monitoring the impurity (H_2O, CO, CO_2, etc.) pressures with a mass spectrometer. These pressures must be a maximum for most effective cleaning. After the cleaning, the impurity pressures must be low to prevent readsorption of impurities at the surfaces. As in baking, the impurity pressure rises usually more than an order of magnitude during discharge cleaning, with a corresponding increase in throughput. Surfaces not reached by the discharge are often degassed by the high-speed pumping of the discharge-cleaned surfaces if the conductance to these surfaces is large enough. In film evaporation the substrate is often cleaned by exposure to a glow discharge. The removal of organic matter is probably accelerated by the presence of oxygen. The pressure is kept constant by admitting air through a leak valve. Because of the high temperature of a gas discharge plasma, adsorbed molecules of higher binding energy are removed also. Adsorption and reemission (Sec. 3-6) of the cleaning gas can be a problem. Cleaning by electron bombardment can be preferable.

A substantial reduction in gassing is obtained by a bake, as explained in Sec. 3-4. After the bake, no water vapor degasses from glass and metals; hydrogen predominates on metal, while approximately equal amounts of hydrogen and CO are present in a glass system. This is stated as a general guide. As is typical for all gassing, there may be large variations.

Power and Robson (63) found that, for baked samples, the gas evolution rate determined by closing off the system and measuring the rate of pressure rise gave a smaller value than the rate measured at constant pressure, while pumping with a known constant speed. The effect of temperature on gassing is shown in Fig. 3-26 from their paper. Around bakeout temperature, desorption of absorbed gas becomes noticeable.

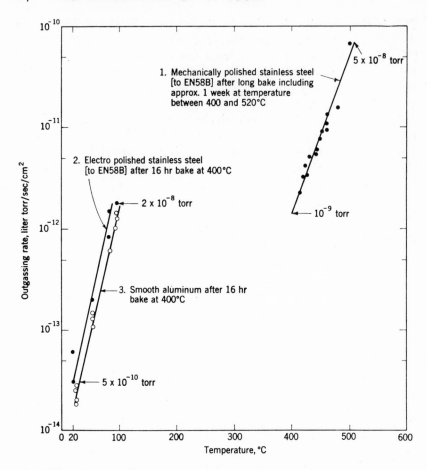

Fig. 3-26 Curves showing outgassing rate against temperature for stainless-steel and aluminum samples after specified baking histories (measured at constant pressure). (From B. D. Power and F. C. Robson, 1961 *Vacuum Symp. Trans.*, p. 1175, 1962.)

To avoid the copious adsorption and some subsequent reemission of water vapor when a system is opened to the air again, dry air (or dry nitrogen) preferably should be admitted. This reduces the pumpdown time. Power and Crawley (64) exposed a large test chamber to dry and undried air for 3 hr. The pumpdown times to 5×10^{-7} torr were 3 and 110 min.

Flecken and Noeller (65) measured the total quantity of gas desorbed from metals during a 2-hr bake at 450°C. The samples were cylinders of 2-cm diameter and 0.2-cm height. Degreasing had some influence.   The amount of gas given off was reduced up to 43 percent. A vacuum degassing of stainless steel at 800°C for 1 hr with subsequent exposure to the atmosphere for 1 hr caused a reduction of 88 to 97 percent, indicating that diffusion is a contributing factor.   Steel plated in various ways gave off up to 86 percent more and up to 68 percent less gas than unplated steel.   The relative amount of H_2 increased 7 to 21 times.

If metal or ceramics are operated hot, high-temperature degassing is required to reduce the gassing caused by diffusion from the interior.   The degassing temperature must be above the operating temperature to obtain more rapid depletion.   As an example, let us consider the removal of N_2 from Fe.   According to Fig. 3-9, D is 10^{-8} cm²/sec for N_2 in Fe at 800°C.   If a sheet 1 cm² and 0.02 cm thick is degassed for 1 hr, $Dt/d^2 = 10^{-8} \times 3600/4 \times 10^{-4} = 0.09$.   It follows from Table 3-2 that two-thirds of the gas is removed.

According to Fig. 3-5, the solubility of N_2 at 800°C is

$$s = 5.6 \times 10^{-2} \text{ cm}^3 \text{ (STP)}$$

for 1 cm³ of iron at 1 atm.   If it is assumed that the iron was saturated with N_2 at this temperature and 1 atm, the initial concentration is $c_0 = 5.6 \times 10^{-2}$ STP and, from Eq. (3-12), the gassing rate after 1 hr is $Q = 2 \times 5.6 \times 10^{-2}(10^{-8}/\pi 3600)^{\frac{1}{2}} = 10^{-7}$ cm³ atm/sec $= 8 \times 10^{-8}$ torr liter/sec.   Equation (3-12) is valid since the concentration in the center of the sheet has only very slightly decreased (see Fig. 3-7).   If the temperature is reduced to 600°C, D drops to 4×10^{-11} cm²/sec according to the extrapolated curve 2 of Fig. 3-9, and the gassing rate is reduced more than one order of magnitude.   After cooling in vacuum, no gas will diffuse into the material again when exposed to the atmosphere, because the diffusion coefficient is very small at room temperature.

Metals contain an amount of gas which is about 10 to 100 percent of their volume, at standard temperature and pressure.   The main constituents are CO, N_2, CO_2, H_2, and, in iron, O_2 [Ref. (58), vol. 2, p. 721].   Stainless steel (type 305) melted twice with consumable electrode in vacuum had 74 percent less O_2 and 79 percent less H_2 than air-melted steel [Ref. (66)].   Burger et al. (67) reduced the gas content of copper electrodes by zone refining.   This method may also be valuable in other cases.

A comprehensive study of the gases in metals and the various methods of degassing was undertaken by Norton and Marshall (68). In particular, they measured the gas content of molybdenum.   They found 5 percent gas (55 percent N_2, 36 percent CO, 9 percent CO_2) by volume if not cleaned at all, 0.44 to 0.82 percent (3 to 70 percent N_2, 30 to 88 percent CO, 4 to 37 percent CO_2) after firing in a tungsten vacuum furnace at about 10^{-3} torr pressure and about 1800°C for about an hour, and 0.16 to 1.2 percent (59 to 95 percent N_2, 9 to 39 percent CO, 3 to 8 percent CO_2) after firing in a H_2 furnace at 1600 to 2000°C for $\frac{1}{2}$ to 1 hr. The lowest value was obtained in high-purity H_2 diffused through Pd. No H_2 and H_2O were found, since they were pumped out during the 800° bake of the quartz container before the gas determination.

When the degassed sample was exposed to wet air for 40 hr, only chemisorbed surface gas equivalent to a monolayer or 0.05 percent (57 percent N_2, 43 percent CO) was given off during a second degassing. Again the water vapor had been removed during the bake. But 8 percent (22 percent N_2, 76 percent CO, 2 percent CO_2) was given off when a degassed sample was handled with bare hands, instead of tweezers. Similar effects of handling with hands, cotton gloves, or rubber cots were reported by Varadi (69) when measuring the gas in Ni. The gas in glass has been investigated by Garbe and Christians (70). It was found that 98 percent or more of the gas is water vapor. The total amount is about 0.1 to 1 torr liter/cm^3.

REFERENCES

(1) F. J. Norton, 1961 *Vacuum Symp. Trans.*, p. 8, 1962.

(2) H. Klumb and H. A. W. Schroeter, *Vakuum Tech.*, vol. 10, p. 175, 1961.

(3) W. A. Rogers, R. S. Buritz, and D. Alpert, *J. Appl. Phys.*, vol. 25, p. 868, 1954.

(3a) P. A. Redhead, J. P. Hobson, and E. V. Kornelsen, *Adv. Electron. Electron Phys.*, vol. 17, p. 323, 1962.

(3b) V. O. Altemose, *J. Appl. Phys.*, vol. 32, p. 1309, 1961.

(3c) H. L. Eschbach, F. Gross, and S. Schulien, *Vacuum*, vol. 13, p. 543, 1963.

(4) B. J. Todd, *J. Appl. Phys.*, vol. 26, p. 1238, 1955.

(5) W. Jost, "Diffusion in Solids, Liquids, Gases," Academic Press Inc., New York, 1960.

(6) C. Hayashi, 1957 *Vacuum Symp. Trans.*, p. 13, 1958.

(6a) G. Ehrlich, *J. Chem. Phys.*, vol. 31, p. 1111, 1959.

(7) B. M. W. Trapnell, "Chemisorption," Butterworth Scientific Publications, London, 1955.
(8) G. Ehrlich, *Ann. N.Y. Acad. Sci.*, vol. 101, art. 3, p. 722, 1963.
(8a) G. Ehrlich, 1961 *Vacuum Symp. Trans.*, p. 126, 1962.
(9) D. M. Young and A. D. Crowell, "Physical Adsorption of Gases," Butterworth Scientific Publications, Washington, D.C., 1962.
(9a) J. P. Hobson, *Brit. J. Appl. Phys.*, vol. 14, p. 544, 1963.
(10) J. Frenkel, *Z. Physik*, vol. 26, p. 117, 1924.
(11) J. H. Hobson, 1961 *Vacuum Symp. Trans.*, p. 26, 1962.
(12) J. P. Hobson, 1961 *Vacuum Symp. Trans.*, p. 146, 1962.
(13) S. Dushman and J. M. Lafferty, "Scientific Foundations of Vacuum Technique," John Wiley & Sons, Inc., New York, 1962.
(14) A. Schram, 1962 *Vacuum Symp. Trans.*, p. 301, 1963.
(14a) M. M. Dubinin and L. V. Radushkevish, *Proc. Acad. Sci. USSR*, vol. 55, p. 327, 1947.
(14b) J. P. Hobson and R. A. Armstrong, *J. Phys. Chem.*, vol. 67, p. 2000, 1963.
(14c) M. Manes and R. J. Grant, 1963 *Vacuum Symp. Trans.*, p. 122, 1964.
(15) D. Alpert, *Le Vide*, no. 97, p. 19, January, 1962.
(16) D. Haneman, *Phys. Rev.*, vol. 121, p. 1093, 1961.
(17) T. W. Hickmott, *J. Chem. Phys.*, vol. 32, p. 810, 1960.
(17a) V. A. Simonov, G. F. Kleymonov, A. G. Mileshkin, and V. A. Kochev, Nuclear Fusion, *Intern. At. Energy Agency*, 1962 Suppl., Pt. I; *AEC Transl.* 5589.
(18) J. L. Robins, 1962 *Vacuum Symp. Trans.*, p. 510, 1963.
(19) R. A. Pasternak and H. U. D. Wiesendanger, *J. Chem. Phys.*, vol. 34, p. 2062, 1961.
(20) J. B. Wood and H. Wise, "Rarefied Gas Dynamics," p. 51, Academic Press Inc., New York, 1961.
(21) J. Blears, *Proc. Royal Soc. (London), Ser. A,* vol. 188, p. 62, 1946.

(21a) R. A. Haefer and J. Hengevoss, 1960 *Vacuum Symp. Trans.*, p. 67, 1961.

(22) E. Apgar, *Proc. Second European Symp., Vacuum*, p. 223, 1963.

(23) P. Clausing, *Physica*, vol. 28, p. 298, 1962.

(24) E. Y. Zandberg and N. I. Ionov, Soviet Phys.—Usp. (*English Transl.*), vol. 2, p. 255, 1959.

(25) R. E. Honig, *RCA Rev.*, vol. 23, p. 567, 1962.

(26) R. E. Honig and H. O. Hook, *RCA Rev.*, vol. 21, p. 360, 1960.

(26a) A. N. Nesmeyanov, "Vapor Pressure of the Chemical Elements," American Elsevier Publishing Company, New York, 1963.

(27) L. Holland, "Vacuum Deposition of Thin Films," Chapman & Hall, Ltd., London, 1956.

(28) J. S. Colligon, *Vacuum*, vol. 11, p. 272, 1961.

(29) D. B. Medved, P. Mahadevan, and J. K. Layton, *Phys. Rev.*, vol. 129, p. 2086, 1963.

(30) H. D. Hagstrum, *Phys. Rev.*, vol. 123, p. 758, 1961.

(31) E. V. Kornelsen, *Can. J. Phys.*, vol. 42, p. 364, 1964.

(32) J. H. Carmichael and J. S. Knoll, 1958 *Vacuum Symp. Trans.*, p. 18, 1959.

(32a) R. E. Fox and J. S. Knoll, 1960 *Vacuum Symp. Trans.*, p. 364, 1961.

(32b) J. P. Hobson and T. Edmonds, *Can. J. Phys.*, vol. 41, p. 827, 1963.

(33) P. G. Smeaton, G. Carter, and J. H. Leck, 1962 *Vacuum Symp. Trans.*, p. 491, 1963.

(34) S. A. Kuchai and A. M. Rodin, *Soviet J. At. Energy* (*English Transl.*), vol. 4, p. 277, 1958.

(35) G. Carter, J. S. Colligon, and J. H. Leck, *Proc. Phys. Soc.* (*London*), vol. 79, p. 299, 1962.

(35a) J. H. Carmichael and E. A. Trendelenburg, *J. Appl. Phys.*, vol. 29, p. 1570, 1958.

(36) J. H. Carmichael and P. M. Waters, *J. Appl. Phys.*, vol. 33, p. 1470, 1962.

(37) L. H. James and G. Carter, 1962 *Vacuum Symp. Trans.*, p. 502, 1963; *Brit. J. Appl. Phys.*, vol. 14, p. 147, 1963.

(38) G. Wehner, *Adv. Electron. Electron Phys.*, vol. 7, p. 239, 1955.

(38a) S. P. Wolsky, 1963 *Vacuum Symp. Trans.*, p. 309, 1964.

(39) R. V. Stuart and G. K. Wehner, *J. Appl. Phys.*, vol. 33, p. 2345, 1962.

(40) O. Almen and G. Bruce, 1961 *Vacuum Symp. Trans.*, p. 245, 1962; or *Nucl. Instr. Methods*, vol. 11, p. 279, 1961.

(41) H. D. Hagstrum and C. D'Amico, *J. Appl. Phys.*, vol. 31, p. 715, 1960.

(42) G. E. Moore, *J. Appl. Phys.*, vol. 30, p. 1086, 1959.

(43) G. E. Moore, *J. Appl. Phys.*, vol. 32, p. 1241, 1961.

(44) L. A. Petermann, *Nuovo Cimento Suppl.*, Ser. 1, vol. 1, p. 601, 1963.

(45) P. A. Redhead, *Surface Phys. Colloq.*, *Can. J. Phys.*, vol. 42, p. 886, 1964.

(46) P. A. Redhead, *Vacuum*, vol. 13, p. 253, 1963.

(47) B. J. Todd, J. L. Lineweaver, and J. T. Kerr, *J. Appl. Phys.*, vol. 31, p. 51, 1960.

(47a) J. L. Lineweaver, *J. Appl. Phys.*, vol. 34, p. 1786, 1963.

(48) R. W. Christy, *J. Appl. Phys.*, vol. 31, p. 1680, 1960.

(48a) S. Garbe, *Vacuum Tech.*, vol. 12, p. 201, 1963.

(49) A. Terenin and Yu. Solonitzin, *Discussions Faraday Soc.*, vol. 28, p. 28, 1959.

(50) W. J. Lange and H. Riemersma, 1961 *Vacuum Symp. Trans.*, p. 167, 1962.

(51) W. J. Lange, *J. Vac. Sci. Techn.*, to be published.

(51a) D. B. Medved, *J. Chem. Phys.*, vol. 28, p. 870, 1958.

(52) J. A. Becker, E. J. Becker, and R. G. Brandes, *J. Appl. Phys.*, vol. 32, p. 411, 1961.

(53) P. O. Schissel, *J. Appl. Phys.*, vol. 33, p. 2659, 1962.

(54) T. W. Hickmott, *J. Appl. Phys.*, vol. 31, p. 128, 1960.

(55) V. J. Mimeault and R. S. Hansen, *Vacuum*, vol. 13, p. 229, 1963.

(56) G. Martin, private communication.

(57) B. B. Dayton, 1959 *Vacuum Symp. Trans.*, p. 101, 1960.

(58) M. von Ardenne, Tabellen Elektronenphysik Ionenphysik und Übermikroskopie, vol. 2, VEB Deutscher Verlag der Wissenschaften, Berlin, 1956.

(59) R. S. Barton and R. P. Govier, *U.K.At. Energy Authority Rept.* CLM-R23, Pt. 2, 1963.

(60) R. S. Barton and R. P. Govier, *U.K.At. Energy Authority Rept.* CLM-R16, Pt. 1, 1962.

(61) J. H. Singleton, 1963 *Vacuum Symp. Trans.*, p. 267, 1964.

(62) Measurements at Princeton Plasma Physics Laboratory, Princeton University, Princeton, N.J.

(62a) A. Schram, *Vide*, no. 103, p. 55, 1963.

(63) B. D. Power and F. C. Robson, 1961 *Vacuum Symp. Trans.*, p. 1175, 1962.

(64) B. D. Power and J. D. Crawley, *Adv. Vacuum Sci. Tech.*, p. 206, 1960.

(65) F. A. Flecken and H. G. Noeller, 1961 *Vacuum Symp. Trans.*, p. 58, 1962.

(66) Allegheny Ludlum Steel Corporation, private communication.

(67) E. E. Burger, J. D. Cobine, and T. A. Vanderslice, *A.I.E.E. Conf. Paper* CP62-137.

(68) J. F. Norton and A. L. Marshall, *Trans. Am. Inst. Mining Met. Engrs.*, vol. 156, p. 351, 1944.

(69) P. F. Varadi, 1961 *Vacuum Symp. Trans.*, p. 73, 1962.

(70) S. Garbe and K. Christians, *Vacuum Tech.*, vol. 11, p. 9, 1962.

The Pumping Process

4

The evacuation of a vacuum vessel is treated in this chapter in a general manner. The application to the design of vacuum systems and their performance will be discussed in Chap. 10.

4-1   Evacuation of a Lumped Volume

It is customary to define pump action in terms of a pumping speed S, expressed in liters per second. S is the volume of gas removed from the container each second at the existing pressure. The pumping speed of many pumps is approximately constant over a large range of pressures. The flow rate into the pump is called the throughput SP of the pump; it decreases as the pressure drops. Room temperature is assumed throughout and $Q = SP$ is used rather than Q/kT, the mass flow (see Sec. 2-1). Hence Q is expressed in torr liters per second at room temperature.

Figure 4-1 is a schematic representation of the evacuation of a container of volume V. The word "pump" refers to the whole pumping system; it includes the pump line, traps, etc. At lower pressures two main sources of gas are present, Q_W gas desorbing from sur-

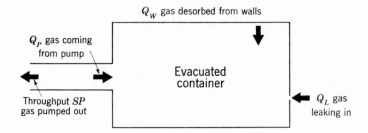

Fig. 4-1 Evacuation equilibrium. (From G. Lewin, *Endeavour*, vol. 22, p. 87, 1961.)

faces and Q_L gas leaking into the container from the outside. For the purpose of analysis, we substitute for the actual pump an ideal or perfect pump of speed S and a gas source Q_P representing the gas that flows back from the pump into the vacuum system. Hence, there are three gas sources, with the gassing rates Q_W, Q_L, and Q_P. These gassing rates are also given in torr liters per second at room temperature. The basic equation describing the pumping action is

$$-V\, dP = dt\, (SP - Q_W - Q_L - Q_P) \tag{4-1}$$

The amount of gas removed from the container during the time dt equals the amount entering the pump less the influx of gas from the three sources. The minus sign applies because dP is negative, corresponding to a drop in pressure. After the initial pumpdown, the gas sources Q determine what gas is left in the container rather than the gas initially filling the volume V. Eventually, an equilibrium will be established and the pressure will not drop any further. When the ultimate pressure P_u is reached, dP/dt is zero and

$$P_u S = Q_W + Q_L + Q_P \tag{4-2}$$

$$S = \frac{\Sigma Q}{P_u} \tag{4-3}$$

We can define an effective pumping speed S_e that takes into account the various gas sources. From Eq. (4-2) there follows

$$S_e P = SP - \Sigma Q = S(P - P_u) \tag{4-4}$$

$$S_e = S\left(1 - \frac{P_u}{P}\right) \tag{4-5}$$

where S_e is a function of pressure; it becomes zero at the ultimate pressure. If Q_L is rendered negligible by proper technology, Q_W and/or Q_P determines P_u.

The gas source Q_L is usually constant, and Q_P and Q_W change only slowly with time.   If we consider those time intervals where the various Q are either negligible or nearly constant and if S is constant, we can integrate Eq. (4-1) and obtain, by Eq. (4-3),

$$P - P_u = (P_0 - P_u)e^{(-S/V)t} \qquad (4\text{-}6)$$

P_0, the pressure at $t = 0$, is large compared with P_u; therefore

$$P = P_0 e^{(-S/V)t} + P_u \qquad (4\text{-}7)$$

For $P \gg P_u$ the time constant is $\tau = V/S$, a useful quantity for judging the performance of a pump system.

If a pump of speed S is connected to the vacuum system through a pipe of conductance C, the pumping speed of the combination is, from Eq. (2-4),

$$S_c = \frac{SC}{S + C} \qquad (4\text{-}8)$$

Therefore, C should be large enough to take advantage of the inherent speed of the pump; in general, $C \approx S$ or larger.   If this is not possible and a large pumping speed is required, it may be necessary to use part of the container wall as a pump by covering it with an adsorbent metal film and/or cooling this surface to attain cryogenic pumping.   It follows from Eq. (2-6) that an area of A cm² which adsorbs or condenses all gas has a pumping speed $S = 3.64(T/M)^{\frac{1}{2}}A$ liters/sec, or, in the case of nitrogen, $11.8A$ liters/sec at 20°C.

Since the flow is viscous during the initial pumpdown, C is not constant in the beginning.   It is usually too complicated and impractical to integrate Eq. (4-1).   But often $C \gg S$ and $S_c = S$ during pumpdown, because of the high viscous-flow conductance.

Let us calculate a typical pump problem (see Fig. 4-2).   A stainless-steel sphere of 100-cm diameter has to be operated at a pressure of 10^{-6} torr after 24 hr of pumping.   At times, nitrogen is bled into the chamber until a pressure of 10^{-3} torr is reached, and this pressure is maintained by a steady nitrogen flow without throttling the pump.   We assume that a diffusion pump is used with a limiting forepressure P_{FL} of 2×10^{-1} torr.   Hence a forepump is needed to pump down to this pressure from atmospheric pressure.

The vacuum chamber has a volume V of 525 liters and a surface area A of 31,400 cm².   We assume a gassing rate of 10^{-9} torr liter/cm² sec (see Table 3-11) or $Q = 3 \times 10^{-5}$ torr liter/sec.   An all-metal system is used.   It follows from Eq. (4-3) that, for $P_H = 10^{-6}$ torr, $S_H = 30$ liters/sec.   Hence it is decided to use a 100-liter/sec pump aggregate and a high-vacuum line of conductance $C_H = 100$ liters/sec,

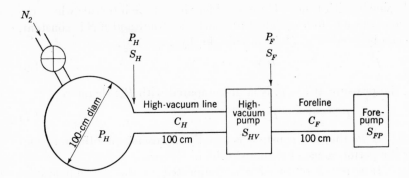

Fig. 4-2   Schematic of a vacuum system.

resulting in $S_H = 50$ liters/sec for the combination.   It follows from Eq. (2-12) that $D_H = (C_H L/12.3)^{\frac{1}{4}} = 9.35$ cm or 4 in.   This can also be gathered from Fig. 2-1.   The gas load with N_2 flowing is $Q_N = P S_H = 5 \times 10^{-2}$ torr liter/sec.   This requires a forepump speed $S = Q_N/P_{FL} = 5 \times 10^{-2}/(2 \times 10^{-1}) = 0.25$ liter/sec, a small value. The size of the forepump is determined by the permissible pumpdown time.   Let us assume that we want to pump down to diffusion-pump vacuum or 10^{-1} torr in 30 min.   At these high pressures, gassing can be neglected or $P \gg P_u$.   Hence, from Eq. (4-7),

$$S_F = \frac{V}{0.434t} \log\left(\frac{P_0}{P_F}\right) = \frac{525}{0.434 \times 1800} \log\left(\frac{760}{10^{-1}}\right)$$

$S_F = 2.6$ liters/second.   As a first trial, we consider a foreline of 2.5-cm diameter and 100-cm length.   It has a conductance $C_F = 1.9$ liters/sec in the molecular-flow range.   From Eq. (2-31), C_F is 8.9 liters/sec at 10^{-1} torr.   This is somewhat small.   Hence we use a diameter of 3.75 cm, which gives a minimum conductance of 42 liters/sec, and a forepump of 3 liters/sec capacity.

4-2   Evacuation of a Distributed Volume

We have discussed thus far systems with lumped volume; i.e., the conductance of the vacuum container is very large and the volume of the connecting pipes is negligible.   We shall now consider a tube with distributed volume and a gassing wall.   Figure 4-3 shows a pipe of length L which is closed at one end and connected to a pump of speed S at the other end.   We assume that the pump is a perfect pump with $Q_P = 0$ and that the pipe is leak-tight.   The only sources of gas

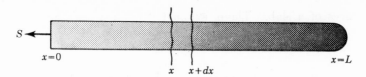

Fig. 4-3   Evacuation of a distributed volume.

are the gas in the volume and the wall gassing Q_W.   We introduce a specific gassing rate $q = Q_W/L$ and a specific conductance or conductivity $c = CL$.   The volume per unit length is $v = V/L$.   The flow rate is $c\,dp/dx$.   If we consider a tube element of length dx, the change of flow between cross sections x and $x + dx$ will be equal to the gassing rate less the removal rate of the volume gas:

$$c\left(\frac{dP}{dx}\right)_{x+dx} - c\left(\frac{dP}{dx}\right)_{x} = -\left(q - v\frac{dP}{dt}\right)dx \qquad (4\text{-}9)$$

The negative sign applies since the flow is opposite to the pressure gradient.   The right side of the equation is the net change of gas in the element of length dx.

We assume first that the gassing rate is negligible and the flow is molecular.   Therefore, from Eq. (4-9),

$$\frac{c}{v}\frac{\partial^2 P}{\partial x^2} = \frac{CL^2}{V}\frac{\partial^2 P}{\partial x^2} = \frac{\partial P}{\partial t} \qquad (4\text{-}10)$$

This equation is identical with the diffusion equation (3-6); D corresponds to CL^2/V.   To solve it, we must know the initial and boundary conditions.   We assume that the tube has initially a uniform pressure P_0.   At $t = 0$, a pump of very large pumping speed ($S \gg C$) is connected at $x = 0$.   Hence,

$$P = P_0 \qquad 0 \leq x \leq L \qquad t = 0$$
$$P = 0 \qquad x = 0 \qquad t > 0$$
$$\frac{\partial P}{\partial x} = 0 \qquad x = L \qquad t \geq 0$$

The last condition follows from the fact that the flow into the closed end is zero.   The solution of Eq. (4-10) is

$$P = P_0\frac{4}{\pi}\sum_{n=0}^{\infty}(2n+1)^{-1}\sin\frac{\pi(2n+1)x}{2L}$$
$$\exp\left[-\frac{\pi^2}{4}(2n+1)^2\frac{C}{V}t\right] \qquad (4\text{-}11)$$

This is identical with Eq. (3-17), the diffusion of gas from the opposite faces of a slab. There, symmetry requires that $\partial c/\partial x = 0$† in the center. L is $d/2$, half the thickness of the slab.

The maximum pressure is at $x = L$.

$$P_{\max} = \frac{4}{\pi} P_0 \exp\left(\frac{-\pi^2}{4} \frac{C}{V} t\right) \quad \text{for } t > 0.1 \frac{V}{C} \tag{4-12}$$

since the higher terms can be neglected when $(\pi^2/4)(C/V)t > 0.25$. If we compare this with Eq. (4-7) for the pumpdown of a lumped volume, we see that, after a time larger than 0.1 times the time constant for the lumped volume, the pressure at the end of the tube continues to drop with a time constant that is 60 percent smaller than the time constant of the lumped volume. Also, P_0 is multiplied by a factor $4/\pi$.

If it is necessary to pump out a capillary tube of circular cross section constituting a void in the vessel wall or an idealized "internal leak," the time constant for pumpout of N_2 is, from Eqs. (3-18) and (2-12),

$$\tau = 2.6 \times 10^{-5} \frac{L^2}{D} \quad \text{sec} \tag{4-13}$$

Here L and D are measured in centimeters. In the rather extreme case of $L = 2$ cm and $D = 10^{-4}$ cm, τ is only 1 sec. Hence, internal capillary voids do not produce virtual leaks, unless a void terminates in a larger cavity.

We now consider the equilibrium condition after pumpdown with a constant gassing rate q. It follows from Eq. (4-9) that

$$c \frac{d^2P}{dx^2} = -q \tag{4-14}$$

The boundary conditions are

$$\frac{dP}{dx} = 0 \quad x = L$$

$$PS = qL \quad x = 0$$

The second condition states that the throughput of the pump equals the total gassing rate. The integration gives

$$P = q\left[\frac{L}{S} + \frac{x}{c}\left(L - \frac{x}{2}\right)\right] \tag{4-15}$$

$$P_{\max} = qL\left(\frac{1}{S} + \frac{L}{2c}\right) \tag{4-16}$$

P decreases parabolically with x from $P_{\max}$ at $x = L$ to $P = qL/S$ at $x = 0$, the pump port.

† c is the concentration in Eq. (3-17).

Vacuum Measurements 5

In this chapter we describe the commonly performed vacuum measurements. For the analysis of the residual gas, a mass spectrometer is used to measure the partial pressures of all gases. These instruments are rather complicated and expensive. A gage that measures only the total pressure often suffices, e.g., if one gas predominates, or the relative abundance of the various gases is known approximately, or a vacuum process has to be monitored. Such gages are much simpler and cheaper.

We shall discuss the total-pressure gages first. We shall then proceed to a description of the mass spectrometers that are suitable for vacuum work. We include in this discussion leak detection, since most leak detectors are mass spectrometers adjusted to measure the probe gas only, usually helium. We also treat two other important vacuum measurements, namely, the measurement of the speed of a pump and of the size of a conductance. The latter measurement is made if it is impossible or impractical to calculate the conductance. Finally, we shall discuss the calibration of gages.

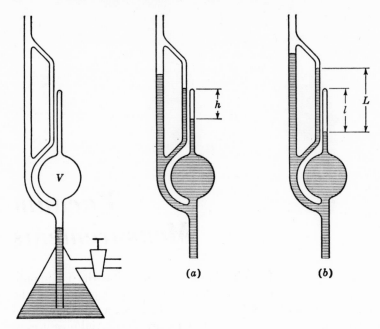

Fig. 5-1   The McLeod gage.

5-1   Total-pressure Gages

We shall describe the most important total-pressure gages and emphasize specifically their limitation and the errors that may be made in their application. A monograph on pressure measurements has been written by Leck (1).

All gages discussed, with the exception of the McLeod and the diaphragm gage, measure density rather than pressure. They are usually calibrated in pressure at room temperature. In most vacuum applications, high precision is neither required nor attainable. An accuracy of ± 10 percent is usually considered quite good.

5-2   McLeod Gage

This gage is one of the oldest gages still in use. It is shown in Fig. 5-1. By raising the mercury with atmospheric pressure or mechanically, the gas in the volume V is compressed. Its pressure is equal to the difference in height between the mercury column in the closed-off volume and the mercury column in the open tube, which is connected to the vacuum system. This gage can be used in two different ways. If the mercury column in the open tube is always raised until it is level with the top of the closed capillary (Fig. 5-1a), the following relation ensues from the equation of state:

$$VP = vp = ah \times h \qquad (5\text{-}1)$$

where P is the pressure in the vacuum system, V is the volume that is closed off, v is the remaining volume after compression, and p is the pressure in this volume. a is the cross section and h is the height of the gas column in the closed capillary. It follows from Eq. (5-1) that

$$P = \frac{a}{V} \times h^2 \qquad (5\text{-}2)$$

where a/V is a constant for the gage. The scale is quadratic and therefore expanded at lower pressures.

To cover a larger range, it is more practical to use the gage in the following manner (Fig. 5-1b): The mercury is raised in the closed capillary to a predetermined point, a distance l from the top. The difference in height between the columns is L.

$$PV = alL \qquad (5\text{-}3)$$

$$P = \frac{al}{V} \times L \qquad (5\text{-}4)$$

Here al/V is a constant of the instrument and P is directly proportional to L. To cover a wider range of pressures, several distances l are commonly used with one instrument. Bakeable McLeod gages have been described in the literature; e.g., see Monk et al. (2).

The gage cannot be used as described for the measurement of vapors. The vapor would condense during the compression, and even before the dew point is reached, departure from the ideal gas law renders the above equations invalid. Hayward (2a) discussed the measurement of gas-vapor mixtures, in particular, air and water vapor. One method of analyzing a binary gas-vapor mixture is to vary l at constant P and plot L, the pressure of the compressed mixture, versus $1/al$. For small L, when the vapor behaves as a gas, the curve is a straight line which goes through the origin. The slope becomes smaller at larger L when the vapor is saturated and its pressure is constant. The pressure of the saturated vapor is the intercept of this second part of the curve with the ordinate. Saturation can be avoided by heating the gage. Precautions must be taken that the glass and the mercury are completely dry, and the proper corrections for local temperature variation must be applied (see Sec. 1-7).

The proper operation of the gage for accurate measurements is discussed by Nottingham and Torney (2b). They explain how to find the effective end of the closed capillary and how to minimize frictional forces between the mercury and the glass wall by tapping. Also, the uniform and equal rise of the mercury in both capillaries must be checked. The wall of the capillaries must be clean to assure uniform capillary depression of the mercury.

A liquid-nitrogen trap is usually used to prevent the mercury from entering the vacuum system. Errors can be caused by condensation or adsorption of gas in the cold trap. If the liquid-nitrogen level varies in the trap, no adsorption equilibrium is established. Another error may be introduced by the pumping action of the mercury streaming into the cold trap from the gage [Ref. (3)]. For N_2, the error is 14 percent at 25°C for a connecting tube of 1-cm diameter between the trap and the gage. The error is approximately proportional to the tube diameter. Meinke and Reich (3a) showed how the error can be reduced by a special design. The tube that dips into the mercury reservoir has a small diameter and the gage is closed off from the trap by a glass valve while the mercury is raised.

The main application of the McLeod gage is for calibration of other gages, since it is an absolute gage. In general, it is reasonable to expect an accuracy of ± 10 percent at 10^{-4} torr for a careful measurement [Ref. (3b)]. The lower limit is 10^{-5} torr or less with reduced accuracy. The main disadvantages of the gage are its fragility, the inability to measure pressures continuously, and the presence of mercury. Also a bakeout is not simple.

5-3   Diaphragm Gage

Diaphragm gages measure differential pressures. A thin diaphragm forms part of the wall of a vacuum system. When the pressure changes, the position of the center of the diaphragm is indicated by a sensitive mechanism; e.g., the diaphragm is one plate of a tuned capacitor. The instrument can be operated as a null indicator by equalizing the pressure on both sides or compensating the deflection by an electrostatic force. Drawin (4) describes two gages that can be baked up to 180°C. Pressures from 10^{-4} to 2×10^{-1} torr and 2×10^{-2}

to 30 torr can be measured.   There is now on the market a gage that
has full-scale ranges from 10^{-1} to 10 torr and can be baked at 450°C.
The calibration is independent of the type of gas.

In dial gages for pressures above 1 torr, the diaphragm is one
wall of an evacuated capsule.   The motion of the diaphragm is transferred to a pointer by direct mechanical linkage.

5-4   Thermal-conductivity Gages

In these gages, a wire is heated electrically.   At low pressures,
when wall collisions prevail, the heat loss is a function of the gas
density, as described in Sec. 1-6.   Two arrangements are commonly
used.   In the Pirani gage the wire forms one branch of a Wheatstone
bridge.   It has a large temperature coefficient of resistance, and the
resistance change unbalances the bridge.   The bridge current is a
direct indication of the pressure.   In the thermocouple gage, a thermocouple is attached to the center of the wire, and the thermocouple
voltage changes with the pressure.   To minimize the heat loss by
radiation, the temperature of the wire is rather low, about 200°C.
Fluctuations of the ambient temperature are compensated in the
Pirani gage by a dummy wire in a sealed-off envelope, which is located
close to the gage and forms the diagonally opposite branch of the
bridge.   Several thermocouples can be arranged in the gage in such a
manner as to compensate for temperature variations, as described by
Benson (5).   He heats the couples directly with alternating current,
which is balanced out in the indicating millivoltmeter.

The lower limit of these gages is about 10^{-3} torr.   The gage can
be used beyond the molecular flow range at higher pressures up to
about 30 torr, since the cooling by convection is a function of gas
density.   The heat loss is, of course, proportional to the accommodation coefficient [see Eq. (1-12)].   The gage is most stable when the wire
is covered with an adsorbed gas layer and the accommodation coefficient approaches unity.   The calibration is a function of the heat conductivity of the gas.   It must be ascertained from time to time that
the calibration has not changed.   This is done by checking some fixed
calibration points, such as zero pressure and atmospheric pressure.

Advantages of the gage are its simplicity, ruggedness, and continuous reading.   It is not damaged by sudden air inrush, and the
temperature of the filament is too low to cause reactions with the gas,
such as occur at incandescent ion-gage filaments.

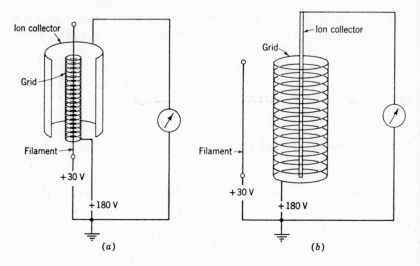

Fig. 5-2 Schematic of ion gages. (*a*) Conventional ion gage; (*b*) inverted ion gage (Bayard-Alpert Gage).

5-5   *Alphatron Gage*

This is a special gage marketed by the National Research Corporation.   A radium source emits alpha rays which ionize the gas. The ionization current is proportional to the gas density.   Two ionization chambers of different size, covering full-scale ranges from 10^{-3} to 10^3 torr, are used.   The sensitivity factor is a function of the type of gas, since the ionization cross sections for alpha rays vary.   Only a nonbakeable version is available.   Advantages of the gage are the absence of a hot filament and the extension of the range to high pressures.   A slight radiation hazard exists.

5-6   *Hot-cathode Ionization Gage*

This gage is one of the most extensively used gages and has been the subject of many investigations.   As initially conceived, the gage has the same electrode arrangement as a common triode radio tube (see Fig. 5-2*a*).   A filament is surrounded by a grid, which in turn is surrounded by a cylinder called the collector.   The collector is grounded, the filament is about 30 V positive, and the grid is 180 V positive.   The electrons emitted from the filament go to the grid.

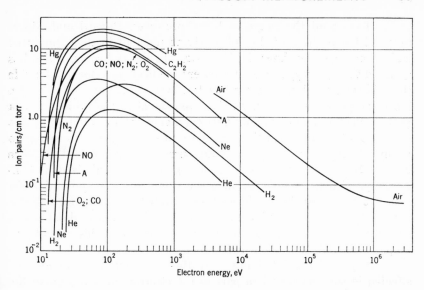

Fig. 5-3 Ionization efficiencies of electrons for some gases as a function of electron energy. (From R. Jaeckel, "Encyclopedia of Physics," vol. 12, p. 535, Springer-Verlag OHG, Berlin, 1958.)

They collide with the gas molecules and ionize them. A number of these ions go to the collector. This ion current is a measure of the gas density. Within a certain pressure range, the following equation applies:

$$i_{ion} = si_{electron}P \qquad (5\text{-}5)$$

The ion current is proportional to the electron current and the pressure. The proportionality constant s is called the sensitivity† of the gage. It has the dimension $torr^{-1}$. Its value depends primarily on the geometry of the gage, the grid voltage, and the ionization cross section of the gas. The ionization efficiencies of electrons for some gases are shown in Fig. 5-3. They have a flat maximum around 100 eV. Typically, $i_{electron}$ ranges from 10^{-5} to 10^{-2} amp.

When the grid is bombarded with electrons, soft x-rays are emitted. These release photoelectrons at the collector, which go to the grid. Hence, a constant current of photoelectrons is added to the ion current and limits the minimum pressure, which can be measured to about 10^{-8} torr.

† The term sensitivity is also used in a more general manner to indicate the minimum pressure that can be detected.

To extend the range to lower pressures, Bayard and Alpert reversed the position of the collector and filament in their "inverted ionization gage," as shown in Fig. 5-2*b*. In the B-A gage, which has replaced the older type, to a large extent the filament is located outside the grid, and the ion collector is a thin wire in the axis of the tube. Since the photoelectron current is proportional to the projected area of the collector, a wire of about 0.01-cm diameter has a thousand times smaller photocurrent and the x-ray current of the gage corresponds to about 5×10^{-11} torr. But the x-ray current is not constant. Hence it must be checked frequently at low pressures. This is done conveniently with Redhead's "modulator" [Ref. (6)]. The potential of a modulator electrode inside the grid is varied between grid and collector potential. Thereby, the ion current to the collector is modulated in a known manner without affecting the x-ray current. This extends the range to about 7×10^{-12} torr [Ref. (7)].

Appelt (8) pointed out that the x-ray current can also be affected in some gages when part of the electron current goes to the modulator. For the modulator will then emit x-rays, while the x-ray emission of the grid decreases for a constant total electron current.

If a molybdenum grid has a layer of adsorbed oxygen, electron bombardment will cause O^+ desorption (see Sec. 3-7). Approximately 3 percent of the ions are collected by the ion collector. They are equivalent to an x-ray current of up to about 10^{-9} torr pressure equivalent. Their presence can be detected by the modulator since the collection efficiency is nearly independent of the modulator potential. Cleaning of the grid by electron bombardment or ohmic heating above 1700°K removes the layer [see Ref. (8a)]. Denison et al. (8b) suspect that alkali impurities evaporated from a tungsten filament and deposited on the grid could increase the x-ray limit in an analogous manner and cause erroneous readings below 10^{-9} torr for $i_- < 1$ ma. This can be ascertained by checking s versus i_-.

The sensitivity of the gage decreases above 10^{-4} torr. If the electron current is reduced one or two orders of magnitude below its usual value of 0.01 amp, s remains constant up to the 10^{-3}-torr range. This high-pressure behavior has been studied by Schulz (9). Eventually the ion current saturates, probably on account of the contribution of secondary electrons to i_-. They have lower energy and less ionization efficiency.

Schulz and Phelps (10) showed how these limitations could be avoided by a well-defined electron path, efficient ion collection at all pressures, and reduced sensitivity to decrease the number of secondary electrons. They proposed two designs. A high-pressure gage con-

Table 5-1   Sensitivity Factors s of Ion Gages, in $Torr^{-1}$

Bayard-Alpert Gage Westinghouse WL-5966 (PPL)

Gas	He	Ne	A	N_2	H_2	CO	CH_4	N_2O
s	2.4	3.7	16.4	11.5	5.0	13.0	18.0	14.2

High-pressure Gage Westinghouse WL-7676

Gas	He*	N_2*	CO*	H_2*	D_2(PPL)	H_2O†
s	0.06	0.40	0.42	0.21	0.24	0.56

	Electrode potential	
	WL 5966	*WL 7676*
Collector	ground	ground
Filament	+30 V	+60 V
Grid	+180 V	+120 V

* From R. J. Melling, *A.I.E.E. Conf. Paper* 60-401, 1960.
† From A. H. Futch, Jr., *Rev. Sci. Instr.*, vol. 32, p. 1263, 1961.

structed according to one of them is now commercially available (11). It has a range of 10^{-5} to 1 torr. This range is intermediate between the Bayard-Alpert ion gage and the diaphragm gage and overlaps the ranges of both gages. When mounted together, the high-pressure gage can be helpful in ascertaining the continuous constancy of the B-A gage calibration. Table 5-1 gives the sensitivity of these two gages for some gases. The sensitivity for Octoil is about 13 times the sensitivity for N_2 [Ref. (12)]. For a general tabulation of sensitivities, see Redhead et al. (13).

Pressure indications of the ion gage can be erroneous for a number of reasons. Smith and Saylor (14) state that the old conventional VG1A ion gage of Consolidated Vacuum Corporation (the collector is a platinum deposit on the glass wall) gives too high or too low a reading after a number of hours, depending on the type of oil, when employed on systems pumped with a glass oil diffusion pump. In one case this was cured by an overnight bake in air. Obviously, pump oil must not accumulate in the gage.

Carter and Leck (15) and Cobic et al. (16) found that a B-A gage with a glass envelope can operate in two different modes, one mode having a 3.5 times higher sensitivity.   The wall stabilized either at cathode (higher sensitivity) or nearer grid potential.   But the wall always stabilized at cathode potential for grid voltages below 250 V, a value well above the customary grid voltage of 180 V.   High-frequency oscillations, so-called Barkhausen-Kurtz oscillations, are often present in the gage.   The grid region constitutes a potential well between the filament and the ion collector and the electrons perform oscillations around the grid.   Pierre (17) describes certain arrangements to suppress them.   A reduction of the electron current often suffices.   If they increase in amplitude, electrons may reach the ion collector, reversing the direction of the collector current, and the wall potential may change.   According to Redhead et al. (13), their amplitude can be limited to a harmless value by a conductive wall coating [e.g., tin oxide; see Gomer (18)].   The wall should be held at a definite potential, preferably ground.   Also, a grounded screen may be provided between the electrode structure and the glass wall.   It was pointed out by Hayward et al. (18a) that photoelectrons released from a grounded screen which reach the grounded collector constitute a reverse x-ray current which lowers the x-ray limit.

Reactions of active gases with the filament can cause dissociation and production of other gaseous compounds.   This subject was discussed in Sec. 3-9.   Such effects can also cause chemical pumping. Eisinger (19) reports that a tungsten filament has a pumping speed of 0.33 liter/cm^2 sec for O_2 at 1800°K and 10^{-5} torr.   At this pressure the speed is a maximum for this temperature.   Some practical filaments are described in Sec. 5-10.   Gages can also pump gases by adsorption after a thorough degassing and by ion pumping.   Alpert (20) reported a maximum speed of 8 liters/sec for N_2 and 30 liters/sec for CO. Nitrogen pumping of an ion gage in ultrahigh vacuum was investigated by Hobson (21).   The maximum combined ion and sorption pumping speed was 2 liters/sec.   The adsorption pumping ceased after 10^{15} molecules had been pumped.   The ion pumping continued with a speed of 0.25 liter/sec at 8-ma electron current and 250-V grid voltage until nearly 10^{17} molecules were bound.

Young (22) found a maximum speed of 4×10^{-3} liter/sec for He at 10-ma electron current and 145-V grid voltage.   Eighty to ninety percent of the ions were collected at the wall.   Appreciable pumping occurred only when the glass was covered with a metallic film.   The maximum speed for N_2 was 0.1 liter/sec.   A clean glass wall or a wall covered by Aquadag pumped as well as a metal film.   There is a rapid drop of speed in the beginning, which may explain the variation of the reported values.   The ion pumping can be reduced by lowering the electron current and, much more effectively, by reducing the grid to collector voltage. The pumping speed drops much faster than the sensitivity when this voltage is lowered.

The gage can also be a source of gas. Hence, provisions are made to bake it and outgas the metal parts, usually by electron bombardment. If a thoria-coated filament is used, a d-c power supply is required since the coating is damaged by alternating current. Gassing and especially pumping are most disturbing at lower pressures, where adsorption equilibrium is established slowly.

A typical tube connecting a gage to a system has an inside diameter of 1 cm and a length of 5 cm. Its conductance is 2 liters/sec (Fig. 2-1). In equilibrium the gas flow into the gage $C(P - P_G)$ [Eq. (2-2)] equals the gas-removal rate by gage pumping $S_G P_G$ [Eq. (4-2)], where P_G is the pressure in the gage. P_G is equal to P if $S_G/C + 1 \approx 1$ or $S_G \ll C$, a condition not complied with in a freshly degassed gage with strong adsorption pumping. In the case of gage degassing, $Q = C(P_G - P)$; hence, for true pressure readings, $Q/C \ll P$. The effects of gage pumping and gassing are greatly reduced if the system has a high pumping speed and/or a large volume and the gage is a nude gage, i.e., a gage that has a large conductance to the vacuum vessel or is located inside the vessel. In the latter case, it should be surrounded by a grounded screen. A nude gage also prevents errors due to adsorption in the connecting tube, as discussed in Sec. 3-4.

If the gage has to be used in magnetic fields, the sensitivity will change. This has been discussed by Martin (23). Sometimes gages act erratically without obvious reason. The author used a nude gage which had an increased sensitivity at higher electron currents, contrary to Eq. (5-5). Also, among a batch of well-behaved gages, one gage was found that exhibited a sensitivity change from 9 to 12 torr^{-1}, when the pressure was increased from 10^{-5} to 10^{-4} torr. Obviously, any gage used for critical quantitative measurements must be recalibrated.

An ion gage of much higher sensitivity is the orbitron of Mourad et al. (23a). The ion collector is a cylinder. A short filament is placed off axis inside the cylinder, near one end. A rod of positive potential is located on the axis. Most electrons do not hit this rod immediately, owing to their angular momentum. They spiral away from the filament in an axial direction, are reflected at the end of the rod, drift back, and are collected near the filament. The average electron-path length is up to 2500 cm compared with 1.25 cm for the B-A gage.

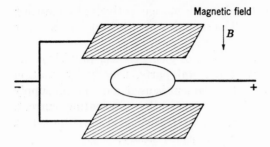

Magnetic field

B

−

+

Fig. 5-4 The Penning or Philips ionization gage (PIG).

5-7 Gages with Crossed Electric and Magnetic Fields

The path length of the electrons and, therefore, the sensitivity are increased in these gages by a magnetic field perpendicular to the electric field, which prevents the electrons from reaching the anode. An early planar arrangement with a hot filament was proposed by Gaede (24) and a magnetron geometry by Slutzkin et al. (25). The planar gage with cold cathodes first described by Penning is commonly called the Penning or Philips ionization gage (PIG). It is shown in Fig. 5-4. The gage contains a pair of cold cathodes and an annular or cylindrical anode. The voltage is typically 2000 V. The magnetic induction, typically of 500 to 1500 gauss, is usually produced by a permanent magnet. The $v \times B$ force prevents most electrons from going to the anode unless they lose energy by collisions with atoms, but ions can reach the cathodes because they are much less deflected by the magnetic field on account of their greater mass and because the cathodes present a larger target. The electrons form a space charge, and their average path length is greatly enhanced; therefore the sensitivity is high, approximately 5 to 10 amp/torr for N_2.

Other advantages are that cold-cathode gages do not exhibit the x-ray effect, since the electron current is barely larger than and proportional to the ion current, and that the cold cathodes avoid gas reactions occurring at hot filaments. The character of this gas discharge is not well understood. Oscillations are always present and probably necessary for the operation. For a more recent theory by Knauer, see Sec. 6-6. The gas-discharge current is pressure-dependent, but the relationship is not always completely linear and reproducible. The operating range is typically from 10^{-2} to 10^{-6} torr. At lower pressures, starting may require many minutes.

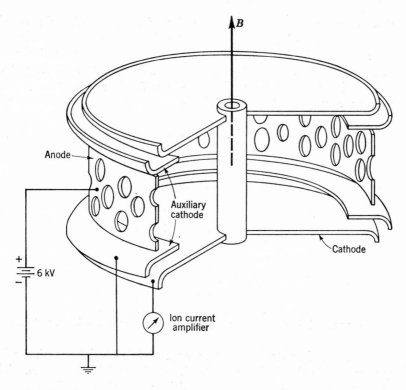

Fig. 5-5 Magnetron gage of Redhead. (From P. A. Redhead, *Can. J. Phys.*, vol. 37, p. 1260, 1959.)

Young and Hession (25a) designed a Penning gage with a hot filament as a starter, located behind a hole in one of the cathodes. The current was nearly proportional to the pressure from the 10^{-11}-torr range to 10^{-3} torr. The pumping speed of the Penning gage is appreciable and is utilized in sputter-ion pumps.

For lower pressures, Redhead (26) used the magnetron configuration shown in Fig. 5-5. This gage, like the Penning gage, has high sensitivity, no x-ray limit, and no hot filament. The lowest measurable pressure is about 10^{-13} torr. The rod-shaped cathode with circular end disks is surrounded by an anode cylinder with the magnetic field in the direction of the cylinder axis. Two annular auxiliary cathodes between the anode and the main cathode disks act as guard rings and prevent field emission from the cathode. The voltage is 6000 V, and the magnetic induction is 1000 gauss. The sensitivity is about 10^{n} amp/torr for N_2. Above 2×10^{-10} torr, $n = 1$. Below this pressure, n is larger and a function of the magnetic field and the anode voltage [Ref. (26a)]. Below 10^{-10} torr the gage must be shielded from ambient light. At low pressures it may require several minutes to start. Barnes et al. (27) determined the relative sensitivity of the gage and the pumping speed for N_2, He, A, CO_2, H_2, and O_2. The average values are given in Table 5-2.

Table 5-2   Relative Sensitivity $s(N_2 = 1)$ and Pumping Speed S in liters per second for Redhead Magnetron Gage

Gas	s	S
N_2	1.0	2.5
He	0.22	0.17
A	2.1	1.7
CO_2	1.35	2.4
H_2	0.48	2.0
O_2	1.1	3.4

SOURCE: G. Barnes, J. Gaines, and J. Kees, *Vaccum*, vol. 12, p. 141, 1962.

In the inverted-magnetron gage [(27a), (13)] the cylinder has guards and is the cathode while the center rod is the anode. The characteristics and operating conditions are similar. In all these gages the power supply must be well stabilized at low pressures. Any fluctuation produces a signal at the current amplifier by capacitive coupling and increases the noise.

Lafferty designed a hot-cathode magnetron gage and described it and later improvements in several papers (28) (see Fig. 5-6). The hairpin-shaped filament is located along the axis; it is surrounded by the cylindrical anode. Two negatively biased end shields close off the volume and prevent the escape of electrons. In the first model, shown in Fig. 5-6, the ions are collected by one end plate. The maximum electron current under cutoff condition is 10^{-6} amp; beyond this value, oscillations render the gage unusable. The sensitivity is increased more than 10^4-fold over the sensitivity of the B-A gage. This reduces the x-ray current of the gage to 2.4×10^{-14} torr. Lafferty improved this sensitivity and reduced the x-ray current even further by focusing the ions onto an electron multiplier through a limiting aperture. This later gage should have a linear response down to 3×10^{-17} torr. A lanthanum boride filament is used. Chemical reactions are minimized because of its low operating temperature of 675°C.

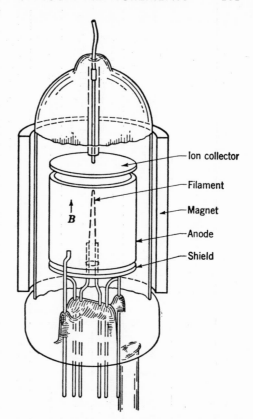

Ion collector

Filament

Magnet

Anode

Shield

B

Fig. 5-6 Hot-cathode magnetron gage. (From J. M. Lafferty, *J. Appl. Phys.*, vol. 32, p.
424, 1961.)

The characteristics of these gages are summarized in Table 5-3.
The amplification of the weak ion currents and the use of some mass
spectrometers as total-pressure gages will be discussed in Secs. 5-11
and 5-13.

5-8   *Measurement of Partial Pressures*

In advanced experimentation, a mass spectrometer is often
indispensable to obtain a complete analysis of all residual gas.   But it
must be kept in mind that a mass spectrometer is an expensive and
complex instrument.   Considerable experience is required to use it
successfully and to interpret the measurements correctly.   Lately a
number of instruments for vacuum work became commercially available, which tends to facilitate their application.   Redhead et al. (7)
emphasized that in ultrahigh vacuum a simple desorption technique

Table 5-3 Some Total-pressure Gages

Gage	Approximate range, torr	Principle	Advantages	Disadvantages
McLeod	10^{-5}–10	Gas compressed by mercury	Absolute pressure gage	Fragile; contains Hg; difficult to measure vapor pressure; no continuous indication; difficult to bake
Diaphragm	10^{-4}–50	Moving membrane	Absolute pressure gage	Only low-temperature bake possible with highest-sensitivity gage
Thermal-conductivity gage	10^{-3}–30	Cooling of heated wire	Cheap; resistant to inrush of air	Limited reproducibility depending on gas adsorption
Alphatron	10^{-4}–10^{3}	Gas ionized by alpha rays from radium	Range extended to high pressures	Not bakeable; slight radiation hazard
Bayard-Alpert ion gage	10^{-10}–10^{-3}	Gas ionization by electrons from hot filament	Measures low pressures	Gas reacting with hot filament; gage may be a source or sink of gas
High-pressure ion gage	10^{-5}–1	Gas ionization by electrons from hot filament	Range extended to higher pressures	Gas reacting with hot filament
Penning or PIG gage	~10^{-7}–10^{-2}	Cold-cathode gas discharge in crossed electric and magnetic fields	Simple, rugged; no hot filament	Pressure indication not always completely linear and reproducible; large gage pumping
Cold-cathode magnetron gage	10^{-13}–10^{-4}	Cold-cathode gas discharge with magnetron configuration and fields	Range extended to low pressures; no hot filament	Large gage pumping; minutes delay in starting at low pressures; pressure indication sometimes not linear
Hot-filament magnetron gage	10^{-13}–10^{-3};lower limit ~10^{-16} with multiplier	Hot-cathode magnetron gage	Extreme low-pressure limit	Not commercially available; hot filament

described below may yield sufficient information, especially in a preliminary experiment, and save much time.

A mass spectrometer for vacuum work, and especially for low pressures, must have high sensitivity and low gassing rate. It has to be bakeable for general applications. Measurements of very low pressure can be made with mass spectrometers since they exhibit no x-ray effect, owing to the optical shielding of the ion collector from the electron collector. Ion pumping is usually no problem, but the surface area should be small to reduce adsorption pumping after degassing. Only moderate resolution is required. High masses are not of particular interest. The cracked pump oil has peaks around mass 40 and 60. With mercury diffusion pumps, it may be important to be able to detect mercury vapor of mass 200.

A mass spectrometer consists of three parts: an ion source where the neutral gas is ionized, a section in which the ions are sorted out according to their ratio of mass to charge, and a collector with an amplifier to measure the weak ion current. Since ion sources and ion-current amplifiers are common to all mass spectrometers, we shall treat them first. We shall then discuss the most common methods of mass separation. Mass spectrometers for vacuum work were reviewed by Huber (28a) and Leck (1).

5-9   Desorption Spectrometer

This is a semiquantitative method (29). It has the advantage of high sensitivity. Gases adsorbed at a cold filament during a time interval are desorbed by gradual heating of the filament. The desorption temperature varies according to the activation energy of desorption. The interpretation of results is complicated by the fact that one gas can be adsorbed in different states with several desorption energies. Figure 5-7 from Ref. (7) is a typical desorption spectrum. Reference (7) gives also a diagram of a circuit suitable for raising the filament temperature linearly with time. Similarly, gases condensed or adsorbed on a cold finger at cryogenic temperatures will desorb approximately in the order of their boiling points when the temperature is raised.

5-10   The Ion Source

Ions are produced by electron impact. Cold-cathode discharges of the Penning type have been used occasionally (30). They have the

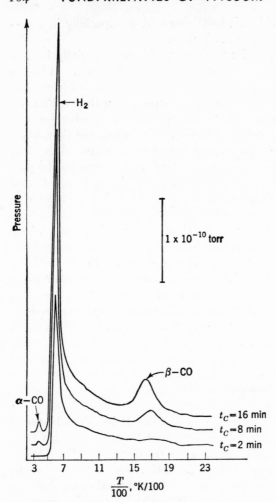

Fig. 5-7 Typical desorption spectra for residual gas at a total pressure of about 10^{-10} torr; t_C is the adsorption time. Horizontal axes of curves have been displaced vertically for clarity. (From P. A. Redhead, E. V. Kornelsen, and J. P. Hobson, *Can. J. Phys.*, vol. 40, p. 1814, 1962.)

advantage that hot-filament reactions are avoided. But the high ion velocity and large velocity spread complicate focusing, and the yield is often not a linear, reproducible function of pressure. Guenther (31) investigated such a source in conjunction with a quadrupole mass spectrometer. He extracted ions of less than 100 eV only, by a suit-

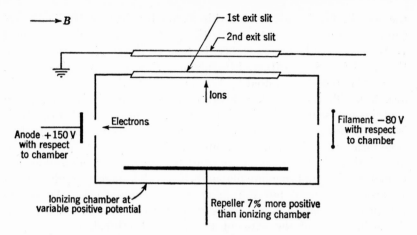

Fig. 5-8   Typical ion source for a mass spectrometer with magnetic deflection.

able electrode arrangement not further described. In a later paper
(51) Guenther and Haenlein describe in greater detail a Penning source
for pressures above 10^{-6} torr that does not have a linear pressure
dependence.

It is more common to use a hot filament as electron emitter and
have the accelerated electrons traverse the ionizing chamber, as first
suggested by Bleakney (32). Guenther reported that his hot-filament
sources had several-times-larger yields than the Penning sources. A
typical source for an instrument with magnetic deflection is shown in
Fig. 5-8. The magnetic field facilitates the focusing of the electrons
moving along the magnetic lines of force, but similar ion sources have
been built without a magnetic field. The electrons are accelerated
toward the ionizing chamber, which they enter through a small hole.
They coast through the chamber, leave through a hole in the opposite
wall, and are collected by the anode. The ions are pushed toward the
first exit slit by the repeller. They are accelerated between the two
slits and move in a circle perpendicular to the plane of the paper under
the influence of the magnetic field. Gas—in particular, oxygen—can
be desorbed from the wall of the ionizing chamber by the impact of
stray electrons and leave with an energy of a few volts. This additional energy is equivalent to a larger mass [Eq. (5-6)] and produces an
oxygen satellite of apparently slightly larger mass. Hartman (33)
observed a large relative increase of the O^+ satellite after adsorption of
oxygen.

The heating of the ion-source region by the hot filament can
cause undesirable gassing, especially in ultrahigh vacuum. To outgas

the source, Davis (34) heated this region by electron bombardment from a separate filament. Also, the parts should be degassed in a vacuum furnace before assembly, to remove the gas from the bulk of the metal (see Sec. 3-10), and the filament should be lit during a bake.

Gas reactions caused by hot filaments have been mentioned in Sec. 3-9. Tungsten filaments are still used extensively. Tungsten contains potassium which is released in bursts of up to 10^6 ions. This is usually not objectionable, with the possible exception of some ion-gage measurements [Ref. (8b)], but pure tungsten can be prepared by dissociation of $W(CO)_6$ on a filament [Ref. (35)]. Rhenium does not form a carbide, and rhenium filaments have advantages in hydrocarbon analysis [Ref. (36)] but not in general vacuum work. An inconvenience of rhenium is less high-temperature strength, which makes the adjustment of the filament tension more critical. Tungsten or burnout-proof iridium filaments coated with thoria are more satisfactory. They have the same emission as plain tungsten at a temperature that is about 600° lower. The cataphoretic coating with ThO_2 was described by Hanley (37).

Lanthanum boride is another low work-function emitter. The preparation of lanthanum boride cathodes on a rhenium core has been explained by Lafferty [(28); 1961 *Vacuum Symp. Trans.*]. At higher emissivity the lanthanum evaporation may be objectionable, at least in ion gages, where it increases the photoeffect of the collector [Ref. (7)]. Oxide- (BaO) coated filaments are not in general use although they operate at the lowest temperature. The oxide coating flakes off when exposed to the atmosphere. Kelley (38) reports a substantial improvement by keeping the cathode at a temperature of 120 to 130°C during such exposure. The filament should be readily replaceable in case of burnout.

In view of gassing and gas reactions, it is not surprising that Alpert (38a) observed that two different types of mass spectrometers connected to the same ultrahigh-vacuum system registered different mass spectra. Some peaks appearing in one instrument were absent in the other, and vice versa. If not nude, the ion source should be connected to the system through a high-conductance tube. See the corresponding discussion for ion gages in Sec. 5-6.

5-11   Ion-current Amplification

Good d-c amplifiers have a signal-to-noise ratio of unity in the 10^{-15}-amp range. The grid resistor of the electrometer tube is usually in the 10^{11}-ohm range at highest sensitivity. These amplifiers have large negative feedback. This reduces the effective input impedance and permits a lower leakage resistance of the collector lead. A vibrating-reed amplifier increases the sensitivity about one order of magnitude. The amplifier response times are several seconds at maximum sensitivity. In the vibrating-reed amplifier the d-c signal is converted to alternating current in a capacitor that has one plate fastened to a vibrating reed, and it is amplified in an a-c amplifier. The signal is demodulated in a synchronous detector followed by an RC circuit. The RC value determines the bandwidth and thereby the noise level [Ref. (39)]. If a vibrating reed is not available, the ion current can be modulated electrically in the mass spectrometer and, after preamplification, amplified with a "lock-in" amplifier [Ref. (40)] whose synchronous detector is connected to the same modulating source. The sensitivity is somewhat lower.

Modulation can be performed in several ways. An a-c voltage can be applied to the ion repeller (see Fig. 5-8), or the electron current can be modulated with a grid, as proposed for ion gages by Hayes et al. (41). Milner (30) modulated the ion-accelerating voltage (see Fig. 5-8). This causes the ion beam to sweep past the exit slit, giving a signal of twice the modulating frequency. Hence the frequency has to be doubled in a frequency doubler before the signal is fed into the lock-in amplifier. An advantage of frequency doubling is that direct capacitive pickup of the modulating signal by the collector is avoided.

Another approach is to amplify the ion current directly inside the vacuum with an electron multiplier. This method gives fast response and large amplification. Often, AgMg or CuBe dynodes with electrostatic deflection are used. Typically, a 10-stage multiplier has a gain of 10^5. The gain can be affected by exposure to the atmosphere and bakeout. Davis (34) reported that multiplier (apparently a Dumont No. 6467 with AgMg dynodes) performance could be greatly improved with regard to gain and noise level by adding a small crystal of $CsNO_3$ to the multiplier housing before the bake. Another multiplier, which is also marketed, was described by Goodrich and Wiley (42). It uses crossed electric and magnetic fields. The proper potential distribution is obtained by the use of two continuous high-resistance strips, one as dynode surface and the other one as field electrode. The gain is 10^7, and the dark current below 10^{-11} amp. The multiplier is bakeable only up to 150°C.

Another scheme of very high sensitivity is shown in Fig. 5-9. The ions hit a target which is biased 40 kV negative. Secondary electrons are emitted and strike a phosphor shielded from light by a thin

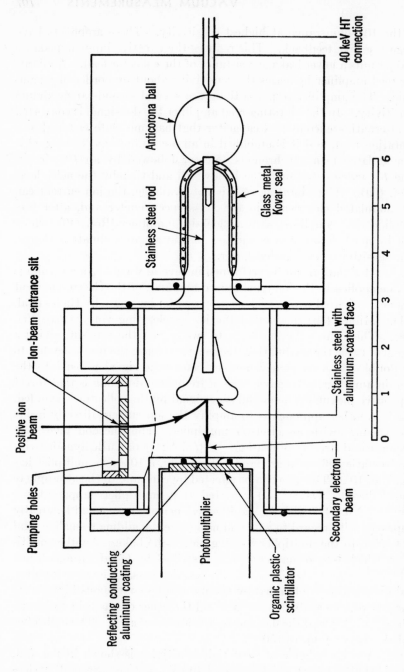

Fig. 5-9 Ion-current amplifier with scintillation counter. (From N. R. Daly, *Rev. Sci. Instr.*, vol. 31, p. 264, 1960.)

aluminum coating.   The light is registered with a scintillation counter.
Such an amplifier with an organic phosphor is being used in the Plasma
Physics Laboratory (PPL) at Princeton.   The aluminum target is
biased 15 kV negative.   When the amplified output is connected to a
pulse height discriminator, most of the dark current is not registered,
and ion currents of one ion per second can be measured [(42a), (43)].
An advantage is that the scintillation counter is outside the vacuum.
Schutze and Bernhard (44) used a ZnO phosphor in a similar arrangement and were able to count a few ions per second.

   To obtain automatic scanning of a certain number of masses,
PPL uses a sequential switching box with six channels.   Each channel
contains a potentiometer to adjust the ion-accelerating voltage to the
desired mass scan [Eq. (5-6)].   The box is connected to a digital
voltmeter which operates a printer.   The channels are switched every
10 sec; first the accelerating voltage is connected for 5 sec to identify
the mass, and the output is recorded during the other 5 sec.

5-12   Mass Separation

   In this section we shall discuss the most important methods of
mass separation and the instruments that utilize them.

   If the ions leaving the ion source enter a homogeneous magnetic
field, they will follow a circular path of radius r.   The following relation exists:

$$r_{cm}B_{gauss} = 143.6 \left(\frac{Vm}{e} \right)^{\frac{1}{2}} \tag{5-6}$$

where m/e is the mass-to-charge ratio expressed in atomic mass units
($m/e = 1$ for H^+) and V the accelerating voltage at the ion source.
This relation is the basis of the magnetic sector spectrometer.   In Fig.
5-10a, S_1 is the second exit slit of the ion source shown in Fig. 5-8.
The magnetic field perpendicular to the plane of the paper extends for
the angle ϕ (60° in this particular case) and deflects the beam.   The
deflected beam passes through the exit slit S_2 and hits the collector.
If the center of the average radius of curvature, slit S_1 and slit S_2, lie
in a straight line and if the central electron beam enters the magnetic
field with normal incidence, as shown in Fig. 5-10a, all ions of the same
energy and m/e but of different directions are focused into slit S_2 in
first order, i.e., for narrow beams.   According to the deflection angle,
these mass spectrometers are classified as 60°, 90°, etc., sector instruments.   Figure 5-10b shows the ion path at 180° deflection.   Usually

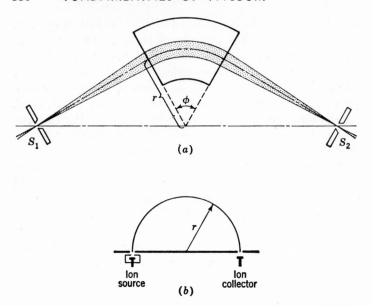

Fig. 5-10   Mass separation by magnetic deflection; magnetic field perpendicular to the plane of the paper.   (*a*) 60° deflection; (*b*) 180° deflection.

B is produced by a permanent magnet and the magnetic field is kept constant.   Ions of different m/e ratio are swept across the exit slit by changing V.

An important characteristic of a mass spectrometer is its resolving power.   It is often defined as the relative resolution $m/\Delta m$, where m is the distance of the center of mass m from the origin and Δm is the line width at a certain fraction of the peak height, usually 1 percent. From a practical viewpoint, it is important to separate adjacent masses.   Therefore Δm should not be more than twice the distance between the centers of mass m and mass $m + 1$.   Hence we define an absolute resolution $1/\Delta m$.   For good separation, $(m + 1) - m \geq 0.5(\Delta m)$ or $1/\Delta m \geq 0.5$.   Let for $\phi = 180°$, Δr be the width of the slits S_1 and S_2. Δr produces a line width Δm.   It follows from Eq. (5-6) that $m/\Delta m = r/2\,\Delta r$. $m/\Delta m$ is constant since r is kept constant by changing V. $\Delta m = 2m\,\Delta r/r$.   The line width caused by the width of the slits increases linearly with m.   Hence the absolute resolution is poor for larger masses.

In the PPL, a small 180° magnetic deflection instrument is used extensively.   The radius is 1 cm.   With a d-c electrometer amplifier, the low-pressure limit is about 10^{-9} torr.   It can be increased to

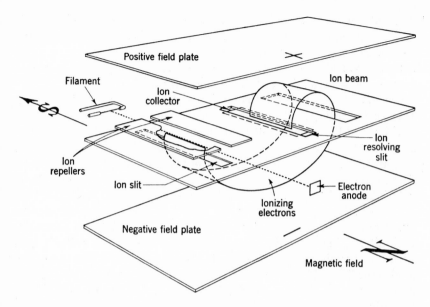

Fig. 5-11 Cutaway view of a mass spectrometer with crossed electric and magnetic fields. (From G. D. Perkins and D. E. Charpentier, 1957 *Vacuum Symp. Trans.*, p. 125, 1958.)

10^{-10} torr by the use of a vibrating-reed electrometer. The volumetric time constant, i.e., the ratio of spectrometer volume to conductance into the instrument, is 1 sec. Good mass separation is obtained up to mass 50. To check for mercury, a special magnet of higher field strength is used. This instrument has a metal envelope. It was modified to render it bakeable. Since the metal parts are made of gold-plated Nichrome, the resolution becomes progressively poorer after several bakes. The gold diffuses into the metal and the Nichrome becomes covered with an insulating layer of chromium oxide. Charges accumulate on these layers and cause defocusing. This condition was cured by a platinum plate.

Davis and Vanderslice (45) describe a bakeable instrument of 90° deflection and 5-cm radius. With the built-in electron multiplier, pressures in the 10^{-13} torr range can be measured, although it is difficult to degas the instrument to such a low level. The resolution $(1/\Delta m)_{1\%}$ is 0.5 at m/e 150. Davis (34) increased the sensitivity to about 10^{-17} torr by reducing the gassing of the ion source and improving the multiplier performance (see Secs. 5-10 and 5-11).

In a so-called cross-field instrument, shown in Fig. 5-11, the ions are simultaneously exposed to homogeneous electric and magnetic fields of perpendicular directions. The ions have a trochoidal path, and ions of equal m/e are focused on the exit slit even if the velocities vary with regard to absolute value and direction. If d is the distance between the ion source and the collector, $d = 2\pi(m/e)(\mathbf{E} \times \mathbf{B})B^{-3}$. Hence $\Delta m = m\,\Delta d/d$. For the same ratio of slit widths to slit distance, the effect of slit widths on line width is half as much as in the 180° sector instrument. Such an instrument has been described by Perkins and Charpentier (46). It has a resolution of $(1/\Delta m)_{1\%} = 0.5$ at mass 80. The low-pressure limit is about 10^{-10} torr with a d-c amplifier. The ions can be focused onto an electron multiplier by a Wein-type electrostatic lens which brings the ions out of the magnetic field into the shielded multiplier [Ref. (46a)].

Another principle is used in the r-f mass spectrometer. An ion beam passes through grids which are connected to an r-f source with alternating polarity. Only those ions having a velocity in step with the changing potential will gain enough energy to pass through a final retarding grid and reach the collector. This instrument has the disadvantage that the sensitivity is a steep function of the r-f voltage. It is difficult to keep this voltage sufficiently constant. The r-f mass spectrometer has no magnet. It can be inserted into the vacuum vessel. Such a nude instrument has been described by Ehlbeck et al. (47). A m/e above 100 can be resolved. This particular instrument has a low-pressure limit of 10^{-8} torr.

An r-f field is combined with a steady magnetic field in the omegatron shown in Fig. 5-12. The r-f voltage is applied between electrodes A and H. Ions, which are in step with the r-f voltage, describe a spiral path of increasing diameter, as in a cyclotron. They eventually reach the collector. The r-f field is homogenized by the rings R connected to a voltage divider. A negative potential is applied to the side plates C to remove the nonresonant ions and render the sensitivity reproducible [Ref. (48)]. The relative resolution $m/\Delta m$ is proportional to m^{-1}. Hence the resolution decreases rapidly for larger masses. The omegatron is used extensively since the instrument and the electronics are relatively simple. It has the disadvantage that an electron multiplier cannot be added. It has about the same sensitivity as the 180° sector instrument described above. The r-f voltage is small (1 to 2 V), and the instrument is affected by changes of contact potentials. Hence, the electrodes must be made of noble metal to ensure stability. Redhead et al. (7) consider this instrument unsuitable for ultrahigh-vacuum work on account of marginal sensitivity and resolution and the extreme care necessary to obtain reproducible results.

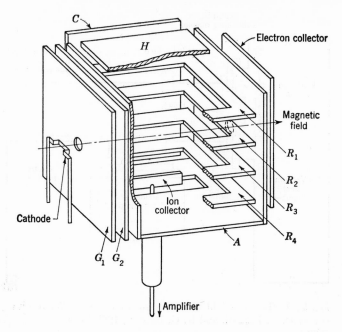

Fig. 5-12   Omegatron with side plates.   (From A. Klopfer, *Adv. Vacuum Sci. Tech.*, vol. 1, p. 397, 1960.)

Another type is the time-of-flight mass spectrometer.   The ions are accelerated and coast in a field free space of length l until they arrive at the collector.   The transit time $l(m/2 \text{ eV})^{\frac{1}{2}}$ is a measure of their mass.   Time-of-flight instruments have the advantage of a small time constant and high repetition rates, but the electronics are rather complicated.   They use electron multipliers for increased sensitivity.   A time-of-flight mass spectrometer with nude ion source has been described by Damoth and Burgess (49).   It is shown in Fig. 5-13.   It is pulsed at a repetition rate of 10^4 pulses/sec.   The electron beam is turned on for 0.3 μsec at the beginning of each pulse. The gain of the multiplier is in excess of 10^8.   The partial-pressure limit is around 10^{-12} torr.   Kendall (50) built an instrument with a usable resolution up to mass 60 and a partial-pressure limit of 5×10^{-13} torr.

Direct-current and r-f fields are combined in the quadrupole mass spectrometer shown schematically in Fig. 5-14.   The ions pass along the axis of four evenly spaced rods to which a d-c and r-f voltage is applied.   The ions perform lateral oscillations under the influence of these fields.   These oscillations do not grow excessively for ions of a

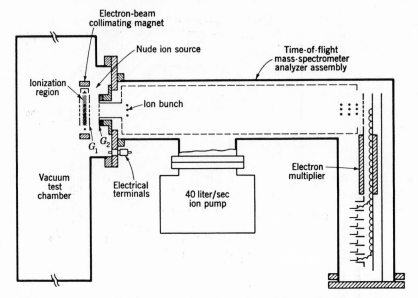

Fig. 5-13 Time-of-flight mass spectrometer adapted for residual-gas analysis. (From D. C. Damoth and R. G. Burgess, 1962 *Vacuum Symp. Trans.*, p. 418, 1963.)

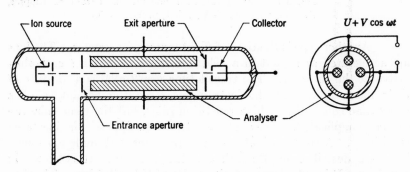

Fig. 5-14 Principle of the quadrupole mass filter. (From K. G. Guenther and W. Haenlein, 1961 *Vacuum Symp. Trans.*, p. 573, 1962.)

specific m/e only. The scanning is usually done by varying the r-f and d-c voltage V and U while the radio frequency is kept constant. The U/V determines the relative resolution. If an additional constant voltage is added to U, Δm becomes nearly constant. Guenther and Haenlein (51) describe an instrument which has a sensitivity of 10^{-10} torr. Recently a simplified version, the monopole spectrometer, was described (51a). It has only two electrodes, a rod inside a channel of right-angle cross section. An advantage is simpler electronics.

The maximum pressure of most mass spectrometers is in the 10^{-4} torr range. The omegatron has a somewhat lower limit because of the long path of the spiraling ions and the ion space charge. The quadrupole mass spectrometer has a somewhat higher limit on account of the continuous focusing. The ratio of partial-pressure sensitivity to total pressure is important for gas analysis. It depends on the resolution and the upper and lower pressure limit. In general, it is around 10^{-5}. A cycloidal mass spectrometer has been described (51b) which has a partial-pressure sensitivity of 10^{-7}.

Carbon monoxide and nitrogen, both common rest gases, have the same mass. Apgar (52) explained how their amounts can be rapidly found in a residual gas containing CO, N_2, CO_2, and CH_4 by means of a nomogram based on the relative amounts of mass 28, 14, 15, and 44.

5-13   Mass Spectrometers as Total-pressure Gages

Some mass spectrometers can also be modified to measure total pressure. Klopfer (53) grounded the ion collector of an omegatron while the other electrodes (Fig. 5-12) had positive, ion-repelling potentials. The low-pressure limit is below 10^{-11} torr. Also, ions can be collected by a negative repeller in the ion source of Fig. 5-8. This requires, of course, good insulation of the repeller. Since the ion collector and the repeller are optically shielded from the electron collector, no x-ray effect exists, as already mentioned.

5-14   Leak Detection

There are several methods available for leak detection. The one employed most in vacuum work uses a special mass spectrometer. In its usual application, helium is applied to the outside of the envelope where a leak is suspected. The helium penetrates and is pumped out by the high-vacuum pump. A mass spectrometer of high sensitivity focused specifically on helium is attached to or acts as the forepump. Leak detection has been described by Briggs et al. (54). Also, the art is taught by the companies that make leak detectors. Hence, we shall not go into this matter here in greater detail.

A typical detection limit is 10^{-10} torr liter/sec; i.e., a leak causing a flow of 10^{-10} torr liter/sec of the probe gas into the leak detector will produce a signal of the same amplitude as the noise at full pumping speed of the leak-detector pump. This is a very small flow indeed, since it amounts to a total flow of 1 cm³ of helium at standard pressure and temperature in 240 years. The sensitivity can be increased by reducing the pumping speed and accumulating He in the mass spectrometer. The slits in leak detectors are usually quite large, to increase the sensitivity. Consequently the resolution is not very high, and the zero level is affected by pressure fluctuation. Hence mass spectrometers with double focusing have been built [(55), (56)]. They also have higher amplification to take advantage of the reduced background. The background of active gases has also been lowered by passing the gas first through a titanium sorption pump. Argon is used instead of helium in special cases where the equipment has a large background of either helium or deuterium.

Leak detectors are complicated instruments. Most of those offered have about equal sensitivity. When buying one, it is important to choose an instrument that is stable and requires little maintenance. Also, the maintenance, such as the replacement of filaments, should be easy to perform.

A change of the composition and/or amount of gas leaking into the system produced by covering the leak with a probe gas or liquid changes the ion current of an ion gage. This effect is utilized in several methods which have high sensitivity at low pressures only. At high pressures the effect of the leak on the total current can be noticed only if the leak is large. Hence these methods are not suited for testing components at higher pressures after a quick pumpdown. The pressure may change significantly when the leak is covered with acetone. It may drop temporarily by plugging of the leak or may increase because of acetone evaporation.

Similarly, when the leak is covered with helium or argon, the ion current changes in a complex manner because of the change of pumping speed, gage sensitivity, and leak conductance. This effect is enhanced in a commercial leak detector which uses a Ti sorption pump and an ion gage with A as the test gas. The pump has high speed for active gases and zero speed for noble gas. Ackley et al. (57) analyzed this effect for sputter-ion pumps. Here the pump current is also a function of the nature of the gas. For some commercial units the minimum detectable leak rate q_{min} in torr liters/sec is $I/5000$, where I is the pump current in amperes. This current is proportional to the pressure. For a pump of 5 liters/sec speed, q_{min} is 2×10^{-8} at 10^{-6} torr. The highest sensitivity of $q_{min} = 2 \times 10^{-11}$ is obtained at pressures below 10^{-9} torr.

Glass tubes sometimes contain small pores where joined by

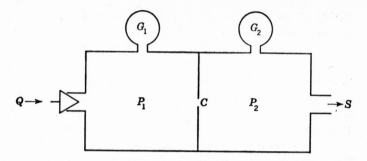

Fig. 5-15   Schematic of vacuum system for measurements of pumping speed and conductance.

glassblowing.   These can be located by going over the joints with a spark coil.   At a leak, the normally bushy discharge penetrates the wall in a concentrated spark at moderate pressures.

5-15   The Measurement of Pumping Speed

Consider the vacuum system shown in Fig. 5-15.   Gas flows into the first chamber at the rate Q; the pressure in this chamber is P_1, measured with the gage $G1$.   This chamber is connected through a conductance C, shown as an aperture, with the second chamber at pressure P_2, measured with the gage $G2$.   This chamber is pumped out by a pump of speed S.   Under stationary conditions, the following equations apply:

From Eq. (2-2)

$$Q = C(P_1 - P_2) \tag{5-7}$$

From Eq. (4-2) $$S = \frac{Q}{P_2} \tag{5-8}$$

Therefore $$S = C\left(\frac{P_1}{P_2} - 1\right) \tag{5-9}$$

If $S \gg C$,

$$S = C\frac{P_1}{P_2} \tag{5-10}$$

For the following, we assume molecular flow or constant C. Depending on what quantities are known, these relations can be used to determine either Q, C, S, or P.   If Q and P_2 are known [Eq. (5-8)], the arrangement is called the "constant-flow method" for the determination of pumping speed.   Pressure P_2 is measured with a gage.   A constant and known gas flow is obtained by dipping a pipet, the upper end of which is connected to the system through a leak valve, into a beaker filled with vacuum oil and observing the rate of rise of the oil in the pipet.   This method can be in error, on account of the change of height of the oil column and change of volume, unless corrections are made.   Stevenson (58) describes a metering device that facilitates these corrections.

A general discussion of this method was given by Dayton (59). He points out the most common errors; e.g., he explains what precautions are to be taken to avoid beaming effects of the gas entering the test dome.   In a later paper (59a), it is shown how this effect can cause erroneous readings in the measurement of the speed of a cryo-surface which closes off one end of a cylindrical test dome.

At low pressures the throughput becomes too small for this technique and Eq. (5-9) or (5-10) has to be used.   The pressures are measured at both ends of a tube or on both sides of an aperture of known conductance.   No absolute calibration of the gages is required. Only the pressure ratio has to be known.   To facilitate the adjustment of Q an auxiliary pump may be attached to the upstream side with pressure P_1 [see Landfors and Hablanian (60)].

Another method for measuring pumping speed is the "constant-volume method."   A volume is pumped out, and the pressure during pumpdown is recorded.   The pressure changes according to Eq. (4-7):

$$P = P_0 e^{-St/V} + P_u \tag{5-11}$$

$$\text{or} \quad \log \frac{P_0}{P - P_u} = 0.434 \frac{St}{V} \tag{5-12}$$

If $P \gg P_u$, P_u can be neglected.   If $\log [P_0/(P - P_u)]$ is plotted against time, the points will lie on a straight line through the origin if Eq. (5-11) is applicable, i.e., if the pumping speed is constant and the gas sources determining P_u are also constant or negligible.   Equation (5-12) can then be used to calculate S.   It is also possible, though less accurate, to plot $P = f(t)$ and to draw the tangent to the curve for any time t.   Then, from Eqs. (4-1) and (4-2),

$$S = \frac{-V}{P - P_u} \frac{dP}{dt} \tag{5-13}$$

Sorption and ion pumps exhibit memory effects.   The pumping speed is affected by the previously pumped gas (see Secs. 6-4 to 6-6). Therefore, the pressure should be measured with a mass spectrometer

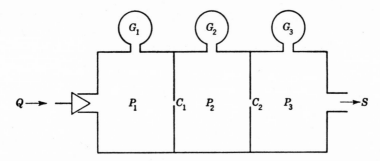

Fig. 5-16 Schematic of vacuum system for measurement of conductance and for gage calibration.

if another gas has previously been pumped. A mass spectrometer
must also be used if the gas contains an impurity that is not handled
by the pump, e.g., if an active gas containing some noble gas is pumped
with a Ti film at room temperature.

5-16   The Measurement of Conductances

A conductance must be measured if it cannot readily be calculated on account of odd shape and/or flow in the transition region.
Either Eq. (5-7) or Eq. (5-9) is used. In addition to the pressures,
either S or Q must be known. Usually Eq. (5-7) is preferred since Q is
easier to determine than S. The Q can be measured with a pipet, as
mentioned in the preceding section. This becomes impractical when
Q is small. In this case, a second known conductance C_2 is put in
series with the unknown C_1 (see Fig. 5-16). It follows that

$$C_1 = C_2 \frac{P_2 - P_3}{P_1 - P_2} \tag{5-14}$$

If $S \gg C_2$, $P_3 \ll P_2$ and

$$C_1 = \frac{C_2}{(P_1/P_2) - 1} \tag{5-15}$$

If, in addition, $C_2 \gg C_1$, $P_2 \ll P_1$ and

$$C_1 = C_2 \frac{P_2}{P_1} \tag{5-16}$$

Another way of obtaining Eq. (5-16) is to consider C_2 a part of the
pumping system. Since it determines the speed, $S = C_2$ and Eq.

(5-16) is equivalent to Eq. (5-10).   The conductance C_2 must have a geometry that facilitates its calculation.   It is usually either a thin aperture or a tube of circular cross section.

5-17   The Calibration of Gages

The McLeod gage is used for absolute pressure measurements above 10^{-5} torr.   If a gage in a clean bakeable system has to be calibrated, the McLeod gage can be used to measure the compensating pressure on the "dirty" side of a bakeable diaphragm gage operated as a null indicator.   A high-pressure ion gage is calibrated with the diaphragm gage.   This gage in turn can be used to calibrate a B-A gage if the ion current is proportional to the pressure.

The linear response of an ion gage was checked by Dushman and Found (61).   They connected the evacuated chamber containing the gage to a gas-filled volume through a small conductance.   As long as the pressure difference is large and the flow molecular, the pressure rises linearly with time, and a linear increase of the ion current with time constitutes a check on the gage linearity.   Since the time becomes too long when the total range of a B-A gage is to be covered, Alpert and Buritz (62) added another chamber connected through a second conductance.   In this chamber the pressure rises quadratically in time. Outgassing and gage pumping can be disturbing effects at low pressures.

Equation (5-16) is used to extend the calibration to lower pressures. P_2 is the pressure in gage $G2$ which has to be calibrated. Hobson (63) applied this method to the calibration of a magnetron gage in ultrahigh vacuum at pressures below the range of the B-A gage. In this case, C_2 was the conductance of the uncooled portion of a cold finger cooled with liquid He which was the pump, with $P_3 \approx 0$, and C_1 was a valve opened slightly. C_1/C_2 was determined at higher pressures by measuring P_1 and P_2 with B-A gages.   But it can also be calculated.   Wall degassing Q_W and gage pumping S_{G2} can be a problem, again especially in ultrahigh vacuum.   If $Q_W \ll P_1 C_1$ and $S_{G2} \ll C_2$, then Q_W and S_{G2} can be neglected.

REFERENCES

(1) J. H. Leck, "Pressure Measurements in Vacuum Systems," Chapman & Hall, Ltd., London, 1964.
(2) G. M. Monk, W. W. Stickey III, and A. T.

Callo, 1961 *Vacuum Symp. Trans.*, p. 531, 1962.

(2a) A. T. J. Hayward, *J. Sci. Instr.*, vol. 39, p. 367, 1962.

(2b) W. B. Nottingham and F. L. Torney, Jr., 1960 *Vacuum Symp. Trans.*, p. 117, 1961.

(3) H. Ishii and K. Nakayama, 1961 *Vacuum Symp. Trans.*, p. 519, 1962.

(3a) Chr. Meinke and G. Reich, *Vakuum Tech.*, vol. 12, p. 79, 1963.

(3b) J. C. Simons, Jr., 1963 *Vacuum Symp. Trans.*, p. 246, 1964.

(4) H. W. Drawin, *Adv. Vacuum Sci. and Technol.*, vol. 1, p. 274, 1960.

(5) J. M. Benson, 1956 *Vacuum Symp. Trans.*, p. 87, 1957.

(6) P. A. Redhead, *Rev. Sci. Instr.*, vol. 31, p. 343, 1960.

(7) P. A. Redhead, E. V. Kornelsen, and J. P. Hobson, *Can. J. Phys.*, vol. 40, p. 1814, 1962.

(8) G. Appelt, *Vakuum Tech.*, vol. 11, p. 174, 1962.

(8a) P. A. Redhead, *Vacuum*, vol. 13, p. 253, 1963.

(8b) D. R. Denison, H. F. Winters, and E. E. Donaldson, 1963 *Vacuum Symp. Trans.*, p. 218, 1964.

(9) G. J. Schulz, *J. Appl. Phys.*, vol. 28, p. 1149, 1957.

(10) G. J. Schulz and A. V. Phelps, *Rev. Sci. Instr.*, vol. 28, p. 1051, 1957.

(11) R. J. Melling, *A.I.E.E. Conf. Paper* 60-401, 1960.

(11a) A. H. Futch, Jr., *Rev. Sci. Instr.*, vol. 32, p. 1263, 1961.

(12) G. Reich, *Z. Angew. Phys.*, vol. 9, p. 23, 1957.

(13) P. A. Redhead, E. V. Kornelsen, and J. P. Hobson, *Adv. Electron. Electron Phys.*, vol. 17, p. 323, 1962.

(14) A. L. Smith and J. C. Saylor, 1954 *Vacuum Symp. Trans.*, p. 31, 1955.

(15) G. Carter and J. H. Leck, *Brit. J. Appl. Phys.*, vol. 10, p. 364, 1959.

(16) B. Cobic, G. Carter, and J. H. Leck, *Vacuum*, vol. 11, p. 247, 1961.

(17) J. Pierre, *Vide*, no. 91, p. 18, 1961.

(18) R. Gomer, *Rev. Sci. Instr.*, vol. 24, p. 993, 1953.

(18a) W. H. Hayward, R. L. Jepsen, and P. A. Redhead, 1963 *Vacuum Symp. Trans.*, p. 228, 1964.

(19) J. Eisinger, *J. Chem. Phys.*, vol. 30, p. 412, 1959.

(20) D. Alpert, *Vide*, no. 97, p. 19, 1962.

(21) J. P. Hobson, *Vacuum*, vol. 11, p. 16, 1961.

(22) J. R. Young, *J. Appl. Phys.*, vol. 27, p. 926, 1956.

(23) G. Martin, 1961 *Vacuum Symp. Trans.*, p. 476, 1962.

(23a) W. G. Mourad, T. Pauly, and R. G. Herb, *Rev. Sci. Instr.*, vol. 35, p. 661, 1964.

(24) W. Gaede, *Z. Tech. Phys.*, vol. 15, p. 664, 1934.

(25) A. A. Slutzkin, S. J. Braude, and I. M. Wigdortschik, *Physik. Z. Sowjetunion*, vol. 6, p. 268, 1934.

(25a) J. R. Young and F. P. Hession, 1963 *Vacuum Symp. Trans.*, p. 234, 1964.

(26) P. A. Redhead, *Can. J. Phys.*, vol. 37, p. 1260, 1959.

(26a) F. Feakes and F. L. Torney, Jr., 1963 *Vacuum Symp. Trans.*, p. 257, 1964.

(27) G. Barnes, J. Gaines, and J. Kees, *Vacuum*, vol. 12, p. 141, 1962.

(27a) J. P. Hobson and P. A. Redhead, *Can. J. Phys.*, vol. 36, p. 271, 1958.

(28) J. M. Lafferty, *J. Appl. Phys.*, vol. 32, p. 424, 1961; *Rev. Sci. Instr.*, vol. 34, p. 467, 1963; 1960 *Vacuum Symp. Trans.*, p. 97, 1961; 1961 *Vacuum Symp. Trans.*, p. 460, 1962; 1962 *Vacuum Symp. Trans.*, p. 438, 1963.

(28a) W. K. Huber, *Vacuum*, vol. 13, p. 399, 1963.

(29) P. A. Redhead, 1959 *Vacuum Symp. Trans.*, p. 12, 1960.

(30) C. J. Milner, *J. Sci. Instr.*, vol. 28, *Vacuum Suppl.* 1, p. 29, 1951.

(31) K. G. Guenther, *Vacuum*, vol. 10, p. 293, 1960.

(32) W. Bleakney, *Phys. Rev.*, vol. 40, p. 496, 1932.

(33) T. E. Hartman, *Rev. Sci. Instr.*, vol. 34, p. 1190, 1963.

(34) W. C. Davis, 1962 *Vacuum Symp. Trans.*, p. 363, 1963.

(35) E. F. Greene, *Rev. Sci. Instr.*, vol. 32, p. 860, 1961.

(36) C. F. Robinson and A. G. Sharkey, Jr., *Rev. Sci. Instr.*, vol. 29, p. 250, 1958.

(37) T. E. Hanley, *J. Appl. Phys.*, vol. 19, p. 583, 1948.

(38) J. W. Kelley, *J. Sci. Instr.*, vol. 39, p. 473, 1962.

(38a) D. Alpert, *Phys. Today*, vol. 8, p. 22, August, 1963.

(39) H. Palevsky, R. K. Swank, and R. Grenchik, *Rev. Sci. Instr.*, vol. 18, p. 298, 1947.

(40) R. D. Moore, *Electronics*, June 8, 1962, p. 40.

(41) R. E. Hayes, A. R. V. Roberts, and R. W. Alsford, *Vacuum*, vol. 12, p. 107, 1962.

(42) G. W. Goodrich and W. C. Wiley, *Rev. Sci. Instr.*, vol. 32, p. 846, 1961.

(42a) N. R. Daly, *Rev. Sci. Instr.*, vol. 31, p. 264, 1960.

(43) H. P. Eubank and T. D. Wilkinson, *Rev. Sci. Instr.*, vol. 34, p. 12, 1963.

(44) W. Schutze and F. Bernhard, *Z. Physik*, vol. 145, p. 44, 1956.

(45) W. D. Davis and T. A. Vanderslice, 1960 *Vacuum Symp. Trans.*, p. 417, 1961.

(46) G. D. Perkins and D. E. Charpentier, 1957 *Vacuum Symp. Trans.*, p. 125, 1958.

(46a) W. J. Lange and L. Hall, *Westinghouse Rept.* 808-D801-R1, April 30, 1961, p. 15.

(47) W. H. Ehlbeck, J. Ruf, and H. J. Schwetz, 1961 *Vacuum Symp. Trans.*, p. 567, 1962.

(48) A. Klopfer and W. Schmidt, *Vacuum*, vol. 10, p. 363, 1960.

(49) D. C. Damoth and R. G. Burgess, 1962 *Vacuum Symp. Trans.*, p. 418, 1963.

(50) R. F. Kendall, *J. Sci. Instr.*, vol. 39, p. 267, 1962.

(51) K. G. Guenther and W. Haenlein, 1961 *Vacuum Symp. Trans.*, p. 573, 1962.

(51a) U. v. Zahn, *Rev. Sci. Instr.*, vol. 34, p. 1, 1963.

(51b) W. K. Huber and E. A. Trendelenburg, 1961
      Vacuum Symp. Trans., p. 592, 1962.
(52) E. Apgar, *Vacuum*, vol. 11, p. 288, 1961.
(53) A. Klopfer, 1961 *Vacuum Symp. Trans.*, p.
     439, 1962.
(54) W. L. Briggs, A. C. Jones, and J. A. Roberts,
     1958 *Vacuum Symp. Trans.*, p. 129, 1959.
(55) J. L. Peters, 1959 *Vacuum Symp. Trans.*, p.
     94, 1960.
(56) M. Poctoroff, S. S. Grossel, and D. W.
     Oblas, 1961 *Vacuum Symp. Trans.*, p. 1081,
     1962.
(57) J. W. Ackley, A. E. Barrington, A. B.
     Francis, R. L. Jepsen, C. F. Lothrop, and
     H. Mandoli, 1962 *Vacuum Symp. Trans.*,
     p. 380, 1963.
(58) D. L. Stevenson, 1961 *Vacuum Symp. Trans.*,
     p. 555, 1962.
(59) B. B. Dayton, *Ind. Eng. Chem.*, vol. 40, p.
     795, 1948.
(59a) W. W. Stickney and B. B. Dayton, 1963
      Vacuum Symp. Trans., p. 105, 1964.
(60) A. A. Landfors and M. H. Hablanian, 1958
     Vacuum Symp. Trans., p. 22, 1959.
(61) S. Dushman and C. G. Found, *Phys. Rev.*,
     vol. 15, p. 7, 1921.
(62) D. Alpert and R. S. Buritz, *J. Appl. Phys.*,
     vol. 25, p. 202, 1954.
(63) J. P. Hobson, *Can. J. Phys.*, vol. 37, p. 300,
     1959.

Pumps 6

Since pumps in vacuum systems operate in a limited pressure range only, pumping is performed in several stages, each stage using a different type of pump. Pump performance is characterized by the pumping speed and the throughput, referring to the removal rate of the volume and the mass of gas, respectively (see Sec. 4-1). A pump has an ultimate minimum inlet pressure, which is the lowest pressure obtainable; it has also an upper limit for the outlet or forepressure. If the forepressure is raised above this value, pump action ceases.

We shall first describe forepumps, capable of pumping down from atmospheric pressure to a pressure at which the high-vacuum pump can operate. We include the Roots pump which covers an intermediate range between a forepump and a high-vacuum pump.

The number of high-vacuum pumps has increased in recent years. Formerly the diffusion pump and its modification for operation at higher pressures, the ejector pump, were virtually the only high-vacuum pumps in general use. Now adsorption pumping, e.g., by metal films produced by evaporation or ion sputtering (often combined with ion

125

pumping), is frequently employed. The adsorption is often increased by cooling of the surface or the gas is condensed at a cold surface. We shall also discuss the molecular drag pump, a mechanical high-vacuum pump. Although this classification is somewhat arbitrary and the ranges overlap, it is a feasible arrangement for a general survey.

6-1 Forepumps

Forepumps reduce the pressure from atmospheric pressure to a value at which high-vacuum pumps begin to operate, usually about 10^{-2} to 10^{-1} torr. The forepump must match the pumping speed of the high-vacuum pump. This means that their pumping speeds must be inversely proportional to the respective inlet pressures. The pumping speed of the forepump must be greater if a fast pumpdown is required. The common forepump is an oil-sealed rotary-vane or rotary-piston pump.

A vane-type pump is shown in Fig. 6-1a. A volume of gas is enclosed in the space bounded by the stator, the rotor, and the two vanes and is transported from the inlet to the outlet. As this gas is compressed, the pressure builds up, the outlet valve opens, and the gas escapes to the atmosphere. With two stages in series, the practical limit is about 10^{-3} torr. Condensation of vapors—in particular, water vapor—in the pump is to be avoided since it causes a deterioration of the pump oil. To this end, most pumps now have a so-called ballast valve attached to the higher-pressure stage. After the gas volume has been closed off from the inlet, gas is bled in through the ballast valve. This causes the outlet valve to open sooner, thereby reducing the compression ratio for the vapor. With the gas ballast, the lowest pressure of a two-stage pump is about 10^{-3} torr.

The rotary-piston pump (Fig. 6-1b) has similar characteristics. The vane-type pumps exhibit some vibration due to the unbalanced vanes. The vibration is greater in pumps with rotating pistons. Figure 6-2 shows typical pumping curves. The speed is nearly constant over a wide range and drops rapidly near the low-pressure limit.

To obtain higher speeds around 10^{-3} to 10^{-2} torr, Roots pumps are sometimes used in conjunction with rotary-vane or rotary-piston pumps, especially if no additional high-vacuum pump is required. Such a pump is shown schematically in Fig. 6-3. It contains two counter rotating rotors of figure-eight cross section. The gap between the rotors and the housing is small, about 0.01 in. Such a pump still

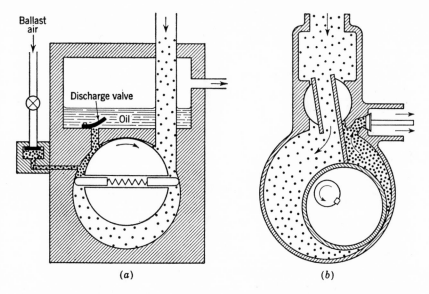

Fig. 6-1 (a) Rotary-vane forepump with gas ballast. (b) Rotary-piston forepump. [Figure 6-1(*b*) from H. A. Steinherz and P. A. Redhead, *Scientific American*, vol. 206, p. 78, March, 1962. Reprinted with permission. Copyright © 1962 by Scientific American, Inc. All rights reserved.]

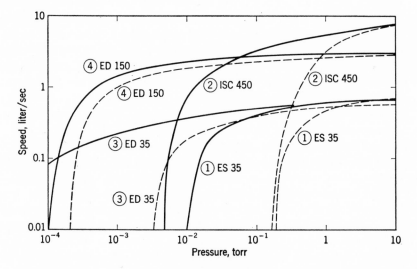

Fig. 6-2 Pumping speeds of rotary-vane forepumps. Solid line, without gas ballast; dotted line, with gas ballast. Curves 1 and 2, single-stage; curves 3 and 4, two-stage pump. Model numbers of Edwards High Vacuum Inc.

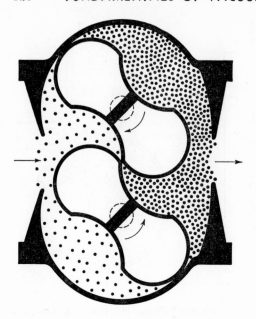

Fig. 6-3 Principle of Roots pump. (From H. A. Steinherz and P. A. Redhead, *Scientific American*, vol. 206, p. 78, March 1962. Reprinted with permission. Copyright © 1962 by Scientific American, Inc. All rights reserved.)

has a good pumping speed in the 10^{-4} torr range. But a large forepump is required to obtain high pumping speed. The upper pressure limit is about 15 torr. Heating of the pump becomes excessive when it is operated continuously at high pressure. Therefore, either a bypass is used at pressures above about 1 torr or the Roots pump coasts at a reduced speed during the initial pumpdown. This, however, cuts down the overall pumping speed. Ejector pumps (Sec. 6-2) cover a similar range.

Cases are known where protracted pumping with only a forepump caused accumulation of forepump oil in the vacuum system. This can be avoided by using a trap between the forepump and the high-vacuum pump. There exists a so-called ion baffle [see Ref. (1)] which reduces hydrocarbon backstreaming from the rotary forepump by means of a cold-cathode discharge in crossed electric and magnetic fields. The hydrocarbons form a solid polymer primarily by ion impact on the cathode. In one experiment with a two-stage oil pump the pressure was reduced from 1.4×10^{-3} to 8×10^{-5} torr. Hydrogen became the major component whereas oil fractions dominated previously. Also, refrigerated or liquid-nitrogen-cooled ($-196°C$) traps are used. But a trap is less effective in the viscous-flow range, and an oil-free forepump can be preferable.

Water aspirators have a lower limit of about 20 torr, or slightly less if the water is chilled. (The water-vapor pressure is 5 torr at 5°C and 18 torr at 20°C.) Steam-ejector pumps have high pumping speeds. By using six stages in series, the low-pressure limit can be extended to the 10^{-3} torr range [Ref. (2)]. Steam backstreaming under no load condition and the necessity of providing live steam can be objectionable.

Another solution for small and medium-size systems with very light gas loads is sorption forepumps. Formerly, mainly charcoal was used as the adsorbent. It has now been partially replaced by zeolites, also called molecular sieves. They are porous aluminum silicates combined with one or more other metallic elements. These materials adsorb large amounts of gas when cooled with liquid nitrogen. Some charcoal and Linde type 5A zeolite adsorb about equal amounts of nitrogen (see Fig. 6-15). When the adsorbent is warmed up to room temperature again, it releases the adsorbed gas. Care must be taken that no excessive pressures can build up under this condition. Such sorption pumps are now commercially available and are in use especially with sputter-ion pumps described in Sec. 6-6. They are valved off after initial pumpdown. According to one manufacturer's specifications, one such pump will pump a 20-liter volume down to 2×10^{-2} torr in $\frac{1}{3}$ hr and to 10^{-2} torr in $1\frac{1}{2}$ hr, including chilling time.

Pumping speed can be improved by more efficient cooling of the zeolite. This also speeds up warming to room temperature for desorption. Grant and Davey (2a) compared a commercial pump, an upright cylinder containing the zeolite with an insert along the axis for additional heat transfer, with their own improved design. They stacked trays with the adsorbent inside the cylinder. These trays were separated by spacers and fastened to a hollow center column. A heating element is inserted into the center cavity for regeneration, and this space is filled with liquid N_2 during chilling. In a test both pumps reached 10^{-1} torr in 25 min. But in 1 hr the commercial pump pumped to 1.5×10^{-2} torr while the new pump pumped to 1.5×10^{-3} torr, although it contained only one-third the amount of adsorbent.

Varadi and Ettre (3) measured the pumping speed of a pump for different gases. Their results are presented in Fig. 6-4. It shows the pumping speed at 10^{-1} torr as a function of the total amount of adsorbed gas normalized to STP for a pump containing 100 g of Linde X13 zeolite. It is interesting to note that the maximum speed is reached only after some gas has been adsorbed. Perhaps the gas improves the chilling of the inner layers of zeolite. All curves have the same general character. The adsorption of hydrogen is small.

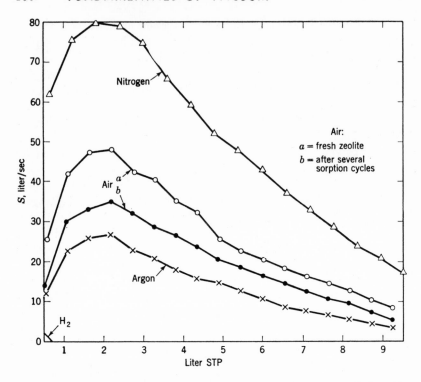

Fig. 6-4 Pumping speed of a sorption pump (filled with 100 g of Linde 13X zeolite) as a function of the pumped gas quantity at 10^{-1} torr. (From P. F. Varadi and K. Ettre, 1960 *Vacuum Symp. Trans.*, p. 248, 1961.)

A comparison of air and N_2 shows that N_2 is adsorbed more readily than O_2.

It is not surprising that the gas composition changes during a pumpdown. Redhead et al. (21) pumped from the atmosphere down to 5×10^{-3} torr with Linde X13. The composition of the gas was 64 percent He, 31 percent Ne, 4 percent A, and 1 percent N_2. The composition of atmospheric air is given in Table 6-1. A correlation with the expected heat of desorption is apparent. Varadi and Ettre observed a reduced sorption after recycling. This is probably caused by water-vapor adsorption. Bannock (4) emphasizes that the water vapor is not desorbed from type 5A zeolite at room temperature. The zeolite has to be heated to 350°C to get rid of most of the water vapor. But it must not be heated above this temperature as this will lead to eventual disintegration. See also Sec. 6-4, for sorption pumps with zeolite and charcoal.

Table 6-1   Composition of Air

Gas	Percent by volume	Partial pressure, torrs
Nitrogen	78.1	593
Oxygen	20.9	159
Carbon dioxide	0.03	0.23
Argon	0.93	7.1
Krypton	1.0×10^{-4}	7.6×10^{-4}
Neon	18×10^{-4}	137×10^{-4}
Helium	5.24×10^{-4}	40×10^{-4}
Hydrogen	0.5×10^{-4}	3.8×10^{-4}

SOURCE: "Handbook of Chemistry and Physics," 41st ed., Chemical Rubber Publishing Company, Cleveland, 1959.

6-2   *Diffusion Pumps and Traps*

In diffusion pumps, the dense vapor of the work fluid, either oil or mercury, emanates from jets into the high vacuum at supersonic speed. It collides with the gas, entrains the molecules, and imparts momentum toward the forevacuum. A typical oil diffusion pump is shown in Fig. 6-5. The boiler is at the bottom. The vapor rises in the chimneylike jet assembly. Three annular jets are arranged in vertical succession. The top jet is designed to operate at the lowest pressure. Above the top jet is a water-cooled baffle and above the baffle a trap. A baffle is a cold wall, used to condense the pump fluid and return it to the boiler. Traps are cold walls to trap gases and vapors, in particular the vapor of the pump fluid. They are usually cooled with liquid nitrogen. In the pump of Fig. 6-5 the baffle is the so-called chevron type. The advantage of this design is the sub-division of the area by the chevron walls. This reduces the mean free path and extends the range of molecular flow. The vapor is directed downward by the jets toward the water-cooled pump wall. There it condenses and streams back to the boiler. The pumped gas is removed through the forevacuum line. In the side wall of the pump one more jet is provided, a so-called ejector stage designed to operate at higher pressures to increase the pump's forepressure tolerance. This stage is often omitted.

The efficiency of a pump is expressed by the speed factor formerly called Ho coefficient, defined as the ratio of the actual pumping speed to the pumping speed of an orifice of the same area as the annular gap between the top jet and the wall. Typically a pump has a

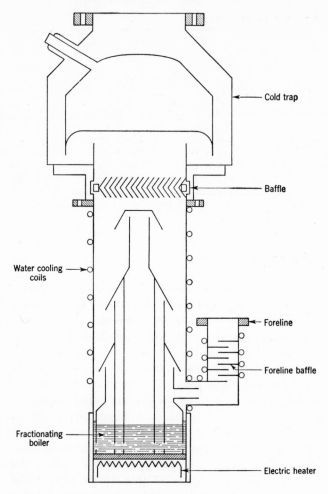

Fig. 6-5 Fractionating oil diffusion pump with ejector stage, chevron baffle, and cold trap.

speed factor of about 0.5. But efficiency is not the most important feature, since the speed can always be improved by using a larger pump.

The pumping speed remains constant as the pressure increases but starts to drop when the limiting forepressure is approached and the vapor stream from the top jet is broken up. When all jets fail, pumping ceases. The limiting forepressure decreases when the throughput is increased. At full load it is 65 to 80 percent of the value for no load or minimum throughput. The values quoted below are the minimum values for maximum throughput. The Committee on Standards of the American Vacuum Society recommends the following definition for limiting forepressure: "The forepressure which corresponds to an inlet pressure about 0.2 millitorr greater than the inlet pressure corresponding to the normal forepressure for a vapor pump at a given load (or throughput)."

A diffusion pump continues to pump at constant speed at low pressures; i.e., gas continues to be entrained and removed by the vapor stream. The actual low-pressure limit is determined by the equilibrium between pumping and gassing. There exist five gas sources: (1) gassing of the walls (not further discussed here; see Sec. 3-10), (2) back diffusion of gas from the forevacuum through the vapor, (3) penetration of fractions of cracked oil into the high-vacuum space, (4) back migration, and (5) backstreaming of the vapor of the pump fluid. Backstreaming is the direct flight of vapor molecules from the top jet toward the mouth of the pump; back migration is the transfer of vapor to the high vacuum by reevaporation from the wall and from baffles. Because of backstreaming, considerably more vapor moves toward the high-vacuum side than would correspond to the vapor pressure at the wall temperature.

Back diffusion depends on the number of stages and the pump design. It varies greatly from pump to pump. Some published data are tabulated by Hablanian and Vitkus (5). The maximum ratios of outlet pressure to inlet pressure varied from 5×10^2 to 7×10^5 for H_2, 10^3 to 2×10^3 for He, and were 10^7 for N_2. Back diffusion decreases rapidly with increasing molecular weight. A high-density ejector stage is beneficial. These authors found a ratio of 10^{10} for He in an oil diffusion pump with ejector stage (NRC HS6 − 1500), and we measured 10^{11} in a small mercury pump with ejector stage [Fig. 6-9 (2)]. Back diffusion presents no basic problem since it can be reduced, if necessary, by increasing the number of stages.

Oil can be cracked in the pump especially by catalytic action of a metal wall, and some light cracking products may migrate to the mouth of the pump. A second oil diffusion pump in series with the first pump reduces back diffusion and removes the light volatile fractions. This can improve the ultimate pressure; see Hengevoss and Huber (7). Also, pumps can be self-fractionating, as shown in Fig. 6-5, by extending the jet partitions to the bottom of the boiler with small connecting holes only. That portion of the oil which, after returning to the boiler, evaporates first goes into the jet nearest the forevacuum.

Most oils decompose when heated only slightly above their

operating temperature. If the pump is exposed to pressures above a few torr while the boiler is hot, the vaporization of the oil is sufficiently retarded and the temperature increased to cause oil decomposition by overheating. An exception is the silicone oils, which may be exposed to the atmosphere while still hot after the heater has been shut off.

Back migration in mercury pumps was discussed by Power et al. (8) in a general survey article on mercury-pump technology. Because of the high vapor pressure of mercury (7×10^{-4} torr at 14°C), back migration is quite large. The rate of evaporation of Hg at 14°C is 1.5×10^{-4} cm³/cm² min. Power measured a back-migration rate of 1.75×10^{-2} cm³/min in a 9-in. pump at this temperature. When the walls were heavily contaminated, the rate increased twelvefold because of poor heat exchange between the wall and the condensing droplets. If a liquid-N_2-cooled trap is used to collect the mercury, the average pump would lose its charge in one to two weeks by freezing out at the trap. Hence a refrigerated baffle cooled to -30°C is used between the pump and the trap. The mercury (freezing point -39°C) condenses at the baffle, still in the liquid state, and drops back into the pump. The vapor pressure of mercury at -30°C is 4.8×10^{-6} torr.

With the baffle, Power measured a back-migration rate of 3.3×10^{-4} cm³/min in a 1500-liter/sec pump, permitting at least one year of continuous operation. This was nine times the rate calculated from evaporation only. Perhaps one reason is that the sticking and accommodation coefficients for mercury are less than unity. It is important that the refrigerated baffle be located directly above the top jet to avoid loss of pumping speed by the diffusion of the gas through the mercury vapor. If this cannot be done, chilling of the top turns of the cooling coils gives improvement.

Diffusion-pump oils have a much lower vapor pressure, of 10^{-7} to 10^{-10} torr at room temperature. Here, backstreaming is appreciable, about 1.5×10^{-5} cm³/min per square centimeter of inlet area for a good pump. Hence, without provisions to return the oil, oil pumps would lose their charge almost as fast as mercury pumps. In their basic investigation of backstreaming, Power and Crawley (9) pointed out that the lip of the top jet is an important source of vapor. The backstreaming was reduced up to 30 times by putting a cooled guard ring around the top jet while the pumping speed increased or decreased slightly.

Hablanian and Steinherz (10) reported that similar cold caps reduced backstreaming rates up to 100 times. But the rate may increase rapidly at higher pressures, as shown in Fig. 6-6 from their paper, after the breakdown of the top jet, when the flow becomes

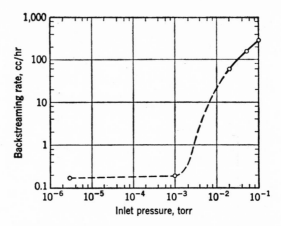

Fig. **6-6**   Backstreaming rate versus inlet pressure
for 32-in. pump (fluid: Narcoil 40) (From M. N.
Hablanian and H. A. Steinherz, 1961 *Vacuum Symp.
Trans.*, p. 333, 1962.)

viscous on account of the high vapor density.   Hence a pump must
not be operated at higher pressure for longer periods, and the pumpdown must be rapid through this range.   They measured backstreaming to an area just above the top jet, a condition not of immediate
practical significance.   At a distance 1.5 diameters from the pump
entrance the backstreaming rate was reduced to 2.5 percent of the
value at the inlet plane.   A baffle or trap or even a piece of straight
pipe will reduce backstreaming.   If the baffle or trap is of the chevron
type shown in Fig. 6-5, the effect of the higher vapor pressure is reduced
since wall collisions predominate even at higher pressures.

Since a baffle reduces the Hg vapor pressure to the 10^{-6} torr
range only, a liquid-N_2-cooled trap is added for operation in ultrahigh
vacuum.   The mercury vapor pressure is negligible at liquid-nitrogen
temperature.   A single-bounce liquid-N_2-cooled trap is inadequate to
prevent all the vapor molecules from entering the vacuum vessel.   It
is possible to obtain pressures of 10^{-10} torr and less with mercury
diffusion pumps, when one or more liquid-N_2-cooled traps are used,
requiring more than one bounce for passage.   Oil diffusion pumps
reach ultrahigh vacuum also with liquid-nitrogen-cooled traps.

More recently there became available new oils that produce
very low pressure even if only a refrigerated trap is used.   Crawley
et al. (11) evaluated silicone oil DC-705.   With one chevron baffle
cooled by water of 16.5°C, the pressure was 5×10^{-9} torr.   In
another pump with a water-cooled baffle and a refrigerated trap at

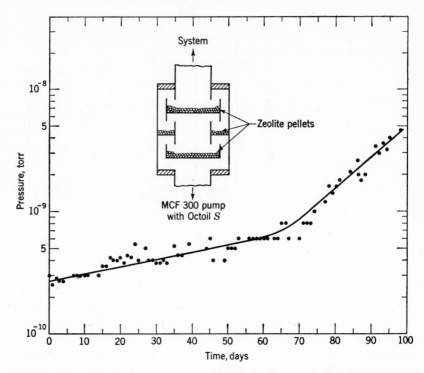

Fig. 6-7 Performance of 8-in.-diameter zeolite (Linde 13X) trap with 4-in.-diameter metal oil diffusion pump with water baffle. (From N. A. Biondi, 1960 *Vacuum Symp. Trans.*, p. 24, 1961.)

$-20°C$, the pressure was 5×10^{-10} torr after several days without a bake and 6.5×10^{-11} torr at $-31°C$ trap temperature after a 160-hr bake at $300°C$. The gage reading was not corrected for x-ray current. Hence the pressure was in the low 10^{-11} range or even lower. We could not reproduce these favorable results in another nonfractionating pump with a different type of boiler.

Alpert (12) discovered that traps filled with coiled sheets of copper foil and kept at room temperature prevent the migration of oil from small glass diffusion pumps into the vacuum system, and a pressure in the 10^{-10} torr range is maintained for several weeks. Then the pressure rises gradually to the vapor pressure of the oil. The trap can be reactivated by a bake. Biondi (13) reported that zeolite or activated alumina is a more powerful adsorbent and permits the design of high-conductance traps for larger metal pumps where copper-foil traps are ineffective. They can also be reactivated by a bake. Figure 6-7 shows a typical performance. But further investigations by the

Westinghouse group revealed the presence of a small influx of gas that is not removed by such a trap. A small amount of ion pumping is necessary to maintain pressures below 10^{-9} torr.

In a comparison of oil and mercury as pump fluids, mercury has the advantage that it is a stable fluid, it may be exposed to the atmosphere while hot, and it can be operated at high forepressures. But it is toxic and has a high vapor pressure that makes a liquid-nitrogen trap mandatory in most applications. In some cases, amalgamation is objectionable; in particular, aluminum forms an amalgam with mercury vapor, which reacts strongly with water vapor to form spongy Al_2O_3. With silicone oil DC-705, ultrahigh-vacuum pressures can be obtained with only refrigerated baffles, and some exposure of the hot oil to the atmosphere is not detrimental, virtues that other oils lack. But the system can be contaminated with hydrocarbons and other oil fractions in case of an accident.

Baffles are cooled to a temperature slightly above the freezing point of the pump fluid. Conventional refrigerators cool to a temperature of about $-30°C$ for Hg pumps. Lately, baffles cooled by the Peltier effect in semiconductor junctions became commercially available. Jean and Liot (14) obtained a temperature difference of 36.5°C between the hot and cold ends. The hot side was cooled to 10°C with tap water. With two stages in series, a cold temperature of $-40°C$ appeared possible.

Traps act as cryogenic pumps for all condensable vapors present in the system, in particular water vapor. Sorption is of no importance since the surfaces saturate rapidly. It follows from Eq. (2-6) that the speed of a liquid-nitrogen trap for water vapor of 20°C is 14.6 liters/sec cm^2. Traps should be designed in such a manner as to avoid the formation of a spot of intermediate temperature on the system side where the water vapor from the system first condenses. As the evacuation progresses, this water would reevaporate only slowly on account of the reduced pressure at the lower temperature, and the evacuation rate would be reduced. Also, part of the cold surface must not warm up when the liquid-N_2 level drops; this would cause the release of some gas. This may require a rather thick wall with high enough heat conduction to assure uniform temperature even if only part of the wall is cooled.

Oil wets all trap surfaces. Hence cold traps should have a cold creep barrier (as shown in Fig. 6-8) so that oil cannot migrate along the surface into the system. Mercury does not wet stainless steel, the metal of which most traps are made. Hence creep barriers are not needed. Automatic devices are available for refilling the trap. The

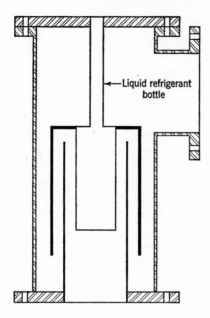

←—Liquid refrigerant
bottle

Fig. 6-8 Cold trap with creep barrier for oil diffusion pump, as proposed by R. Post. (From "Encyclopedia of Physics," vol. XII, Springer Verlag OHG, Berlin, 1958.)

danger is that ice formed by condensation of the moisture from the atmosphere settles at a spot where it interferes with the proper operation of the filling system. A trap should be filled only after some pumping has removed most of the water or at the end of the bake, if the system is baked. In ultrahigh vacuum two traps in series are preferable. The trap nearer the system is filled last after the system has been cooled.

Traps and baffles cut down the speed. In a balanced pump aggregate the trap and baffle together have a conductance numerically at least 40 percent of the pump speed.

The advantages of diffusion pumps are their reliability and high pumping speed independent of any change of throughput, or, to put it differently, their lack of memory effect; i.e., the speed is not affected by the type or amount of previously pumped gas. Diffusion pumps with speeds up to 90,000 liters/sec are commercially available. Typical pumping-speed curves for air of oil and mercury pumps with and without ejector stage and of an oil-ejector pump are shown in Fig. 6-9. The speeds were measured on pumps without traps or baffles. The small 80-liter/sec mercury pump with ejector stage is remarkable on account of its very high forepressure limit of 35 torr. It can be operated with a water aspirator as forepump. The lowest limiting forepressures at maximum throughput are given. The forepressure limit for oil diffusion pumps with and without ejector stage is in the upper and

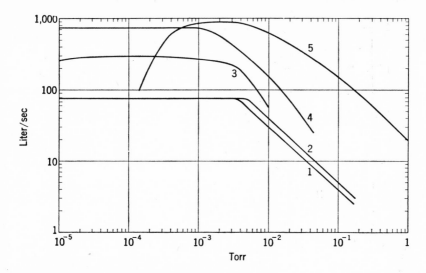

Fig. 6-9 Speeds of pumps without baffle or trap:

1. Three-stage mercury diffusion pump; limiting forepressure, 0.5 torr. Edwards High Vacuum 2M3B.
2. Four-stage mercury diffusion pump with ejector stage; limiting forepressure, 35 torr. Edwards High Vacuum 2M4A.
3. Oil diffusion pump; limiting forepressure, 0.22 torr. Consolidated Vacuum Corp. MCF 300.
4. Oil diffusion pump with ejector stage; limiting forepressure, 0.45 torr. National Research Corp. HS4-750.
5. Oil-ejector pump; limiting forepressure, 2 to 3 torr. Edwards High Vacuum 9B3.

lower half of the 10^{-1} torr range and for mercury pumps around 1 torr. Oil-ejector pumps operate effectively in the 10^{-4} to 10^{-1} torr range with a forepressure limit in the 10^{0} torr range. Their range is similar to that of Roots pumps. Pumping speed for lighter gases is higher. In measurements at the Oak Ridge National Laboratories on two oil diffusion pumps, the pumping speeds for air and hydrogen at 10^{-5} torr were 18,000 and 25,000 liters/sec (NRC H-32-P) and 1500 and 2600 liters/sec (CVC MCF-1400), respectively (14a).

6-3   Molecular Drag Pump

In this pump, first introduced by Gaede, a high-speed rotor imparts momentum to the impinging gas molecules. To avoid excessive heating by gas friction, a forevacuum pump is required. The

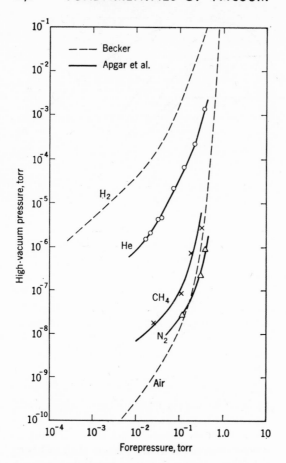

Fig. 6-10 High-vacuum pressure versus forepressure for several gases in a molecular drag pump under zero flow condition. (From E. Apgar, G. Lewin, and D. Mullaney, *Rev. Sci. Instr.*, vol. 33, p. 985, 1962, and W. Becker, *Vakuum Tech.*, vol. 7, p. 149, 1958.)

theory has recently been treated by Kruger and Shapiro (15) for the molecular flow range.   The high speed of rotation combined with close spacing was an undesirable feature of older designs.

Becker (16) described a new pump which, though also operating at 16,000 rpm, has a 1-mm gap between rotor and stator.   A large pressure ratio between inlet and outlet is obtained for heavier gases by the use of 19 stages in series.   Figure 6-10 shows this pressure ratio for several gases.   The rapid increase with increased molecular weight explains the absence of oil vapor on the high-vacuum side although the

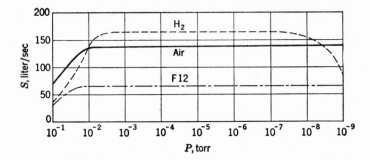

Fig. 6-11 Pumping speed of a molecular drag pump for H_2, air, and Freon 12. (From W. Becker, *Vakuum Tech.*, vol. 7, p. 149, 1958.)

vapor pressure of the oil is high, 0.05 torr nitrogen equivalent on a thermocouple gage. Figure 6-11 from Becker's paper gives the pumping speed for hydrogen, air, and Freon 12. Without baking, a pressure in the 10^{-9} torr range is obtained. An ultimate pressure of less than 10^{-9} torr is reached after a mild bake, the only one permissible. This pump is commercially available. Apgar et al. (17) showed that this pump can be used as a combination pumping and gas injection system for hydrogen and helium in the 10^{-4} to 10^{-3} torr range by admitting the gas on the forevacuum side at high enough pressure to have it diffuse to the high-vacuum side.

Beams (17a) developed a magnetic rotor suspension and used it in the design of a bakeable molecular drag pump. One such pump has a one-stage rotor of 9-in. diameter which is spun at speeds up to 27,000 rpm. The gap between rotor and stator is 0.05 cm. Pumping speeds of the order of 10 liters/sec have been reached. The lowest pressure was 4×10^{-10} torr with a pressure ratio of 150. The highest ratio was 8.3×10^4 at a high-vacuum pressure of 1.2×10^{-7} torr; all measurements were conducted with the residual gas.

The molecular drag pump, like the diffusion pump, has a constant pumping speed over a wide pressure range, a rather low ultimate pressure, and no memory effect. It does not require baffles or traps. But it rotates at high speed and, therefore, is inherently less reliable. Only one size is commercially available, and the cost per liter per second speed is high.

6-4 Sorption Pumping

Physical and chemical adsorption and chemical reactions at surfaces are utilized for pumping. Substances pumping by chemical adsorption and reaction are sometimes called getters. Mostly metals are employed. They are usually used in the form of a thin film evaporated onto a surface, often the wall of the container. We shall first discuss the gettering qualities of various metals and methods of preparation of metal films. We shall consider the performances of these pumps at room temperature and liquid-nitrogen temperature. Adsorption forepumps filled with zeolite were mentioned in Sec. 6-1. Here we shall discuss the general use of zeolites and charcoal in cryogenic sorption pumping. The term cryogenic refers to any low-temperature process. While cryogenic sorption pumping is treated in this section, Sec. 6-7 will deal with cryogenic condensation pumps and cryotrapping, the trapping of a noncondensable gas by a condensable vapor at a cold surface.

Sorption pumping has two advantages:

1. The pump is clean; there is no pump fluid or pump-fluid vapor which may enter the system.

2. High pumping speeds can be obtained by depositing the adsorbing layer on the wall of the vacuum vessel itself.

It follows from Eq. (2-6) that the pumping speed S of 1 cm^2 surface area of an adsorbent with a sticking coefficient s is

$$S = 3.64s \left(\frac{T}{M}\right)^{\frac{1}{2}} \quad \text{liters/sec cm}^2 \quad (6\text{-}1)$$

For N_2 and H_2, S is $11.8s$ and $44s$ liters/sec cm^2 at room temperature. This is a high speed. Even if an area of only moderate size is covered with the adsorbent, S can be large when the pumping occurs in the vessel itself. With a separate pump, the speed is reduced by the limited conductance of the connecting pipe.

But sorption pumps also have drawbacks. They are recommended only for light gas loads (small throughputs), since the gas is not removed to a forepump. The rate of adsorption is a function of the type of gas and is affected by the presence of other gases. In extreme cases, previously sorbed gas may be replaced by the new gas (see Sec. 3-4). The sticking coefficient drops as a monolayer is approached. Hence the metal films have to be renewed continually. Noble gases are not adsorbed at room temperature on account of their low heat of desorption. Cooling of the surface enhances the sorption since physical adsorption, especially adsorption of noble gas, occurs also. But a cooled surface will release physically adsorbed gas when warmed to room temperature. An auxiliary pump of small speed, about 1 percent of the speed of sorption may be necessary to retain good vacuum during evaporation and, in some cases, to remove gases that are not sorbed. Ion pumps may perform the latter function.

Getters have been used for a long time to produce and maintain a low pressure in electron tubes. Reports on properties of getters differ considerably. Many getters are porous, and diffusion of gases occurs. The equilibrium pressure depends upon the degree of saturation. Table 6-2, compiled by Holland, lists the characteristics of some suitable metal films. Titanium is used most extensively. It getters all common chemically active gases except methane. When heated, mainly H_2 is released above 200°C [(19), (20)]. Titanium, zirconium, tantalum, and molybdenum have been used in ultrahigh vacuum. Selective getters are sometimes useful, e.g., for gas purification or a crude gas analysis [Ref. (21)]. An evaporated rhodium film adsorbs H_2, CO, O_2, and simple hydrocarbons but does not adsorb N_2. Gold adsorbs CO and simple hydrocarbons but does not adsorb H_2, N_2, and O_2.

A fresh metal surface is provided by evaporation. A number of filamentary heaters have been described for titanium. Clausing (22) used a heater consisting of a tantalum rod overwound with one layer of columbium wire and two layers of titanium wire. The columbium alloys with the titanium and raises its melting point. Another heater was a homogeneous filament made of an alloy of Ta and Ti. This also permitted higher operating temperatures. Herb et al. (23) twisted two titanium wires of 0.2-mm diameter together with two tantalum wires of 0.1-mm diameter and wound the twisted wires closely onto a 0.4-mm-diameter tungsten wire.

The capacity of such filaments is limited. To increase it, titanium wire was formerly kept on a spool inside the pump and fed by an externally driven mechanism onto the evaporator. It consisted of a hot post heated by electron bombardment, or the wire tip was melted directly into a bead by electron bombardment. The wire feeder has been abandoned in favor of titanium rods [Refs. (23), (24)] or cartridges [Ref. (25)]. The cartridges are formed from a stiff tungsten wire overwound with stranded titanium and tantalum wire. The rods or cartridges are usually heated by bombardment with electrons supplied by a tungsten wire. The temperature of the rods is kept below the melting point and the titanium sublimes or the end is molten.

A barium sorption pump for H_2 and O_2 has been investigated in the 10^{-5} to 10^{-3} torr range by Cloud et al. (26). They use an auxiliary diffusion pump of 59 liter/sec speed for H_2. The barium charge of 1.2 kg maximum is put in open air into a lower stainless-steel appendage of the pump and heated to 800 to 900°C with an electric oven. The barium evaporates and deposits on vanes attached to the water-cooled housing. The initial (and highest) speed at 10^{-5} torr is 1800

Table 6-2 Some Characteristics of Metal Films of Importance in Determining Their Usefulness as Getters

$\mu = 10^{-3}$ torr C = chemical reaction. Ch = chemisorption. D = diffusion. L = linear law of oxidation.

Getter film	Gas	Initial adsorption rate ($\simeq 20°C$) $(-s^{-1}\,cm^{-2})$*	Film temperature for continuous sorption (°C)	Sorptive capacity $l\mu/mg$ $(T°C)$†	Adsorption rate enhanced by ionization	Remarks
Aluminum mp = 660°C 1291°C (vp = 100 μ)	O_2	C	500°	7.5–38.5 (20)	—	
	H_2	0.0	—	0	—	
	N_2	0.0	—	0	—	
	CO_2	<0.005 l.	—	0	—	
	CO	<0.005 l.	—	—	—	
Barium mp = 717°C 730°C (vp = 100 μ)	Air	Ch	>40°	56 (400)	No	H_2 gettering increased by presence of heated cathode. Commercially available metal requires extensive degassing or distillation to remove impurities. Can be obtained in alloy form with Al.
	O_2	0.3 l.	200°	57 (300)	No	
	H_2	0.05 l.		100 (400)		
	H_2O	C	>100°	72 (300)	Yes	
	N_2	0.003 l.		{ 3–25 (<100) 43–51 (>100) }		
	CO_2	5.0 l.	>80°	66 (400)	No	
	CO	3.5 l.		100 (400)		
	C_2H_2, C_2H_4	Ch				
Calcium mp = 810°C 700°C (vp = 100 μ)	O_2, N_2, CO, C_2H_2, CO_2, H_2O, SO_2, NH_3, C_2H_4	C Ch Ch Ch	425°L	—	—	Electrolytically prepared metal may contain CaH_2 which dissociates at the evaporation temperature. Distilled metal is commercially available and cheaper than Ba.
Magnesium mp = 651°C 515°C (vp = 100 μ)	O_2	C	>450°L	20–200 (20)	—	H_2 gettering increased by presence of heated cathode.
	H_2	0.0	—	—	Yes	
	N_2	0.0	—	—	—	
	CO_2	<0.005 l.	—	≃0.0	Yes	
	CO	<0.005 l.	—	— (30)		
Titanium mp = 1660°C 1742°C (vp = 100 μ)	O_2	C	—	1.9–2.5 (30–300)	—	Vacuum-melted metal in form of wire and sheet is commercially obtainable, contains ≃0.008 percent of H_2.
	H_2	Ch	—	4.3 (20)	—	
	N_2	3.0 l.	—	3.4–4.2 (30–200)	—	
	CO_2	4.3 l.	—	—	—	
	CO	12.0 l.	—		—	
	SF_6		—		—	
	C_2H_2, CH_4, C_2H_4, CCl_2F_2, NH_3	Ch Ch Ch	—		—	

Material	Gas	Film type	Temp	Speed	(°C)	Getter	Remarks
Titanium (solid)	O_2	2.01 μ (800°) D	>650°L	90	(800)	—	CH$_4$ dissociates when striking Ti at 1200°C; C is sorbed and H$_2$ taken up at lower temperature. H$_2$ is only gas released by heating. Surface oxide reduces H$_2$ sorption below 300°C.
	H_2	D	20–400° D			—	
	N_2		>700°			—	
	CO_2	0.08 μ (1000°)	>700°	160	(1000)	—	
	H_2O	0.81 μ (1100°)	300°–400°	50	(1100)	—	
Zirconium mp = 2127°C 2212°C (vp = 100 μ)	H_2	C				—	
	C_2H_2, C_2H_4	Ch				—	
		>2.5 l.				—	
Zirconium (ribbon)	O_2	C	885°	1.99	(400)	No	
	H_2	D	300°–400°	13.3	(350)		
	N_2	C	1527°	1.46	(800)		
	CO_2	C		3.04	(800)	Yes	
	CO			3.65	(800)	No	
Tantalum mp = 2996°C 2820°C (vp = 1 μ)	O_2	C				No	Difficult to evaporate—low vapor pressure.
	H_2, C_2H_2, C_2H_4	Ch					
	N_2	>2.5 l.					
	CO	>2.5 l.				No	
Molybdenum mp = 2622°C 2533°C (vp = 10 μ)	O_2	C		1.0	(30)		Difficult to evaporate thick films —low vapor pressure. May be sublimated.
	H_2, C_2H_2, C_2H_4	Ch					
	N_2	2.7 l.		3.0	(30–200)		
	CO	3.5 l.					
Tungsten mp = 3382°C 3309°C (vp = 10 μ)	O_2	Ch				—	Difficult to evaporate thick films —low vapor pressure. May be sublimated.
	H_2, C_2H_2, C_2H_4	Ch				—	
	N_2	>2.5 l.				—	
	CO					—	
Thorium mp = 1827°C 2431°C (vp = 100 μ)	O_2	C	450°L	7.5–33.1	(20)	—	Difficult to evaporate—low vapor pressure.
	H_2	Ch	650°	19.5–53.7	(20)	—	
	CO_2	Ch				—	
Uranium mp = 1132°C 2098°C (vp = 100 μ)	O_2	C	240°L	10.6–9.3	(20)	—	
	H_2	Ch		8.9–21.5	(20)	—	
Misch metal Cerium mp = 785°C 1439°C (vp = 100 μ)	O_2	C		21.7–51	(20)	—	Chiefly cerium and lanthanum.
	H_2	Ch		46.1–64	(20)	—	
	N_2	Ch		3.2–16	(20)	—	
	CO_2	Ch		2.2–45	(20)	—	

* Initial adsorption rates are given in terms of volumetric and mass speeds (that is, $ls^{-1}\,cm^{-2}$ and $\mu s^{-1}\,cm^{-2}$) according to author.

† Generally values are for bright films, where two values are quoted the second figure is for a black deposit.

SOURCE: L. Holland, J. Sci. Instr., vol. 36, p. 109, 1959.

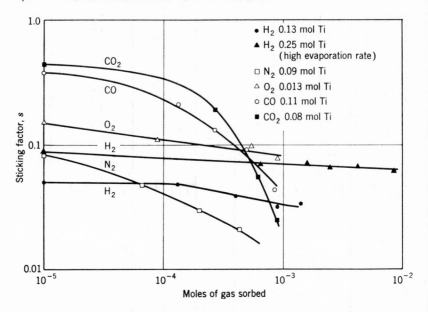

Fig. 6-12 Sorption of gases onto films formed by titanium evaporation in high vacuum onto a surface of 34,000 cm² at 10°C. (From R. E. Clausing, 1961 *Vacuum Symp. Trans.*, p. 345, 1962.)

liters/sec for H_2 and 2000 liters/sec for O_2, corresponding to about 10^{-1} liter/sec cm² (a rather low value). The speed dropped 75 percent after sorption of 50,000 torr liters of gas.

Hunt et al. (27) evaporated molybdenum filaments onto the wall of an 85-liter stainless-steel vessel. A small diffusion pump produced a pressure of less than 10^{-7} torr. The filaments were degassed and then heated to evaporation temperature in 1-min pulses with 5-min intervals. After the first pulse the pressure remained below 10^{-7} torr and decreased gradually. At 10^{-7} torr, the time for adsorption of a monolayer is a few seconds, long enough to prevent immediate film saturation. Pressures in the 10^{-10} torr range were produced and maintained in an unbaked and a moderately baked system. The initial sticking probability for H_2 and D_2 was about 0.3. They measured also the relative pumping speed for H_2 at room temperature and at $-196°C$ at low pressures in a baked system [Ref. (28)]. The speed increased several times when the Mo film was cooled. Warming and recooling had no effect. The speed as a function of coverages had a maximum and a minimum at room temperature. It increased at $-196°C$ with coverage to a maximum just before saturation.

Clausing (22) investigated the sorption characteristics of Ti

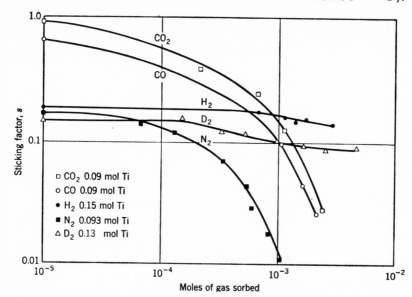

Fig. 6-13 Sorption of gases onto films formed by titanium evaporation in the presence of 2.5×10^{-3} torr pressure of helium onto a surface of 34,000 cm² at 10°C. (From R. E. Clausing, 1961 *Vacuum Symp. Trans.*, p. 345, 1962.)

films for H_2, D_2, N_2, CO, and CO_2 in a 500-liter tank, also equipped with a small diffusion pump. He used continuous evaporation during pumping and batch evaporation. Figures 6-12 and 6-13 show how the sticking factor s (and the pumping speed) decreases as more gas is adsorbed. The slow decrease for H_2 indicates diffusion. Evaporation in inert gas is helpful, since the deposits have a larger surface. Table 6-3 gives his initial sticking factors. The table shows that the initial sticking probability is enhanced if the films are deposited and kept at −196°C. But the pumping speed for H_2 and D_2 drops faster at low temperature since the diffusion is smaller, as shown in Fig. 6-14. The sticking coefficient of CO_2 remains almost unity since the gas condenses at the cold surface. Films deposited at 10°C did not sorb much better when cooled, while films deposited at −196°C lost their high sorption when allowed to warm up temporarily. The higher sorption for low-temperature deposition is due, at least in part, to a different type of deposition with poorly developed crystal structure. But there are other unknown factors contributing to the observed behavior.

Elsworth and Holland (28a) investigated the sorption of N_2 by Ti films. They found an extrapolated initial sticking factor of 0.32 at 10^{-8} torr. The molecules dissociate on chemisorption, and the atoms diffuse into the interior along grain boundaries.

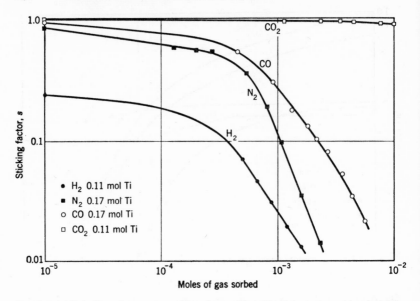

Fig. 6-14 Sorption of gases onto films formed by titanium evaporation in high vacuum onto a surface of 34,000 cm² at −195°C and kept at this temperature. (From R. E. Clausing, 1961 *Vacuum Symp. Trans.*, p. 345, 1962.)

Table 6-3   Initial Sticking Factors for Various Gases on Titanium Films Deposited under Several Conditions

Gas species	High vacuum, 10°C		0.002 torr helium 10°C batch evaporation	High vacuum, −195°C		0.002 torr helium −195°C batch evaporation
	Continuous evaporation	Batch evaporation		Continuous evaporation	Batch evaporation	
Hydrogen	0.07	0.05	0.19	0.14	0.24	0.85
Deuterium	—	—	0.14	—	—	0.78
Nitrogen	>0.20*	0.08	0.17	>0.5	0.85	0.93
Carbon monoxide	0.86	0.38	0.66	—	0.95	—
Oxygen†	0.63	0.85	0.82	—	0.86	—
Carbon dioxide	>0.5*	>0.4*	0.92	—	0.98	—
Helium	<0.0005*	—	—	—	—	—
Argon	<0.0005*	—	—	—	—	—
Methane	<0.0005*	—	—	—	—	—

* These data are estimated.

† The oxygen used in this measurement contained some argon, thereby possibly producing a lower value of s than would be expected for pure oxygen.

SOURCE: R. E. Clausing, 1961 *Vacuum Symp. Trans.*, p. 345, 1962.

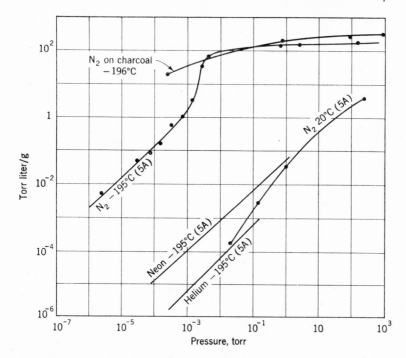

Fig. 6-15 Adsorption isotherms: N_2, Ne, He on Linde Molecular Sieve type 5A zeolite (from F. T. Turner and M. Feinleib, 1961 *Vacuum Symp. Trans.*, p. 300, 1962) and N_2 on activated charcoal (from J. de Dios Lopez-Gonzalez, F. S. Carpenter, and V. R. Dietz, *J. Res. Natl. Bur. Std.*, vol. 55, p. 11, 1955).

Cooled zeolites and activated charcoal can also serve as high-vacuum pumps, after they have been degassed by a bake in vacuum. The sorption of charcoals varies greatly, depending on type and preparation. Lopez-Gonzalez et al. (29) reported an order-of-magnitude or more improvement after several sorptions at low temperature and desorptions at room temperature in addition to an initial bake at 400°C. Figure 6-15 shows the adsorption isotherm at 77°K for N_2 on activated charcoal which was baked and improved by sorption cycles and on type 5A zeolite which was baked only. The isotherms for He and Ne on type 5A zeolite are also given. Figure 6-16 plots the isotherms for A on type 13X zeolite and activated charcoal at 77°K after a bake. Here the charcoal sorbed about 100 times as much argon. The isotherm gives the saturation coverage at which the pumping speed becomes zero but does not indicate what the pumping speed is at lower coverage. Adsorption of gases by zeolites does not always increase

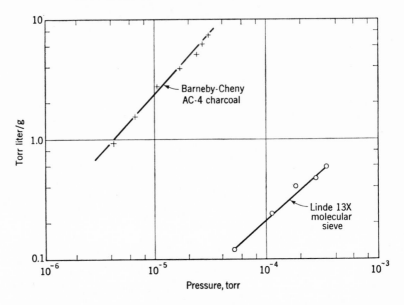

Fig. 6-16 Argon sorption isotherms at 77°K and low pressures. (From N. M. Kuluva and E. L. Knuth, 1962 *Vacuum Symp. Trans.*, p. 237, 1963.)

with decreasing temperature for all gases. It can have a maximum at a temperature between 77 and 300°K.

Lazarev and Fedorova (32) tripled the pumping speed for H_2 of a particular sorption pump filled with charcoal by cooling with liquid H_2 instead of N_2. The composition of gas mixtures can change drastically during sorption (see Sec. 6.1). It is conceivable that cooling of charcoal and zeolite can become a problem at low pressures where heat conduction by the gas is negligible. But heat exchange can be improved by proper design, as mentioned in Sec. 6-1. Read (32a) used type X13 zeolite for pumping high- and ultrahigh-vacuum systems.

In comparing activated charcoal with zeolites, Turner and Feinleib (30) make the preliminary statement that advantages of charcoal are higher thermal conductivity, lower regeneration temperature, and lower cost. Synthetic zeolites have lower dusting and greater ease of outgassing, namely, 15 to 30 min compared with several hours for activated charcoal. Obviously, the collection of further data, including data on simultaneous sorption of different gases, is very desirable.

Hunt et al. (60) adsorbed H_2 at 11°K on A, N_2, N_2O, O_2, H_2O, and CO_2 films. Sticking probabilities at a coverage with 10^{11} H_2

molecules/cm^2 are 0.4 for H_2O and 0.09 for A and O_2; s was 0.3 on N_2O for a coverage of 6×10^{13} to 2×10^{16} molecules/cm^2, a high sorption rate far beyond a monolayer. Helium was not adsorbed in comparable quantities. Most or all of the gas was desorbed below 20°K. They demonstrated that H_2 can be pumped by this method in the ultrahigh-vacuum range and that the gas can be desorbed and the surface reactivated by a slight temperature increase.

6-5   Ion-Sorption Pumps

Pure ion pumps are rarely used [Ref. (33)]. In these pumps the gas is ionized and the ions are driven toward an auxiliary pump. Usually sorption and ion pumping are combined. The ions are captured by metal surfaces, mainly Ti, which also pump by sorption. These pumps are called ion-sorption or getter-ion pumps. The ion pumping removes the gases that are not sorbed. The electrons that ionize the atoms are in most cases produced by a hot filament. Ion-sorption pumps (and sputter-ion pumps; see Sec. 6-6) are well suited to retain vacuum in systems while unattended. If the pump stops because of a power failure, a small amount of gas may be reemitted, but large quantities of gas enter the system if a cold trap warms up or a diffusion pump ceases operating.

Molecules are dissociated and metastable atoms are formed in a gas discharge, although the cross sections for these events are usually much smaller than for ionization. It has been mentioned by several investigators that, in such states, gas is sorbed more readily. Hence the combined pumping action of an ion-sorption pump is larger than that of either part alone. Also, krypton [Ref. (34)] was recovered from the anodes of sputter-ion pumps. But Francis and Jepsen (36) stated recently that the sorption speed of titanium for CO, CO_2, H_2, N_2, O_2, and H_2O is not affected by a discharge and titanium did not sorb A, He, and CH_4 when a discharge was present. Klopfer (37) confirmed their results for N_2 and CO. Conflicting reports are explained by the presence of impurities which are not sorbed but can be removed by ion pumping.

Surfaces that capture ions saturate (see Sec. 3-6). Table 6-4 lists the number of molecules pumped at saturation in some ion gages and the small ion pump of Fig. 6-17. It is interesting to estimate the pressure rise that can be expected when the pump stops because of spontaneous reemission. Let us assume that the small ion pump is connected to a volume of 1 liter and that 50 percent of the gas pumped

Table 6-4 Number of Ions Pumped at Saturation

Type of gage	Pumping area, cm²	Material of pumping surface	Maximum ion energy, eV	Saturation number (molecules × 10⁻¹⁶)						
				He	Ne	A	Kr	Xe	N₂	O₂
Bayard-Alpert gage (WL5966)	~200	Glass, W on glass	150						~60	~60
Cylindrical anode Penning	~6	Ni Mo Al	4000	10	4.0	2.3	0.17		2.2	1.0
Bayard-Alpert gage	~200	Glass	250	>10	2.0	2.0	2.0	2.0		
Inverted-magnetron pump (Fig. 6-17)	26	Titanium	6000	75		4.0				

SOURCE: P. A. Redhead, J. P. Hobson, and E. V. Kornelsen, *Adv. Electron. Electron Phys.*, vol. 17, p. 323, 1962.

at saturation will be reemitted. The pressure would rise 6×10^{-4} and 10^{-2} torr for A and He, respectively. No reemission of tightly bound chemisorbed gases will occur. (See Sec. 6-6 for some reemission measurements on sputter-ion pumps.) On account of the saturation of sorption and ion pumping, the surfaces have to be renewed.

Kornelsen (38) developed the pump, shown in Fig. 6-17, for pumping of small ultrahigh-vacuum systems. It is patterned after the inverted-magnetron gage of Redhead et al. [(21), (39)]. A cylindrical box is the cathode. The anode is a helical coil along the axis. The voltage is 6000 V. A magnetic induction of about 2000 gauss in axial direction is obtained from a permanent magnet. The anode is also the titanium evaporator. It consists of a 0.25-mm-diameter titanium wire and a 0.1-mm-diameter tungsten wire wound together onto a 0.25-mm-diameter tungsten wire, and the combination is wound on a 1-mm-diameter sapphire rod. A total amount of 30 mg of titanium is available. This titanium increases the ionic pumping capacity for He and A more than two orders of magnitude. The unit pumps 0.5 torr liter of argon and about 10 times as much helium. The speed is 0.03 liter/sec for helium, 0.25 liter/sec for argon, and 1 liter/sec for N₂. A base pressure of 3×10^{-13} torr was obtained in a test system. (See Sec. 10-2.)

Huber and Warnecke (40) designed a series of ion pumps built like conventional triode or tetrode electron tubes. The water-cooled metal envelopes are the ion collectors. The tungsten grid is coated with titanium and heated by electrons from the axial filament. Such

Herb, who built the first ion pumps combined with titanium evaporation. A wheel of 4-in. diameter contains 14 cartridges arranged around its circumference. The evaporator filament emits the electrons that bombard the cartridge. The grid filament is for ion pumping. The short grid (3 in. high and 4.75 in. in diameter) gives a sticking probability above 0.5 for argon, 5 to 10 times higher than older designs with longer grids. The reason for the improvement is that the ions approach the wall from directions similar to that of the titanium vapor from the evaporator. Hence they do not hit shadowed areas. The pumping speed for air is 1000 liters/sec. A similar pump of 12-in. diameter had a pumping speed in excess of 7000 liters/sec for air, close to the theoretical maximum. The pumping speed for argon was 104 liters/sec between 6×10^{-7} and 5×10^{-6} torr at a grid current of 0.5 amp. The sticking probability was 0.5 or more.

6-6   Sputter-ion Pumps

It appears particularly attractive to combine ion pumping with ion sputtering to form fresh surfaces. To obtain continuous ion pumping, metal sputtered from a nonpumping saturated cathode surface region has to be deposited on the pumping cathode surface area in a growing layer that remains unsaturated. There the metal pumps more gas than was released when it was sputtered. At the same time, it reduces or prevents reemission from the metal underneath. Therefore, the rates of sputtering must vary over the cathode surface. Chemisorption of neutral gas will also occur on metal films deposited on the anode. Such pumps are called sputter-ion pumps. They were first described by Gurewitch and Westendorp (41) and are now marketed by several manufacturers, in sizes from 0.2 to 10,000 liters/sec. All designs are derived from the Penning-gage geometry (Fig. 5-4). The pumps are an agglomerate of many small units, as shown in Fig. 6-20. The anodes are tubes about 1 in. long. The cathodes are titanium plates on both sides of the anode. An anode voltage of several thousand volts and a magnetic inductance of about 1000 gauss are used.

The PIG discharge at low pressure is not well understood. Knauer and coworkers (41a) found that the potential at the axis is near cathode potential and rises steeply near the anode. Hence he surmises that the discharge is concentrated in a plasma sheath near the inner anode surface. The electrons rotate in the sheath under the influence of the radial electric and axial magnetic field. He picked

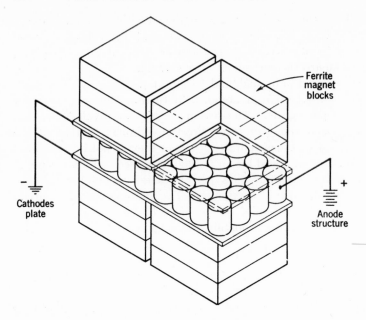

Fig. 6-20 Modular pumping element of diode sputter-ion pump. (Courtesy Ultek Corp.)

up a 70-Mc signal with a tuned receiver connected to an axially split anode and attributes it to this rotation. Modified geometries are suggested to enhance the pumping action.

Nonuniform sputtering can be obtained by varying the angle of incidence for the ions. Carter (42) recommends Ta as cathode material in several geometries, since its sputtering rate at a 20 to 40° angle is about 10 times larger than at normal incidence. This method has also been applied in slotted Ti cathodes [Ref. (43)]. The pumping speed for argon relative to air was increased by a factor of 5 to 0.1 S_{air}, and formerly existing instabilities disappeared although the pumping speed for air improved only slightly. A more drastic solution is the triode pump [Ref. (44)]. Two pairs of Ti cathodes are provided, one pair of high-current density and high-voltage sputter cathodes, and one pair of pumping cathodes. The pumping speed for argon was 0.32 S_{air}.

Pumps start operating at about 10^{-2} torr. The power consumption is high at higher pressures. This heats the pump. If the pump has handled much gas previously, it causes degassing. The pressure rises, the power input increases further, which in turn increases the gas evolution, and so on. In one test a triode pump showed less tendency to "run away." In less severe cases the pumping speed is low until a pressure of 10^{-4} torr is reached. This is called slow starting. A pump with water-cooled cathodes is now marketed for applications requiring extensive pumping in the 10^{-4} to 10^{-2} torr range. Slow starting can be avoided by pumping to 10^{-3} torr or less with the fore-pump. The main contaminant causing slow starting is water vapor [Ref. (46)]. Its accumulation can be prevented by filling the system with dry air when it has to be let down to the atmosphere. If the pump is contaminated, a vacuum bake is an effective means of degas-sing. Hydrocarbons (from forepump oil) can be removed by an air bake at 400°C. Starting is slow initially after the bake until the titanium oxide has been sputtered away. Kelly and Vanderslice (47) removed carbonaceous matter by a discharge in oxygen at lower pressures.

Sputter-ion pumps have reduced pumping speeds in ultrahigh vacuum. Fischer (48) suggests that the gas given off by the system during the bakeout contaminates the cathode surfaces. He demon-strated that a diode pump's nominal pumping speed for N_2 of 130 liters/ sec can be enhanced after a bake by operating the pump in argon of 10^{-4} torr pressure for 10 min at a temperature of 200°C. He pumped N_2 at pressures in the 10^{-10} torr range for 24 hr. The speed dropped from 250 percent nominal speed to 120 percent.

After a bake before the argon treatment, the "sensitivity" $s = i/P$ of the pump is constant between 10^{-7} and 10^{-8} torr but decreases below 10^{-8} torr and the measurement points scatter. There-fore the pump cannot be used as a pressure gage. After the argon treatment, s is still erratic but much higher, more than an order of magnitude greater in the 10^{-8} torr range than before the treatment. This can be explained partly by the presence of large amounts of argon in the residual gas.

Rutherford (48a) found that the drop of S at low pressures could also be avoided by increasing either the magnetic field or the diameter of the anode cylinders. Rutherford and Jepsen (49) enhanced the hydrogen pumping at 10^{-5} torr several times by opera-tion in argon of 10^{-5} torr pressure at room temperature. Davis (50) tested the performance of a 5-liter/sec diode pump at pressures below 10^{-11} torr. Helium, argon, and methane pressures were kept below 2×10^{-13} torr; pumping speeds were 0.1, 1, and 2 liters/sec, respec-tively. Reemission of previously pumped gas was quite noticeable. Many hours are required to start the pump below 10^{-12} torr at the rated voltage of 3000 V. This time was reduced to 15 min by increas-ing the voltage to 6000 V with a magnetic induction of 1500 gauss.

Table 6-5   Absolute (liter per second) and Relative (N$_2$ = 1)
Speeds of Sputter-ion Pumps for Various Gases

Gas	Diode pump 912-6014	Varian Associates	Triode pump PDV-300A	Consolidated Vacuum Corp.
N$_2$	250	1	338	1
Air	250	1.0	355	1.05
H$_2$	680	2.7	710	2.10
D$_2$	480	1.9		
O$_2$	140	0.57	390	1.15
CO$_2$	250	1.0		
He	25	0.1	71	0.210
A	15	0.06	106	0.314

As in a Penning gage, starting should also be improved by a hot-filament starter, as described in Sec. 5-7.

The life of a pump is limited by the erosion of the cathodes, caused by sputtering and flaking of the deposited metal. Hence it is inversely proportional to the ion current or the pressure. The rated life of commercial pumps is over 50,000 hr at 10^{-6} torr.

Pumping speeds of various gases for a commercial diode and triode pump are given in Table 6-5. The diode pump has slotted cathodes to improve argon pumping. The triode pump is superior for pumping of noble gases. The pumping mechanism for H$_2$, He, N$_2$, O$_2$, and A was discussed by Rutherford et al. (35).

To study the memory effect, Milleron and Reinath (50a) operated the 300-liter/sec triode pump of Table 6-5 with varying throughputs in N$_2$, He, and H$_2$ and compared it with a "perfect" pump, represented by a well-trapped oil diffusion pump. Table 6-6 summarizes their findings. They regret the lack of suitable specifications taking into account the memory effect. They state:

We were pleasantly surprised to find very little gas belching by the triode ionic pump. On the other hand, we were surprised to find that the ionic pump lost its appetite for gas much sooner than predicted by the manufacturer. We submit that the performance characteristics of any pump should be given in terms of gas type, amount, and equilibrium pressure. For our purposes we would like to know how much gas a given pump will handle at a given equilibrium pressure. Where large and/or varying gas loads must be handled and where rapid cycling is necessary, we call attention to other methods of pumping.

The memory effect of a 140-liter/sec diode pump under varying gas loads was demonstrated by Normand and Knox (50b). Another

Table 6-6 Ionic versus "Perfect" Pump Histories

Ionic Pump = C. V. C. PDV-300 DriVac
"Perfect" Pump = C. V. C. PMC-1440 + trap, baffle, and variable high impedance

Glass chamber wall °C	Test gas	P pump	Initial base pressure after bakeout Torr	Initial dp/dt speeds		Steady leaks admitted at pressure P for time T		Subsequent dp/dt speed after steady leak, Max. speed for 1/10 sec	New base pressure after steady leak	Average recovery speed from new base to initial base	Range of operational system speeds
				Average over pressure change of one decade	Max. speed during 1/10 sec	P, torr	T, sec				
			Torr	liter/sec	liter/sec			liter/sec	Torr	liter/sec	liter/sec
25–30	N_2	Ionic	5×10^{-8}	34	76	2.5×10^{-6}	225	37	8×10^{-7}	0.2	1/1000–300*
		"Perfect"	4×10^{-8}	72	125			14	4×10^{-8}	14	14–130
140–160	N_2	Ionic	4×10^{-7}	1.5	83	4×10^{-6}	500	23	2.8×10^{-6}	0.17	1/90–300*
		"Perfect"	3×10^{-7}	87†	89†			69	3×10^{-7}	69	69–89†
	He	Ionic	3×10^{-7}	Pressure change < one decade	25	3×10^{-6}		23	1.4×10^{-6}	0.45	1/2–90*
		"Perfect"	3×10^{-7}	100†	115†			87		87	87–100†
	H_2	Ionic	1.7×10^{-7}	Pressure change < one decade		4×10^{-6}	820	18	2.7×10^{-6}	0.08	1/12–530*
		"Perfect"	2.7×10^{-7}	121†	137†			120	2.7×10^{-7}	120	120–140†

* Steady-state speeds.
† With higher impedance connection than at room temperature.
SOURCE: N. Milleron and F. S. Reinath, 1962 Vacuum Symp. Trans., p. 356, 1963.

manifestation of the memory effect is the reemission of gas when the pump current is switched off. Martin (45) measured the gassing rates of a diode and a triode pump after pumpdown of the residual gas from about 10^{-2} to 10^{-6} torr. After power shutoff, the pumps continued to pump CO and CO_2 emitted from the attached small system while H_2 and CH_4 were given off.

There are now available sputter-ion pumps that are combined with a Ti sorption pump with hot-filament evaporators to obtain increased pumping speed of active gases during peak loads.

6-7 Cryogenic Condensation Pumps and Cryotrapping

Condensation pumps have the advantage that the surface does not saturate under high loads, as in ion and sorption pumps. The only possible limitations are that a thick layer of solidified gas may flake off and that the surface of a heavy layer may attain a substantially higher temperature than the condensing wall. At high pressures film boiling can raise excessively the surface temperature. High pumping speed is easily obtained, as in sorption pumps. Mostly, liquid hydrogen (20.4°K) or liquid helium (4.2°K) is used for cooling. Liquid hydrogen requires special precautions in handling on account of the explosion hazard [Ref. (51)]. At 4.2°K, only He and H_2 have an appreciable vapor pressure. The vapor pressure of H_2 is 3.5×10^{-7} torr [Ref. (52)]. At 20.4°K, Ne has also an appreciable pressure. Sometimes the coolant is liquid nitrogen (77°K). At this temperature, the vapor pressure of CO_2 is about 10^{-8} torr and the vapor pressure of ice and mercury is immeasurably small. But other gases such as CO have high vapor pressures (see Fig. 3-20). A small auxiliary pump is sometimes used to remove noncondensable gases.

Because of thermal transpiration [Eq. (1-15)], the ultimate or equilibrium pressure P_u in the system at temperature T is higher than P_v, the vapor pressure at T_v, the temperature of the cold surface. If s and s_v are the condensation coefficients for gas temperature T and T_v,

$$P_u = s_v P_v s^{-1} \left(\frac{T}{T_v} \right)^{\frac{1}{2}} \tag{6-2}$$

Assuming s_v and s to be unity, P_u/P_v is 8.3 for liquid He and 3.8 for liquid H_2 for $T = 300°K$. ΔN, the difference between the number of molecules condensing and leaving the unit surface area each second, is, from Eq. (1-7),

$$\Delta N = sP(2\pi mkT)^{-\frac{1}{2}} - s_v P_v (2\pi mkT_v)^{-\frac{1}{2}} \tag{6-3}$$

It follows from Eq. (1-1) that the throughput $PV = \Delta NkT$, and $S = Q/P = \Delta NkT/P$ or, from Eqs. (6-3), (6-2), and (1-7),

$$S = s \left(\frac{kT}{2\pi m}\right)^{\frac{1}{2}} \left(1 - \frac{P_u}{P}\right) = 3.64s \left(\frac{T}{M}\right)^{\frac{1}{2}} \left(1 - \frac{P_u}{P}\right)$$
$$\text{liters/sec cm}^2 \quad (6\text{-}4)$$

For $P \gg P_u$, Eq. (6-4) becomes Eq. (6-1). $S = 0$ for $P = P_u$. It is assumed that the evaporated molecules attain the temperature T by collisions with warm walls before they hit the cryogenic surface again.

Wang et al. (54) found s to be 0.81 to 0.89 for H_2O at 77°K and a pressure of 10^{-6} to 10^{-4} torr. Buffham et al. (55) measured $s = 1$ for CO_2 at 77°K. The pressure was 10^{-4} torr and the CO_2 temperature 150 to 400°K. Clausing (Fig. 6-14) found a value of 0.9. Foner et al. (56) measured 0.6 for A at 4.2°K. Baechler et al. (53) measured the condensation coefficients s for N_2 and H_2 between 26 and 29°K and 3.6 and 4.4°K, respectively. At 29°K, the condensation coefficient s_{N_2} became unity for $(P - P_u)/P_u > 10$. But s_{H_2} was only 0.5 at 3.6°K for $1 < \Delta P/P_u < 40$. It is difficult to understand why s should be greater when P is higher. Chubb (65) found $s_{H_2} = 0.93$ for $T_v = 3.7$°K, $T = 293$°K, and $\Delta P/P_u = 53$.

Liquid-helium cold fingers are sometimes employed in small ultrahigh-vacuum systems. But cryogenic pumping is used primarily in large installations for space simulation, wind tunnels, and rocket testing, where the gas loads are high and large pumping speeds are needed. In most pumps, heat shields, cooled with liquid nitrogen, are used to retard evaporation of the cryogenic liquid. Again, surfaces at intermediate temperatures may become a source of gas, especially water vapor, after initial condensation when the pressure drops, as mentioned for cold traps in Sec. 6-2.

Several investigations (57) discuss optimization of design. Mullen and Jacobs (58) observed a pumping speed up to three times the theoretical one for multilayer deposits of N_2 at 20°K and CO_2 at 20°K or 77°K, which is difficult to understand. It appears possible that beaming effects in the test dome (see Sec. 5-15) are at least a contributing factor. As to be expected, CO_2 was pumped equally well at either temperature. They emphasize that cryosurfaces should be properly oriented to minimize flaking of deposits. Borovik et al. (59) describe a hydrogen condensation pump with a speed of 37,000 liters/sec for air. They use a hydrogen liquefier which is part of the pump.

Cryotrapping is the trapping of noncondensable gases by a condensing vapor. Cryotrapping by water vapor was first observed by Brackmann and Fite (61). It was theoretically and experimentally

Table 6-7 Vacuum Pumps

Pump	Principle	Approximate pressure range, torrs	Approximate speed range for N_2, liters/sec	Typical forepressure for N_2, torrs	Remarks
Rotary oil forepump	Rotary piston or vanes	10^{-3}–10^3	1–400		Common for pumpdown from atmospheric pressure; may require trap for oil vapor.
Sorption forepump	Sorption on cooled zeolite or charcoal	10^{-2}–10^3	Small commercial units		Initial pumpdown for oil-free systems with small gas load.
Roots pump	Counter moving rotors	5×10^{-4}–10^0	40–6000	10^0	For medium to high loads at intermediate pressures.
Steam ejector pump	Steam jet	10^{-3}–10^3	High to very high		For high loads; large backstreaming under no load; live steam needed.
Oil, mercury ejector pump	Vapor jet	10^{-4}–10^{-1}	40–20,000	10^0	For medium to high loads; requires trap.
Oil (a), mercury (b) diffusion pump	Vapor jet	10^{-11}–10^{-2}	1–10^5 (without traps or baffles)	(a) 10^{-1} (b) 10^0	Has high throughput; vapor must be trapped.
Molecular drag pump	(Grooved) high-speed rotor	10^{-9}–10^{-1}	140	10^0	Low compression ratio for light gases; no trap required; expensive.
Ion-sorption and sputter-ion pumps	Renewed metal layer bombarded with ions	10^{-11}–10^{-4}	10^{-1}–10^4		Small throughput; memory effect; small speed for inert gases.
Cryogenic condensation pump	Condensation on cold surface	10^{-10}–10^{-2}	Medium to very high		High throughput; cryogenic liquid required.

investigated by Schmidlin et al. (62).   They trapped N_2 with H_2O at 77°K and found that the condensed water has a porous structure with a surface area of 600 m^2/g.   One percent of the H_2O sites are true trapping centers, while surface adsorption accounts for only 7 percent of the trapping.   Hengevoss and Trendelenburg (63) studied the cryotrapping of H_2 and He with A at a cold surface of 4.2°K temperature.   The temperature of the gases was 83°K.   In the presence of A, the maximum sticking probability was about 0.5 for H_2 and 0.03 for He.   Under optimal conditions, one A atom traps one H_2 molecule, but about 30 A atoms are required to trap one He atom.   The cryotrapping of H_2 by A and N_2 at 4°K was also studied by Degras (64). He found a much larger trapping ratio, 16 H_2 molecules for one A atom and 10 H_2 molecules for one N_2 molecule.   When the H_2 throughput exceeded one monolayer per second, the sticking coefficient decreased to zero.   Increasing the A or N_2 throughput until it became equal to the H_2 throughput had no effect.

REFERENCES

(1) R. A. Haefer, 1961 *Vacuum Symp. Trans.*, p. 1346, 1962.
(2) V. V. Fondrk, 1957 *Vacuum Symp. Trans.*, p. 88, 1958.
(2a) H. L. Grant and J. E. Davey, *Rev. Sci. Instr.*, vol. 34, p. 587, 1963.
(3) P. F. Varadi and K. Ettre, 1960 *Vacuum Symp. Trans.*, p. 248, 1961.
(3a) "Handbook of Chemistry and Physics," 41st ed., Chemical Rubber Publishing Company, Cleveland, 1959.
(4) R. R. Bannock, *Vacuum*, vol. 12, p. 101, 1962.
(5) M. H. Hablanian and P. L. Vitkus, 1963 *Vacuum Symp. Trans.*, p. 140, 1964.
(6) P. A. Redhead, J. P. Hobson, and E. V. Kornelsen, *Adv. Electron. Electron Phys.*, vol. 17, p. 323, 1962.
(7) J. Hengevoss and W. K. Huber, *Vacuum*, vol. 13, p. 1, 1963.
(8) B. D. Power, N. T. M. Dennis, and D. J. Crawley, 1961 *Vacuum Symp. Trans.*, p. 1218, 1962.
(9) B. D. Power and D. J. Crawley, *Vacuum*, vol. 4, p. 415, 1954.
(10) M. N. Hablanian and H. A. Steinherz, 1961 *Vacuum Symp. Trans.*, p. 333, 1962.

(11) D. J. Crawley, E. D. Tolmie, and A. R. Huntress, 1962 *Vacuum Symp. Trans.*, p. 399, 1963.

(12) D. Alpert, *Rev. Sci. Instr.*, vol. 24, p. 1004, 1953.

(13) N. A. Biondi, 1960 *Vacuum Symp. Trans.*, p. 24, 1961.

(14) R. Jean and R. Liot, *Vide*, no. 98, p. 186, 1962.

(14a) F. A. Knox, *Oak Ridge Natl. Lab. Rept.* 60-5-94, 1960; C. E. Normand, *Oak Ridge Natl. Lab. Rept.* 59-11-70, 1959.

(15) C. H. Kruger and A. H. Shapiro, 1960 *Vacuum Symp. Trans.*, p. 6, 1961.

(16) W. Becker, *Vakuum Tech.*, vol. 7, p. 149, 1958.

(17) E. Apgar, G. Lewin, and D. Mullaney, *Rev. Sci. Instr.*, vol. 33, p. 985, 1962.

(17a) C. E. Williams and J. W. Beams, 1961 *Vacuum Symp. Trans.*, p. 295, 1962.

(18) L. Holland, *J. Sci. Instr.*, vol. 36, p. 105, 1959.

(19) V. L. Stout and M. D. Gibbons, *J. Appl. Phys.*, vol. 26, p. 1488, 1955.

(20) J. Morrison, 1959 *Vacuum Symp. Trans.*, p. 291, 1960.

(21) P. A. Redhead, E. V. Kornelsen, and J. P. Hobson, *Can. J. Phys.*, vol. 40, p. 1814, 1962.

(22) R. E. Clausing, 1961 *Vacuum Symp. Trans.*, p. 345, 1962.

(23) R. G. Herb, T. Pauly, R. D. Welton, and K. J. Fisher, *Rev. Sci. Instr.*, vol. 35, p. 573, 1964.

(24) C. L. Gould and P. Mendel, 1962 *Vacuum Symp. Trans.*, p. 360, 1963.

(25) T. Pauly, R. D. Welton, and R. G. Herb, 1960 *Vacuum Symp. Trans.*, p. 51, 1961.

(26) R. W. Cloud, H. Milde, and S. F. Philp, 1961 *Vacuum Symp. Trans.*, p. 357, 1962.

(27) A. L. Hunt, C. C. Damm, and E. C. Popp, *J. Appl. Phys.*, vol. 32, p. 1937, 1961.

(28) A. L. Hunt, C. C. Damm, and E. C. Popp, *Adv. Cryog. Eng.*, vol. 8, p. 110, 1963.

(28a) L. Elsworth and L. Holland, *Brit. J. Appl. Phys.*, vol. 14, p. 593, 1963.

(29) J. de Dios Lopez-Gonzalez, F. S. Carpenter,

and V. R. Deitz, *J. Res. Natl. Bur. Std.*, vol. 55, p. 11, 1955.

(30) F. T. Turner and M. Feinleib, 1961 *Vacuum Symp. Trans.*, p. 300, 1962.

(31) N. M. Kuluva and E. L. Knuth, 1962 *Vacuum Symp. Trans.*, p. 237, 1963.

(32) B. G. Lazarev and M. F. Fedorova, *Soviet Phys.-Tech. Phys. (English Transl.)*, vol. 6, p. 624, 1962.

(32a) P. L. Read, *Vacuum*, vol. 13, p. 271, 1963.

(33) J. S. Foster, E. O. Lawrence, and E. J. Lofgren, *Rev. Sci. Instr.*, vol. 24, p. 388, 1953.

(34) W. Baechler, *Vakuum Tech.*, vol. 11, p. 33, 1962.

(35) S. L. Rutherford, S. L. Mercer, and R. L. Jepsen, 1960 *Vacuum Symp. Trans.*, p. 380, 1961.

(36) A. B. Francis and R. L. Jepsen, *Supplemento al Nuovo Cimento*, serie I, vol. 1, p. 694, 1963.

(37) A. Klopfer, *Proc. Second European Symp. Vacuum*, p. 271, 1963.

(38) E. V. Kornelsen, 1960 *Vacuum Symp. Trans.*, p. 29, 1961.

(39) J. P. Hobson and P. A. Redhead, *Can. J. Phys.*, vol. 36, p. 271, 1958.

(40) H. Huber and M. Warnecke, *Vide*, no. 74, p. 84, 1958.

(41) A. M. Gurewitch and W. F. Westendorp, *Rev. Sci. Instr.*, vol. 25, p. 389, 1954.

(41a) W. Knauer and E. R. Stack, 1963 *Vacuum Symp. Trans.*, p. 180, 1964.

(42) G. Carter, 1962 *Vacuum Symp. Trans.*, p. 351, 1963.

(43) R. L. Jepsen, A. B. Francis, S. L. Rutherford, and B. E. Kietzmann, 1960 *Vacuum Symp. Trans.*, p. 45, 1961.

(44) A. R. Hamilton, 1961 *Vacuum Symp. Trans.*, p. 388, 1962.

(45) G. D. Martin, private communication.

(46) A. E. Barrington and A. B. Francis, *Vide*, no. 104, p. 189, 1963.

(47) J. E. Kelly and T. A. Vanderslice, *Vacuum*, vol. 11, p. 205, 1961.

(48) E. Fischer, *Proc. Second European Symp. Vacuum*, p. 261, 1963.

(48a) S. L. Rutherford, 1963 *Vacuum Symp. Trans.*, p. 185, 1964.

(49) S. L. Rutherford and R. L. Jepsen, *Rev. Sci. Instr.*, vol. 32, p. 1144, 1961.

(50) W. D. Davis, 1962 *Vacuum Symp. Trans.*, p. 363, 1963.

(50a) N. Milleron and F. S. Reinath, 1962 *Vacuum Symp. Trans.*, p. 356, 1963.

(50b) C. E. Normand and F. A. Knox, *Oak Ridge Natl. Lab. Rept.* 60-1-26, 1960.

(51) Hazards of Liquid Hydrogen in Research and Development Facilities, Rept. ASD-TDR-62-1027, Wright-Patterson Air Force Base, Ohio, December, 1962.

(52) E. S. Borovik, S. F. Grishin, and E. Ya. Grishina, *Soviet Phys.-Tech. Phys.* (*English Transl.*), vol. 5, p. 506, 1960.

(53) W. Baechler, G. Klipping, and W. Mascher, 1962 *Vacuum Symp. Trans.*, p. 216, 1963.

(54) E. S. J. Wang, J. A. Collins, Jr., and J. P. Haygood, *Adv. Cryog. Eng.*, vol. 7, p. 44, 1962.

(55) B. A. Buffham, P. B. Henault, and R. A. Flinn, 1962 *Vacuum Symp. Trans.*, p. 205, 1963.

(56) S. N. Foner, F. A. Mauer, and L. H. Bolz, *J. Chem. Phys.*, vol. 31, p. 546, 1959.

(57) R. W. Moore, 1961 *Vacuum Symp. Trans.*, p. 426, 1962; and F. C. Hurlbut and R. J. Mansfield, *Adv. Cryog. Eng.*, vol. 8, p. 46, 1963.

(58) L. O. Mullen and R. B. Jacobs, 1962 *Vacuum Symp. Trans.*, p. 220, 1963.

(59) E. S. Borovik, B. G. Lazarev, and I. V. Mikgailov, *Vide*, no. 99, p. 231, 1962.

(60) A. L. Hunt, C. E. Taylor, and J. E. Omohundro, *Adv. Cryog. Eng.*, vol. 8, p. 100, 1963.

(61) R. T. Brackmann and W. L. Fite, *J. Chem. Phys.*, vol. 34, p. 1572, 1961.

(62) F. W. Schmidlin, L. O. Heflinger, and E. L. Garwin, 1962 *Vacuum Symp. Trans.*, p. 197, 1963.

(63) J. Hengevoss and E. A. Trendelenburg, 1963 *Vacuum Symp. Trans.*, p. 101, 1964.

(64) D. A. Degras, *Proc. Second European Symp. Vacuum*, p. 95, 1963.

(65) J. N. Chubb, private communication.

Equipment Components 7

7-1 Selection of Components; Reliability

Most components of vacuum systems are now commercially available in a variety of designs made by an increasing number of manufacturers. Also, bakeable components needed for ultrahigh vacuum are readily obtainable. Reliability is of paramount importance. A breakdown often manifests itself in only a small leak that is not easy to find. The cost of time lost in leak hunting and repair is greater than the saving that can be made by buying an inferior product. Often the manufacturer cannot supply sufficient statistics on the probability of failure, but it may be possible to inquire from some of his customers. Statistics on reliability are especially lacking for new products. Therefore, brand new improvements are questionable. If they cannot be avoided on account of special features, a test program is required. Adherence to a proved design also permits standardization, which reduces the stock of spare parts. This situation is even more pronounced in the case of bakeable components since the heating puts an additional strain on them, especially when dissimilar parts are joined (see also Sec. 9-1).

167

To give two examples of the importance of reliability: The C stellarator at PPL has about 100 detachable joints. They must be very dependable to avoid frequent breakdowns. Hence the reliable corner-type gold seal (Fig. 7-4) is used almost exclusively. Most mass-spectrometer leak detectors have approximately equal sensitivity. They are rather intricate instruments, and freedom from breakdown and ease of servicing are the decisive considerations when making a choice. Hardware in general is discussed in Ref. (1).

7-2   Stopcocks and Ground Joints

These have been used for many years. In most cases, ground joints have now been replaced by gasketed joints and stopcocks by metal valves. They are discussed in the next two sections. For vacuum work, stopcocks and ground joints must be ground to a high degree of perfection and greased.

All vacuum greases, with the exception of silicone grease, soften rapidly when the temperature is raised above 30°C. This causes the stopcocks to run dry and freeze. It can happen even at room temperature after frequent use. A tougher grease prolongs useful life. If the grease is too stiff, the stopcock may develop streaks around the bore and leak. Tougher grease is always used in ground joints. The vapor pressure of most greases is about 10^{-6} torr at room temperature. They often contain and release occluded gas. Grease must be applied sparingly since it penetrates further after assembly. Silicone grease cannot be removed by common solvents but requires special cleaning methods; see Ref. (48), p. 332.

7-3   Detachable Joints and Leadthroughs

Detachable joints are needed in most systems to assemble the various parts. They consist of flanges screwed together, with a gasket between (Fig. 7-1). Sometimes tubes have reinforced ends and are pressed together with separate clamps (Fig. 7-2). Such glass-tube joints with molded grooves for elastomer O rings are commercially available. The design of joints depends on the type of gasket. Many shapes and combinations have been proposed. We shall limit ourselves to the most common ones.

The O-ring seal shown in Fig. 7-1 is widely used. Relatively small pressures are needed since the O ring is made of an elastomer, in particular, Neoprene, Viton A, or Teflon. Teflon is somewhat harder

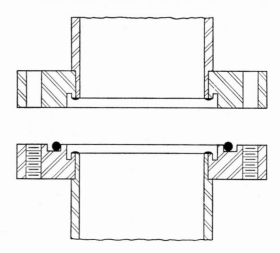

Fig. 7-1   Flanges with elastomer O-ring seal.

than Neoprene and Viton A.   The maximum bakeout temperatures are 90, 200, and 250°C for Neoprene, Viton A, and Teflon, respectively. All show permanent set at elevated temperatures and Viton A and especially Teflon even at room temperature.   The O ring is located in a groove to prevent lateral motion caused by atmospheric pressure and to facilitate assembly, especially in the case of inclined flanges. The groove has rounded corners; its width is about 40 percent larger than the O-ring diameter.   It may be slightly wider or narrower at the bottom.   The height is 75 percent of the O-ring diameter for Neoprene and 65 percent for Viton A and Teflon to compensate for their permanent set.   The ring is $\frac{1}{16}$ to $\frac{1}{8}$ in. thick up to 5-in. torus diameter and $\frac{1}{8}$ to $\frac{1}{4}$ in. for larger sizes.

Robins et al. (3) measured He leak rates of less than 5×10^{-5} cm³/sec for Viton A and Neoprene seals compressed 80 percent between flat flanges at temperatures down to 20°K.   Indium or lead gaskets (see below) may be preferable for cryogenic purposes.

Gassing rates of elastomers, exclusive of permeation, are given in Table 3-11.   Permeation constants for Neoprene are given in Fig. 3-2.   Jordan and Young (6) report the values for permeability of elastomers to air given in Table 7-1.   Butyl rubber has the lowest permeation.*   Permeation through gaskets can be a large source of gas.

* R. S. Barton measured permeation rates of rubberlike materials [*At. Energy Res. Estab. (Gr. Brit.) Repts.* AERE-Z/M 210, 1958] and some plastics [CTR Div., *At. Energy Res. Estab. (Gr. Brit.) Repts.* AERE-M 599, 1960] to H₂, He, N₂, O₂, and A at room temperature.   The permeability of Teflon to N₂ is 2.4×10^{-8} cm²/sec (same unit as in Table 7-1).

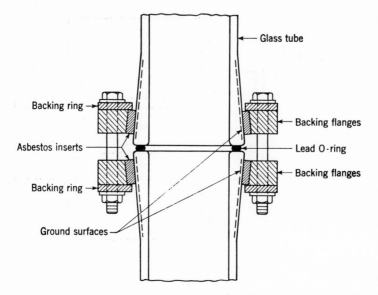

Fig. 7-2 Detachable joint with external clamps. (From A. L. Green, H. T. Mills, and A. C. Richardson, *J. Sci. Instr.*, vol. 36, p. 324, 1959.)

Consider a Neoprene gasket with an exposed area 1 mm wide and 2 mm thick. For a diameter of 5 cm, the gassing rate due to permeation is 6×10^{-8} torr liter/sec for N_2. The gassing of Viton was studied by Addiss et al. (7) with a mass spectrometer. Below 250°C, only H_2O, CO, CO_2 were released; no hydrocarbons were present, as is typical for Neoprene and Buna N. But Young (8) reports that the evolution of hydrocarbons from Neoprene and other rubbers caused by the cleaning fluid could be substantially reduced by an air bake at 100°C for several hours. Holland and Bateman (9) found indium and Viton A gaskets superior to Buna N or Silastic in a bell jar equipped with a liquid-nitrogen trap (see Fig. 10-2). The latter materials exhibited gas permeation. Targets exposed to a glow discharge in a bell jar with a liquid-nitrogen trap were coated with optically absorbing carbonaceous material in the case of Neoprene or Buna N seals but stayed clean with indium or Viton seals [Ref. (10)]. Gassing of elastomers can be reduced and ultrahigh vacuum be attained by refrigeration. Shabeck (11) operated a 550-liter vessel pumped with a 10-in. diffusion pump in the low 10^{-11} torr range. The six flanges with butyl rubber O rings were refrigerated to -20 to -25°C. The refrigeration system was also operated during the bake.

It can be concluded from the published data that synthetic and

Table 7-1   Permeation of Air in
Cubic Centimeters (STP) at 760-torr
Pressure Differential and 80°C
through a Section of 1 cm² Area,
1 cm Thick

Material	Permeability, cm^2/sec
Butyl rubber	3.2×10^{-8}
Kel-F	8×10^{-8}
Viton A	8.8×10^{-8}
Natural rubber	44×10^{-8}
Silicone rubber	450×10^{-8}

SOURCE: J. R. Jordan and R. Young, Research and Development, p. 74 (December 1961), quoted by H. A. Steinherz, "Handbook of High Vacuum Engineering," p. 150, Reinhold Publishing Corporation, New York, 1963.

natural rubbers, except butyl rubber, have high permeation and gassing rates. They are not recommended for pressures below 10^{-7} to 10^{-6} torr. Refrigerated butyl rubber is satisfactory even in ultrahigh vacuum. No permeation has been noticed with Viton A in high vacuum. It can be baked at 200°C. This improved performance will in many cases justify the higher cost.

Instead of organic elastomers, soft metals can be used, in particular indium and lead. Indium melts at 156°C and lead at 327°C. We made gaskets from wires of $\frac{1}{16}$-in. diameter. The ends of the wires were welded together but, at least in the case of indium, crossing of the wire ends suffices. The rings were compressed to $\frac{1}{32}$ in. between flat flanges, using the same type and number of bolts as for elastomers. Flanges 2 to 8 in. in diameter with lead gaskets were baked at 200°C and sometimes up to 300°C and remained leak-tight. No springs were used to compensate for gasket flow. It is possible that adequate pressure was maintained by the atmospheric pressure. These metals are also useful as gaskets for glass tubes [Ref. (4)] (see Fig. 7-2) and windows. Indium and lead O rings, in V-shaped grooves, have been used in bubble chambers at liquid-hydrogen temperature [Ref. (5)]. Both metals are dissolved in mercury and cannot be used in a mercury pump.

For bakeout temperatures above 250 to 300°C up to 450 to 500°C, aluminum, copper, or gold gaskets have to be used. Figure 7-3 shows several more common designs for flat copper gaskets. Figure 7-3a is a step seal [Ref. (12)]. The author has used only one step seal, which became leaky, apparently owing to oxidation, after several hundred hours of baking. The opinions of his colleagues regarding its

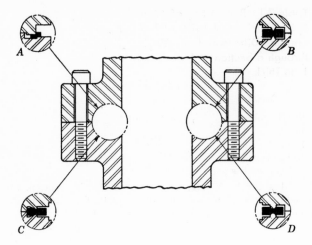

Fig. 7-3   Flanges with flat copper gaskets.

reliability are divided.   Figure 7-3*b* is a double knife-edge seal [Refs. (13), (14)], and Fig. 7-3*c* shows a conflat seal.   Figure 7-3*d* is a modification of 7-3*b* which permits the use of harder gaskets without damaging the flange.   Wheeler and Carlson (15) tested seals *a*, *b*, and *c* and came to the conclusion that the conflat seal ranks highest.   Some seals developed only high-temperature leaks that closed again on cooling. Hence all leak tests must also be performed at bakeout temperature. In the designs of Fig. 7-3*b*, *c*, and *d* both mating flanges are identical, a desirable feature.

Gold-wire seals are made between flat flanges or, preferably, as the so-called corner-type seal shown in Fig. 7-4 [Ref. (16)].   Sometimes both flanges have clearance holes, and a split ring with tapped holes is put behind one flange.   If a bolt cannot be removed after a bake and the head is sheared off, the split ring can be taken off for repair.   Flat flanges are sometimes gouged by the wire while corner flanges are not damaged.   Wires have 0.020 to 0.030 in. diameter and are compressed to half their original thickness.   Proper compression can easily be assured by having the two flanges hit each other after compression, as shown.   The radial gap between the two cylindrical surfaces into which the gold is squeezed in the corner seal is 0.001 to 0.002 in. in small sizes up to 5-in. diameter for 0.020-in. wire and 0.002 to 0.004 in. for larger sizes and 0.030-in. wire.   The surface finish is 16 μin. Stainless-steel flanges have to be stress-relieved before final machining to avoid warpage during baking.   At PPL they are kept at 430°C for several hours.   At least $\frac{1}{32}$ in. has to be machined off the seat after an

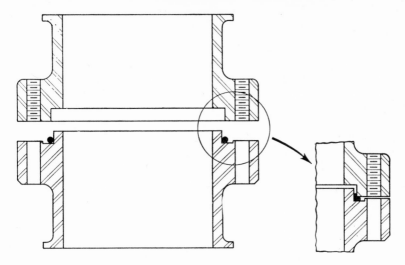

Fig. 7-4   Flanges with corner gold seal.

annealing treatment to work harden the sealing surface.   The forces
and stresses in the bolts are high.   If made of type 304 stainless steel,
they are usually loose after a bake.   But the flanges stay together and
the seal is tight since the gold diffuses into the stainless steel.   Bolts
made of A286 stainless steel are stronger.   The bolts must be coated
with a graphite or MoS_2 grease to reduce galling during bake.   In case
of galling, bolts made of A286 can still be removed most of the time
without the head being sheared off.   The bolt circle must be close to
the gold ring to reduce the bending moment.   Above 5-in. diameter,
double gold rings are preferable, as shown in Fig. 7-5, if the flange is
thin and bends easily.   Above 10-in. diameter, uniform pressure
should be assured by spring-loaded bolts, e.g., Bellville washers made
of Inconel X, since strain storage in the flanges and/or bolts is very
small and nonuniform expansion due to temperature variation becomes
unavoidable.   Jackscrews are used to pry the flange apart for dis-
assembly.   Holes terminating near the gold ring are drilled in flanges
where necessary to facilitate injection of He for leak testing.

When making an O ring, the gold wire is cut approximately
$\frac{1}{2}$ percent shorter than the required length, the ends are butt-welded
with a torch, and the ring is annealed in the flame.   A tapered mandrel
is inserted into the flange, and the ring is slipped over the mandrel and
put onto the flange, being stretched to size in the process.   Although
gold amalgamates, we had only one leak due to amalgamation after
approximately one year of operation.   The seal was at the lower end

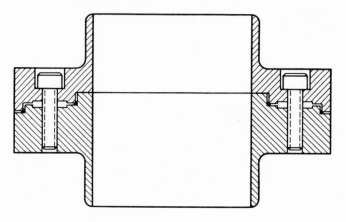

Fig. 7-5 Double gold seal flanges. (From J. T. Mark and K. Dreyer, 1959 *Vacuum Symp. Trans.*, p. 176, 1960.)

of a refrigerated baffle above a mercury pump. Although a new gasket is required each time, gold wires are not as expensive as it may appear, since used gaskets are returned to the vendor for credit. Occasionally some gold adheres to the flange. It must be removed and the seal repolished with emery cloth before remaking a seal.

Aluminum gaskets have been investigated primarily by the Edwards group. They were reviewed by Steckelmacher (18). Aluminum wire 0.036 in. in diameter was compressed to 0.011-in. thickness between flat flanges. It stuck to the flange tenaciously when baked above 370°C. We found it much harder to remove than gold. The rather high pressure required to obtain sufficient strain storage to compensate for the plastic flow of the aluminum can be reduced when springs are used. If the wire is coated with indium, the pressure is also reduced, since indium acts as a lubricant. Attack by mercury is greatly lessened if the aluminum is alloyed with 3 to 5 percent silicon. Aluminum rings are butt-welded with a torch and application of flux and the bead is filed to size. An interesting design is the aluminum-foil seal of Batzer and Ryan (19) shown in Fig. 7-6. The angle Θ is about 1 to 2°, depending on the flange diameter. The bolts are tightened until the opposing seal faces are nearly parallel. Strain energy is stored in the rotated flanges. The seal can be cycled from −196 to 450°C. Table 7-2 lists the compression forces required for various seals.

The experience at PPL has been that properly made corner gold seals are dependable. If baked, they require springs above 10-in.

Table 7-2   Compression Forces for Some Seals

Type of seal	Maximum force, lb/lin in. of circumference	Ref.
Step seal	2100	(15)
Knife-edge	2500	(15)
Conflat	2800	(15)
Flat gold seal 0.020 in.	800	(17)
Flat gold seal 0.030 in.	1500	(17)
Corner gold seal 0.020 in.	1400	(17)
Corner gold seal 0.030 in.	1500	(17)
Aluminum-wire seal 0.036 in.	5000	(18)
Aluminum-wire seal with springs	2500	(18)
Aluminum-wire 0.036 in., indium-coated	2500	(20)
Aluminum-foil seal	3000	(19)

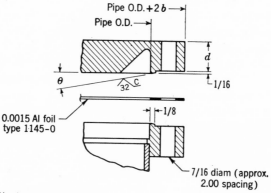

Maximum stress in flange:

$$\sigma_{max} = \frac{MR}{Z}$$

Rotational deflection in flange:

$$\theta = \frac{MR^2}{EI}$$

where M = moment due to bolt load and gasket reaction

R = radius of bolt circle

Z = $bd^2/6$ flange section modulus

I = $bd^3/12$ moment of inertia of flange section

E = modulus of elasticity of flange

Fig. 7-6 Aluminum-foil seal. (From T. H. Batzer and J. F. Ryan, 1963 *Vacuum Symp. Trans.*, p. 166, 1964.)

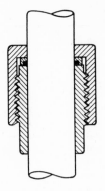

Fig. 7-7 Demountable leadthrough.

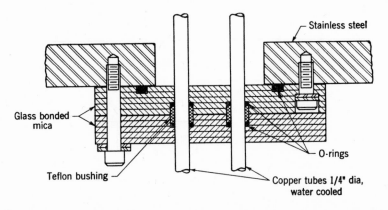

Fig. 7-8 Water-cooled r-f leadthroughs for brazing in vacuum bell jar.

diameter.   Aluminum wires are also reliable.   They require springs when baked.   They should not be used above 300°C since they stick to the flanges, and it is much harder to refinish the sealing surface than in the case of gold wires.   Limited but good results were achieved with lead wires up to 200°C.   Indium wire is satisfactory at room temperature.

If a seal develops a leak, the leak can usually be closed by injection of a dilute solution of Glyptol if no further baking is necessary. A commercial sealer that permits baking is available [Ref. (19a)].

Demountable leadthroughs are O-ring seals to tubular members. Two examples are shown in Figs. 7-7 and 7-8.   Figure 7-7 is a so-called compression port for attaching a tubulation.   Figure 7-8 shows a leadthrough for a r-f coil which is used in bell-jar brazing.

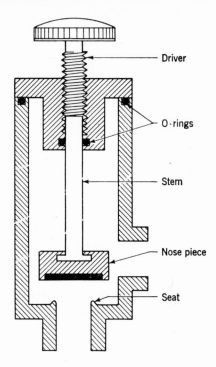

Fig. 7-9   Vacuum valve.

7-4   Valves

Besides stopcocks, there are other simple means to close off parts of a system, such as the mercury column in a McLeod gage. Here we are concerned with metal valves that are in many respects similar to detachable joints, with the additional requirement that the same "gasket" has to be used constantly.

Figure 7-9 shows a typical vacuum valve. The valve stem or plunger has a nosepiece (here a Neoprene washer) at its end which is pressed against the valve seat, a rounded-off knife edge. The force is provided by the driver, located outside the vacuum to simplify lubrication. It is screw-operated with a hand wheel. For opening the valve, the stem must move axially at least a distance equal to the diameter of the seat opening to assure high conductance. An O-ring seal is used to seal the stem against the housing and permit axial motion (see Sec. 7-6). As demonstrated by this valve, the three significant elements, which we shall now discuss, are (1) the driver, (2) the vacuum-

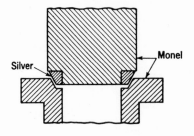

Fig. 7-10 Nose-seat design for small bakeable valve. (From D. G. Bills and F. G. Allen, *Rev. Sci. Instr.*, vol. 26, p. 654, 1955.)

tight coupling of the stem to the driver, and (3) the nose-seat combination.

Besides manually operated screws, hydraulic, pneumatic, and solenoid-operated drives are used. They are of conventional design. In a bakeable valve, screws and bearings are lubricated with a high-temperature lubricant to avoid galling when the valve is baked in the closed position. None of these lubricants is completely satisfactory. Therefore, the drive is removed during a bake whenever possible and the valve kept open with a special clamp.

The O-ring stem seal shown in Fig. 7-18 is frequently used in nonbakeable valves. Sometimes two O rings are used in series with pumping between the rings. In small bakeable valves with a short stroke the stem is often fastened to the center of a metal diaphragm which is part of the valve housing. For longer strokes, bellows have to be used (see Sec. 7-5 and Fig. 7-11).

For less stringent gassing requirements, elastomers, either O rings or flat washers, seal the nose against the seat; otherwise bakeable all-metal nose-seat combinations must be employed. They require large closing forces. Before large all-metal valves were developed, a low-melting, low-vapor-pressure metal such as indium or tin was used in a solder seal. The rim of a cup which is attached to the stem dips into an annular trough filled with molten metal. The trough is heated electrically above the melting point of the metal [Ref. (21)]. The seat of such a valve must be horizontal. The danger exists that, owing to oxidation, the metal may not wet and thus cause a leak.

Alpert (22) designed the first bakeable all-metal valve for his ultrahigh-vacuum research. He used a small polished Kovar cone pressed into a copper seat. For slightly larger valves of $\frac{1}{2}$-in. opening the silver-Monel combination of Fig. 7-10 gives very dependable service. Contact is made along the beveled faces. When the valve is baked in the closed position, the silver sticks to the seat, but it breaks away from the seat without damage when the valve is opened. The necessary closing force is high because of the large contact area.

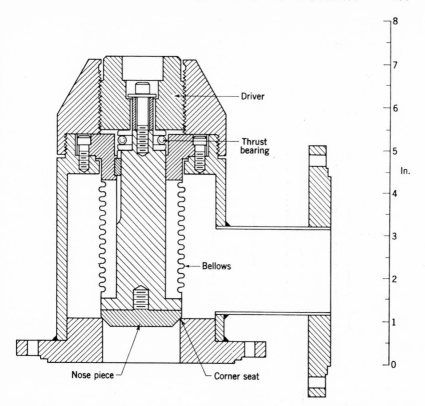

Fig. 7-11   Two-inch bakeable valve with copper nose cone and stainless-steel corner seat.   (From W. J. Lange, *Rev. Sci. Instr.*, vol. 30, p. 602, 1959.)

The unit force is less in Lange's design of Fig. 7-11.   The corner of the stainless-steel seat penetrates into a copper nosepiece to form the seal.   Careful alignment is necessary to seat the corner always in the same groove.   Also, uniform temperature must be maintained during the bake when the valve is kept closed by a screw-type driver, to avoid transient leaks.   This difficulty, typical for larger valves with insufficient strain storage, can be overcome by a different type of driver (e.g., pneumatic or spring).   Occasionally, some copper sticks to the seat and the nose is damaged when the valve is opened after a bake in the closed position.   We found that oxidized stainless steel and copper have less tendency to coalesce, and copper does not adhere at all to molybdenum.

The driving force is considerably reduced and the alignment less critical in Mullaney's valve (Fig. 7-12).   The nose is stainless steel

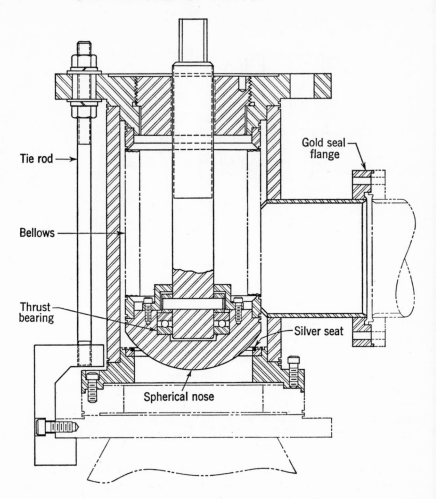

Fig. 7-12   Four-inch bakeable valve with spherical stainless-steel nose and silver corner seat.   (From D. Mullaney, *Rev. Sci. Instr.*, vol. 33, p. 1003, 1962.)

and the seat silver.   The silver has initially a sharp corner, and a seat of small cross section is formed during the first closure.   It is essential that the angle between the axis of the stem and the radius drawn from the center of the sphere to the point of contact with the seat be 45°. At PPL this valve is used in sizes from 1 to 4 in.   It was baked successfully in the closed position a few times.

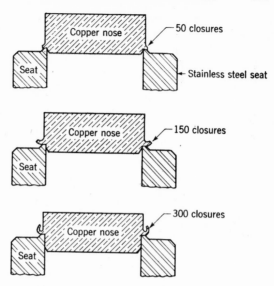

Fig. 7-13   Broaching seat of 8-in. bakeable valve.
(From W. B. Parker and J. T. Mark, 1960 *Vacuum
Symp. Trans.*, p. 21, 1961.)

For 8-in. valves PPL uses the design of Mark (Fig. 7-13).   The
stainless-steel seat acts as a broaching tool to form the seal at the
copper nose.   These valves were not baked in the closed position.   A
danger of all-metal designs is that dirt particles may ruin the sealing
area.   This danger is reduced in Mark's design.   Knife-edge and
rounded-edge seat-nose combinations have been described in the
literature [(27) to (29)].   Usually a copper disk is pressed against a
stainless-steel knife edge.   The closing force is moderate.   We used
a 1-in. valve with a stainless-steel knife-edge nose on a copper-plated
stainless-steel seat.   After baking, the copper had disappeared and the
valve did not close properly.

Medicus and Jehn (30) made a seal between two spherical
tungsten carbide surfaces.   A thin platinum gasket was diffused onto
the seat.   Chromium had to be sputtered onto the nose to prevent
sticking of the platinum in the larger valves ($\frac{3}{8}$-in. max.).   The valves
were baked in the open position only.   Table 7-3 lists the closing forces
per unit length of perimeter for some metal valves.   The lower the
cross section of contact, the less is the force.

Maximum conductance and minimum valve height are obtained
in the design of Fig. 7-14.   The closing vane slides sideways over the

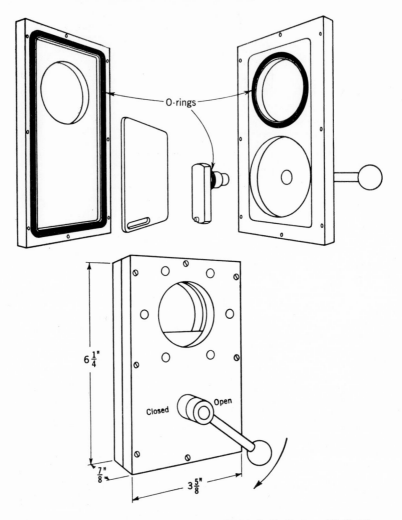

Fig. 7-14   Flat gate valve.   (From J. S. Wahl, S. G. Forbes, W. E. Nyer, and R. N. Little, *Rev. Sci. Instr.*, vol. 23, p. 379, 1952.)

O rings into position.   In an improved design now marketed by several companies the O ring is located in a groove on the vane and the vane is pressed against the mating surface by lever action after the lateral travel has been completed.   Another advantage of this valve is that, when open, it gives a straight optical path between the two sides.   This has also been attained by the use of a ball as the nose; it has a hole and is rotated around an axis perpendicular to the hole (see

Table 7-3   Closing Force for Some Metallic Seat-Nose Combinations

Type of seat		Fig.	Ref.	Force, lb/in. of perimeter
Nose	*Seat*			
Silver cone	Monel cone	7-10	(23)	12,000
Copper cone	Stainless-steel corner	7-11	(24)	4,000
Stainless-steel sphere	Silver corner	7-12	(25)	400
Copper cylinder	Stainless-steel broach	7-13	(26)	1,800 to form seat
				1,100 to keep closed
Tungsten carbide sphere	Platinum foil on tungsten carbide sphere		(30)	>6,000

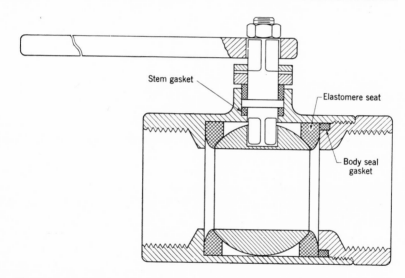

Fig. 7-15   Principle of ball valves.   (Courtesy Jamesbury Corp.)

Fig. 7-15).   The space between the ball and the housing may be connected to one side or a separate pump.   A bakeable valve with a stainless-steel ball and silver corner seat was designed by Fry (32) of PPL.   It performed well under limited testing.   The simplest method for obtaining an optical path is to arrange the inlet and outlet tubes in a straight line which forms a 45° angle with the axis of the stem.

Customarily, needle valves are employed for flow control.   The design of Fig. 7-10 is well suited to serve as a leak valve and allows fine regulation.   Such a leak valve driven with a servomotor is now com-

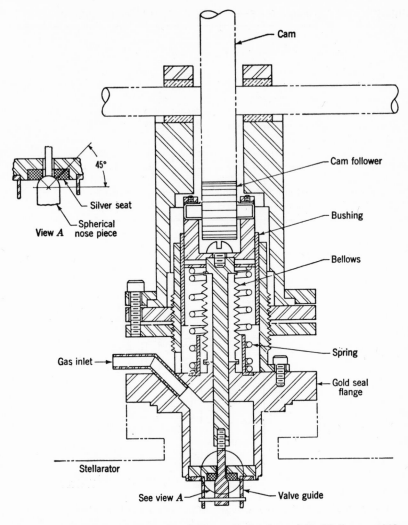

Fig. 7-16 Pulsed bakeable valve. (From G. Lewin and D. Mullaney, 1963 *Vacuum Symp. Trans.*, p. 176, 1964.)

mercially available.   Sometimes valves have to be pulsed to admit gas for a short time only.   Fast-acting valves for opening times of about 10^{-4} sec have been described [(33), (33a)].   They use an O-ring gasket and an epoxy-insulated coil which drives the flat aluminum nosepiece electrodynamically by a capacitor discharge; it is reseated by a spring.

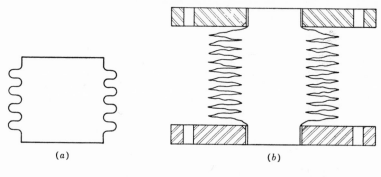

Fig. 7-17 Flexible bellows. (a) Corrugated bellows; (b) washer-type bellows.

Opening times of 15 to 100 msec were obtained by Lewin and Mullaney (34) with a cam-operated all-metal valve, shown in Fig. 7-16. The seal is of the same type as in Fig. 7-12. The valve was mass-spectrometer leak-tight after 50,000 operations.

The experience at PPL has been that the valve designs shown in Figs. 7-10, 7-12, and 7-13 are reliable. Silver–stainless steel is a good combination for baking in the closed position; Mo-Cu does not coalesce at all. The author expects Mo-Ag to be as good as Mo-Cu.

7-5   *Flexible Tubing and Bellows*

Heavy-wall rubber and plastic tubing are used for forevacuum lines. Flexible vinyl plastic tubes are employed in the PPL. Pure gases passing through rubber or vinyl tubing pick up impurities. The total length of rubber or plastic tubing is reduced if they are used only as short connectors between metal (copper) tubes.

Metal bellows are employed for clean flexible connections between components and to transfer motion into the vacuum. Two types are shown in Fig. 7-17. Stainless-steel bellows are used exclusively at PPL, and the maximum deflection is kept within the specifications of the manufacturers, regardless of the frequency of flexing. Typically, the total motion (compression and extension) is 20 to 40 percent of total length. The ends of the bellows must be fixed to prevent collapse under atmospheric pressure. Bellows can be deformed into an S shape. This is necessary to connect two misaligned flanges that are parallel but not coaxial.

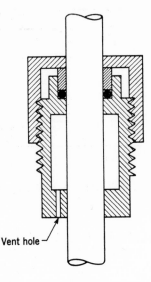

Vent hole

Fig. 7-18   O-ring seal for sliding and rotary motion.

7-6   Motion in Vacuum

Parts attached to the end of bellows and flexible tubes can be moved in vacuum to some extent.   Iron slugs are sometimes moved inside the vacuum by means of an external magnet.   Formerly, axial and rotary motion was often provided by a "Wilson seal."   It consists of a conical rubber washer backed by a metal plate of the same shape through which the drive shaft passes.   This is now superseded by the O-ring design shown in Fig. 7-18 which is similar to the leadthrough of Fig. 7-7.   The shaft must have a smooth surface finish.   If the O ring is made of Neoprene, it has a short life unless it is lubricated with stopcock grease.   Teflon has such a low friction coefficient that the seal can be operated dry.   The seal is first tightened.   To allow motion, it is loosened just enough that the rod can be moved.   The proper pressure can be provided by a spring.   Since Teflon exhibits a permanent set, hollow Teflon O rings that are slit open and have a rubber insert are marketed [Ref. (35)].   The Teflon reduces the friction and the rubber the permanent set.

The wobble drive shown in Fig. 7-19 permits high bakeout temperatures but is rather expensive and usually requires deformation of the bellows far beyond the recommendations of the manufacturer. Another low-speed high-torque drive [Ref. (36)] which is commercially available is based on a traveling deflection wave in a flexing non-

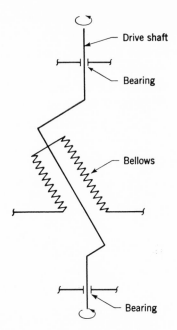

Drive shaft

Bearing

Bellows

Bearing

Fig. 7-19 Wobble drive.

rotating spine element which constitutes the hermetic seal.   The same principle is used by Hunter (37).

Magnetic drives have higher speeds and are also commercially available.   One for speeds up to 10,000 rpm was described by Coenraads and Lavelle (38).   The separating wall between the magnets was a 0.080-in.-thick quartz disk, of $2\frac{3}{8}$-in. diameter.   Clark of the PPL built the drive shown in Fig. 7-20.   Since it was designed for lower speeds, a stainless-steel diaphragm was used.   The bearings in the center permit a minimum gap between magnets of only 0.038 in.   The maximum torque is 10 in.-lb.   If the torque is removed from the driver, it returns to its zero position with respect to the driven member within 15 min of an arc.   The Alnico 5 magnets can be baked.   They lose only 10 percent of their remanence at 400°C.   When they are cooled, the remanence recovers somewhat and returns to the previous high-temperature value when heated again to 400°C.   Iron may be substituted for one of the magnets, if less torque is needed.

A motor suitable for operation in vacuum was developed by Baudot (39).   Such motors use "printed coils," consisting of interconnected copper foils of spiral shape, deposited on both sides of a Mylar, epoxy-glass, or ceramic plate.   A stator outside the vacuum with a squirrel-cage-type rotor has been employed for a long time in

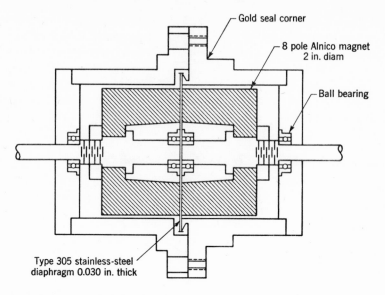

Gold seal corner

8 pole Alnico magnet
2 in. diam

Ball bearing

Type 305 stainless-steel
diaphragm 0.030 in. thick

Fig. 7-20 Magnetic drive. (C. Clark.)

x-ray tubes with rotating targets.   It is also used in some mechanical
pumps to avoid the shaft seal.   A laboratory unit, for ultrahigh-
vacuum use, bakeable after removal of the stator, is commercially
available.

All drives require lubrication.   Activity in this field was stimu-
lated by the requirements of space technology.   References can be
found in the paper by Buckley et al. (40).   Behavior of materials in
vacuum is very different from that in air.   Dry steel ball bearings run
well in ultrahigh vacuum at $-196°C$ but have short life at room temperature [Ref. (41)].   A 0.0004-in. coating of Pb, Au, or Ag on 440-C
stainless steel gives low friction and wear [Ref. (40)], but a Cr coating,
though good in air, is poor in vacuum [Ref. (42)].   Silver is being used
in x-ray-tube bearings.   Willans (43) found a thin layer of Teflon to
be a good lubricant.   The bearing surface was coated with Teflon by
rubbing against it; e.g., the cage of a ball bearing was made of Teflon.

Blackmon et al. (44) tested a number of lubricants for ball
bearings.   Among others, some diffusion-pump oils (DC704, Apiezon
K) and some silicone greases and reinforced Teflon gave good results.
The pressure was around 10^{-7} torr.   A dry film lubricant, which is
also used in the drive described in Ref. (38), is a mixture of MoS_2,
graphite, and sodium silicate.   It was found satisfactory in limited use
in ultrahigh vacuum after a $400°$ bake [Ref. (45)].   There are on the

market self-lubricating materials consisting of a matrix of 60 to 70 percent Ag and/or Cu, 20 to 30 percent Teflon, and 10 percent WSe_2. Their operating range is -196 to $250°C$. They were operated successfully under heavy loads in 10^{-9} torr vacuum. Heindl and Belanger (46) had good results at 10^{-7} torr at low speeds with a shaft coated with MoS_2 in a sodium silicate binder which ran in a sleeve bearing consisting of a sintered matrix of 80 percent Ag and 20 percent MoS_2.

Recently a comprehensive test program of ball bearings and slip rings lubricated with oils, dry films, and self-lubricating materials was conducted by Parcel et al. (2). Oils and greases gave the longest life. No gassing rates have been reported for any of these materials. Perhaps decomposition occurs during operation. Hence metal coatings are safest for critical applications.

7-7 Gas Purifiers

Gas purification is treated in Ref. (47) and, in greater detail, in Ref. (48). A general discussion is outside the scope of this text. Selective gas sorption of some getters which could be used for gas purification was mentioned in Sec. 6-4. There is on the market equipment that produces pure H_2, D_2, O_2, and He by permeation through solids (see Sec. 3-1). Hydrogen and D_2 have been purified by permeation through palladium at 200 to 300°C for a long time. But Pd changes from the α to the β phase when cooled below 157°C in H_2. This is accompanied by a volume change.

Repeated phase changes can cause fatigue cracks. Hence an alloy of 75 percent Pd and 25 percent Ag, which does not exhibit this phase transformation, is now used. Palladium and Pd-Ag have approximately the same permeability. We measured 5×10^{-3} torr liter/sec cm^2 for 0.010-in. thickness at 200°C and 400 torr on the high-pressure side. The downstream pressure was below 1 torr. The purity of the gas is very high [Ref. (49)]. Permeation through nickel is less recommended since it requires higher temperatures. In a test the purified H_2 contained at least 1 ppm of CO [Ref. (49)].

Oxygen is diffused through silver. Whetter and Young (50) found a permeation rate of 4×10^{-5} torr liter/sec cm^2 for 0.010-in. thickness at 760 torr and 700°C. Helium diffusing through quartz was also studied by Young and Whetter (51). A quartz tube of 0.010-in. wall thickness has a permeation rate of 8×10^{-6} torr liter/sec cm^2 at $<750°C$ and 760 torr. The only major impurity, they found, was H_2 (10 ppm). Its relative concentration was reduced one order of

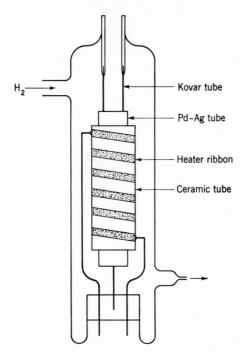

Fig. 7-21 Small hydrogen purifier.

magnitude by the diffusion, as was to be expected since the permeation constant of He is about 10 times larger than that of H_2.

A typical small purifier for H_2 is shown in Fig. 7-21.   One end of a Pd-Ag tube is brazed to a Kovar tube which is sealed to the glass tube on top. The other end is closed off. The Nichrome heater ribbon is wound over a ceramic tube which surrounds the Pd-Ag tube. The whole assembly is located inside a glass jacket through which the impure gas passes. A low flow rate is sustained to prevent accumulation of impurities.   Oxygen and helium purifiers are similarly constructed.

REFERENCES

(1) M. Pirani and J. Yarwood, "Principles of Vacuum Engineering," Reinhold Publishing Corporation, New York, 1961.
(2) R. W. Parcel, F. J. Clauss, C. F. O'Hara, and W. C. Young, 1963 *Vacuum Symp. Trans.*, p. 3, 1964.
(3) R. F. Robins, D. H. Weitzel, and R. N.

Herring, *Adv. Cryog. Eng.*, vol. 7, p. 343, 1962.

(4) A. L. Green, H. T. Mills, and A. C. Richardson, *J. Sci. Instr.*, vol. 36, p. 324, 1959.

(5) H. Bridge, R. Budde, A. Burger, H. Filthuth, D. R. O. Morrison, Ch. Peyrou, and J. Trembley, *Adv. Vacuum Sci. Tech.*, vol. 2, p. 481, 1960.

(6) J. R. Jordan and R. Young, quoted by H. A. Steinherz, "Handbook of High Vacuum Engineering," p. 150, Reinhold Publishing Corporation, New York, 1963.

(7) R. R. Addiss, L. Pensak, and N. J. Scott, 1960 *Vacuum Symp. Trans.*, p. 39, 1961.

(8) J. R. Young, *Rev. Sci. Instr.*, vol. 30, p. 291, 1959.

(9) L. Holland and S. K. Bateman, 1961 *Vacuum Symp. Trans.*, p. 1201, 1962.

(10) L. Holland, *Vacuum*, vol. 13, p. 173, 1963.

(11) J. C. L. Shabeck, Jr., 1962 *Vacuum Symp. Trans.*, p. 278, 1963.

(12) W. J. Lange and D. Alpert, *Rev. Sci. Instr.*, vol. 28, p. 726, 1957.

(13) P. J. van Heerden, *Rev. Sci. Instr.*, vol. 26, p. 1130, 1955.

(14) R. Carpenter, *J. Sci. Instr.*, vol. 39, p. 533, 1962.

(15) W. R. Wheeler and M. Carlson, 1961 *Vacuum Symp. Trans.*, p. 1309, 1962.

(16) D. J. Grove, 1958 *Vacuum Symp. Trans.*, p. 9, 1959.

(17) J. T. Mark and K. Dreyer, 1959 *Vacuum Symp. Trans.*, p. 176, 1960.

(18) W. Steckelmacher, *Vacuum*, vol. 12, p. 109, 1963.

(19) T. H. Batzer and J. F. Ryan, 1963 *Vacuum Symp. Trans.*, p. 166, 1964.

(19a) J. R. Young, *Rev. Sci. Instr.*, vol. 35, p. 116, 1964.

(20) B. D. Power and F. C. Robson, 1961 *Vacuum Symp. Trans.*, p. 1175, 1962.

(21) F. L. Reynolds, 1955 *Vacuum Symp. Trans.*, p. 74, 1956.

(22) D. Alpert, *Rev. Sci. Instr.*, vol. 22, p. 536, 1951.

(23) D. G. Bills and F. G. Allen, *Rev. Sci. Instr.*, vol. 26, p. 654, 1955.

(24) W. J. Lange, *Rev. Sci. Instr.*, vol. 30, p. 602, 1959.

(25) D. Mullaney, *Rev. Sci. Instr.*, vol. 33, p. 1003, 1962.

(26) W. B. Parker and J. T. Mark, 1960 *Vacuum Symp. Trans.*, p. 21, 1961.

(27) H. L. Eschbach and W. Peperle, *Vakuum Tech.*, vol. 10, p. 210, 1961.

(28) D. Baker, *Vacuum*, vol. 12, p. 99, 1962.

(29) R. B. Thorness and A. O. Nier, *Rev. Sci. Instr.*, vol. 32, p. 807, 1961.

(30) G. Medicus and W. Jehn, *Rev. Sci. Instr.*, vol. 33, p. 1265, 1962.

(31) J. S. Wahl, S. G. Forbes, W. E. Nyer, and R. N. Little, *Rev. Sci. Instr.*, vol. 23, p. 379, 1952.

(32) W. A. Fry, U.S. Patent 3036811.

(33) R. S. Lowder and F. C. Hoh, *Rev. Sci. Instr.*, vol. 33, p. 1236, 1962.

(33a) E. D. Andryukhina, A. Ya. Safronov, and I. S. Shpigel, *Instr. Exp. Tech. (U.S.S.R.) (English Transl.)*, p. 178, 1961.

(34) G. Lewin and D. Mullaney, 1963 *Vacuum Symp. Trans.*, p. 176, 1964.

(35) D. E. Armstrong and N. Blais, *Rev. Sci. Instr.*, vol. 34, p. 440, 1963.

(36) C. W. Musser, *Machine Design*, April 14, 1960, p. 160.

(37) W. R. Hunter, *Vacuum*, vol. 13, p. 193, 1963.

(38) C. N. Coenraads and J. E. Lavelle, *Rev. Sci. Instr.*, vol. 33, p. 879, 1962.

(39) J. H. Baudot, *Vide*, no. 98, p. 173, 1962.

(40) D. H. Buckley, M. Swikert, and R. L. Johnson, *Am. Soc. Lubrication Engrs.*, *Preprint* 61 LC-2.

(41) J. Mark, private communication.

(42) Z. J. Atlee, J. T. Wilson, and J. C. Filmer, *J. Appl. Phys.*, vol. 11, p. 611, 1940.

(43) R. H. Willans, *Rev. Sci. Instr.*, vol. 31, p. 574, 1960.

(44) P. H. Blackmon, F. J. Clauss, G. E. Ledger, and R. E. Mauri, 1961 *Vacuum Symp. Trans.*, p. 1244, 1962.

(45) S. E. Openshaw, private communication.
(46) J. C. Heindl and R. J. Belanger, 1963 *Vacuum Symp. Trans.*, p. 27, 1964.
(47) Max Knoll, "Materials and Processes of Electron Devices," 484 pages, Springer-Verlag OHG, Berlin, 1959.
(48) Werner Espe, "Materials Technology of High Vacuum Technique," vol. 3, Auxiliary Materials, 542 pp., VEB Deutscher Verlag der Wissenschaften, Berlin, 1961. (In German.)
(49) J. R. Young, *Rev. Sci. Instr.*, vol. 34, p. 891, 1963.
(50) N. R. Whetter and J. R. Young, *Rev. Sci. Instr.*, vol. 30, p. 472, 1959.
(51) J. R. Young and N. R. Whetter, *Rev. Sci. Instr.*, vol. 32, p. 453, 1961.

Materials for Vacuum Systems

8

Here we shall give a short survey of only the main materials for vacuum systems. Several books treat the materials for and the technology of electron-tube production [(1) to (4)]. They contain a large amount of valuable information for the vacuum engineer. Reference (3) is by far the most comprehensive text.

8-1 Metals

Larger systems are made of metal; smaller ones are still often made of glass. Mild steel is impractical. Rust must be avoided since a rusty surface takes much longer to degas. Brass has the disadvantage that the zinc evaporates on moderate heating. Aluminum cannot be used in the presence of mercury (see Sec. 6-2), and it is difficult to make a permanent joint to other metals. Copper begins to oxidize around 200°C. It migrates in vacuum during a bake when exposed to water vapor, because of the formation of volatile oxide. Stainless steel such as type 304 is the preferred choice for most metal systems. It is rust-free, nonmagnetic, strong, relatively easy to machine, and resistant to many chemicals, including mercury. Precipitation-hardening stainless steel (type A286) is indicated where greater strength, especially at elevated temperature, is required.

Although type 304 stainless steel is the main construction material, other metals are used for special functions. Table 8-1 lists the main physical properties of metals and alloys of interest to the vacuum engineer. Graphite is also included. For the vapor pressures of the elements, see Figs. 3-16 to 3-18.

8-2 Glasses

Glass is used in vacuum systems mainly in the form of tubes and windows. If ultraviolet transmission is required, quartz or sapphire is substituted. But Corning glass 9741 also has fair ultraviolet transmission, 50 percent at 2200 Å for 1-mm thickness, and it is easier to join to other glasses. Table 8-2 gives characteristics of some common glasses. The low-expansion borosilicate glasses are used almost exclusively since they have higher softening points and are less susceptible to thermal shock. A short survey of glass properties can be found in Ref. (5). Here and in the next chapter we discuss quartz, together with the glasses.

Glass is brittle; this means it does not flow at room temperature when stressed excessively. The elastic limit and ultimate strength coincide. If a force is applied through a point contact and produces a large pressure in a ductile metal, the metal flows, the contact area widens, and the pressure is reduced. In the case of glass, a fracture must be avoided by inserting a layer of ductile material, such as lead, between the glass and the contact point. Glass is also weakened by surface scratches which cause stress concentrations. While glass is strong in compression, it is relatively weak in tension and shear. A conservative design limit is a maximum tensile stress of 1500 psi. We never go beyond 2500 psi. The need for great strength can usually be circumvented by a clever design.

8-3 Ceramics

Ceramics are good insulators. They are stronger than glass and withstand higher temperatures. Envelopes are made of mullite or high-alumina ceramic. The author has found in some cases that mullite resisted thermal shock better than alumina, despite its lower strength and heat conductivity, on account of its lower expansion. In general, alumina is preferred because it has high strength and can be joined to metals by brazing (see Sec. 9-7). The alumina ceramics

Table 8-1 Properties of Some Metals and Alloys

Metal or alloy	A	B	C	D	E	F	G	H	I	J	K
Ag	10.5	960.8	low	19–23	9–12*	0.055	206	0–500	1.0	1.5	4.1
Al	2.7	659	~5	10–16	8.5–9.7*	0.031	277	20–500	0.52	2.8	4.1
Au	19.3	1063	very low	18–20	12*	0.09	142	0–100	0.71	2.4	4
Cu	8.9	1083	10	33	17–18*	0.11	186	0–600	0.94	1.7	6.8
Fe	7.86	1530	21	26–41	32*	0.11	140	0–500	0.174	9.6	5.6
Hg	13.6	−38.9				0.033			0.027	95.8	
Mo	10.2	2630	up to 57	~120†	46*†	0.062	56–60	0–500	0.38	4.8*	4.1*
Ni	8.9	1453	10–30	59–81	26–33	0.112	144	25–300	0.2	8.7*	4.7
Pt	21.4	1773		24	15–26	0.033	95	0–500	0.167	11.4	4
Ta	16.8	3000		51‡	28†	0.034	66	0–500	0.130	~13.0	3.8
Ti	4.52	1690		79	17*	0.127	82	0–300	0.041	~47	~3.3
W	19.3	3382	63	260†	46¶	0.034	46	0–600	0.31	5.5	4.8
Kovar (29 Ni, 17 Co, 54 Fe)	8.3	1450	55	85	22	0.16	52	30–450	0.046	49	
Stainless steel, type 304, nonmagnetic	7.9	1400–1430	30	80	29	0.12	180	20–500	0.039	72	
Stainless steel, type 430, magnetic	7.7	1450–1480	35	60	29	0.11	108	20–500	~0.05	60	
Monel (67 Ni, 30 Cu)	8.84	1300–1350	25–40	70–88	27		145	20–300	0.062	48	
Inconel (14 Cr, 6 Fe, 80 Ni)	8.51	1395–1425	25–50	82–100	32	0.109	137	20–300	0.036	98	1.1
Yellow brass (65 Cu, 35 Zn)	8.47	905–930	~17	~49	15	0.09	203	20–300	0.28	6.4	
Graphite	1.5–1.75§	3700		2.2–3.7		0.20			0.3–0.4		

A = Density, g/cm^3
B = Melting point, °C
C = Yield strength annealed, psi 10^{-3}
D = Tensile strength annealed, psi 10^{-3}
E = Modulus elasticity, psi 10^{-6}
F = Specific heat, cal/g °C
G = Coefficient thermal expansion, °C^{-1} × 10^7
H = Temperature range (°C) of coefficient thermal expansion
I = Thermal conductivity, cal/cm sec °C
J = Electrical resistivity at 20°C, ohm cm 10^6
K = Thermal coefficient of electrical resistivity, °C^{-1} × 10^3

* Annealed.
† Wire 0.1 cm diameter.
‡ Sheet 0.025 cm thick.
¶ Hard-drawn wire 0.01 cm in diameter.
§ Apparent density.

Table 8-2 Glasses of Corning Glass Works

Glass code	Type	Principal use	Thermal expansion coeff.-/°C from 0 to 300°C	Upper working temperatures (mechanical considerations only) Annealed Normal service, °C	Extreme limit, °C	Strain point, °C	Anneal-ing point, °C	Soften-ing point, °C	Work-ing point, °C	Modulus of elasticity lb/in.²	Log₁₀ of volume resistivity 25°C	250°C	350°C	Power factor, %	Dielec-tric constant	Loss factor, %	Glass code
0010	Potash soda lead	Soft glass; general purpose	93×10^{-7}	110	380	395	435	625	985	8.9×10^6	17.+	8.9	7.0	0.16	6.7	1.0	0010
0080	Soda lime	Soft glass; general purpose	92×10^{-7}	110	460	470	510	695	1005	10.0×10^6	12.4	6.4	5.1	0.9	7.2	6.5	0080
0120	Potash soda lead	Soft glass; general purpose	89×10^{-7}	110	380	395	435	630	980	8.6×10^6	17.+	10.1	8.0	0.12	6.7	0.8	0120
1720	Aluminosilicate	Low helium permeation	42×10^{-7}	200	650	670	715	915	1190	12.7×10^6	—	11.4	9.5	0.38	7.2	2.7	1720
1990	Potash soda lead	Iron sealing	124×10^{-7}	100	310	330	360	500	755	8.4×10^6	—	10.1	7.7	0.04	8.3	0.33	1990
3320	Borosilicate (canary color)	Tungsten sealing	40×10^{-7}	200	480	500	540	780	1155	9.4×10^6	—	8.6	7.1	0.30	4.9	1.5	3320
7050	Borosilicate	Sealing	46×10^{-7}	200	440	460	500	705	1025	8.7×10^6	16.0	8.8	7.2	0.33	4.9	1.6	7050
7052	Borosilicate	Kovar sealing	46×10^{-7}	200	420	435	480	710	1115	8.2×10^6	17.0	9.2	7.4	0.26	4.9	1.3	7052
7070	Borosilicate	Low loss electrical	32×10^{-7}	230	430	455	495	—	1070	7.4×10^6	17.+	11.2	9.1	0.06	4.1	0.25	7070
7720	Borosilicate	Tungsten sealing	36×10^{-7}	230	460	485	525	755	1140	9.1×10^6	16.0	8.8	7.2	0.27	4.7	1.3	7720
7740	Borosilicate	General purpose	33×10^{-7}	230	490	515	565	820	1245	9.1×10^6	15.0	8.1	6.6	0.50	5.1	2.6	7740
7750	Borosilicate	(Kovar sealing) tungsten sealing	40×10^{-7}	230	400	431	467	704	—	—	17.0	9.5	7.7	0.24	4.3	—	7750
7910	96% Silica	Ultraviolet transmission	8×10^{-7}	800	1090	820	910	1500	—	9.6×10^6	17.+	11.2	9.2	0.024	3.8	0.091	7910
7940	Fused silica	Ultraviolet transmission	5.5×10^{-7}	900	1100	990	1050	1580	—	10.5×10^6	—	11.8	10.2	0.001	3.8	0.0038	7940

contain about 90 to 99 percent Al_2O_3.   The balance is mostly SiO_2, to render the ceramic gas-tight.   Alumina is also available as a polycrystalline high-purity, high-density translucent alumina (Lucalox of the General Electric Company), and as single-crystal sapphire. Sapphire is sensitive to heat shock since the thermal expansion parallel to the axis is 9 percent greater than in the direction perpendicular to the axis.   Corning Pyroceram is glass that is converted to a ceramic by devitrification in a special heat treatment.

The manufacturing processes for ceramics are not suited to the quick production of a few samples, a frequent requirement in research. Few ceramic parts, except some tubes, are stocked by the manufacturers.   Although Pyroceram is made from glass, it is not easily made in small quantities, since these glasses have to be formed by casting or spinning and do not lend themselves to glassblowing. Sometimes it is possible to purchase partially sintered ceramic, machine it, and return it to the manufacturer for final firing.   It is simpler to use natural lava.   This material can also be machined and fired afterwards.   It grows or shrinks about 2 percent in firing, depending on the grade.   The variation from piece to piece is about $\pm\frac{1}{4}$ percent. Fired ceramics are very hard and can be machined only with diamond tools.   The American Lava Corporation markets a fired ceramic (type 222) that can be machined with a high-speed steel tool.   This ceramic is very porous and can be used inside the vacuum only.   We never found excessive gassing due to porosity in any ceramic.   Two machinable materials which in some cases can be used in place of ceramics are treated in the next section.   Also, quartz is often a suitable substitute.

Some physical properties of these ceramics are listed in Table 8-3.   Further data on Pyroceram 9606 can be found in Ref. (6).   The design stress has to be considerably less than the average strength given in the table.   Its value depends on the uniformity of the body, which can be judged to some extent by the scattering of the strength-test results.   Based on his very limited experience, the author estimates that, similar to glass, a maximum design stress of 20 percent of the average ultimate strength may be a reasonable value and 10 to 15 percent a safe value.

8-4   *Boron Nitride and Glass-bonded Mica*

Boron nitride (BN) is a gas-tight high-temperature insulator which can easily be machined.   It contains 2 to 3 percent B_2O_3 as a

Table 8-3 Properties of Some Ceramics

	Unit	Natural lava, grade A	Alsimag 222 machinable aluminum silicate	Typical values of mullite ~40% silica ~60% alumina	Typical values of high alumina, ~95%	Pyroceram 9606
Specific gravity		2.3	2.0	3.2	3.7	2.6
Porosity		not gas-tight	highly porous	gas-tight	gas-tight	gas-tight
Average coefficient of thermal expansion, 25–700°C	$°C^{-1} \times 10^6$	3.6	10	~4	~8	5.7 (25–300°C)
Thermal conductivity	g cal/cm sec °C	0.003	0.005	~0.014	~0.07	0.0087
Modulus of elasticity	$psi \times 10^{-6}$				45	17.3
Tensile strength	$psi \times 10^{-3}$	2.5	2.5	18	30	
Compressive strength	$psi \times 10^{-3}$	40	10	110	300	
Flexural strength	$psi \times 10^{-3}$	9	5	20	50	20
Volume resistivity, 100°C	ohm cm	6×10^{11}	$> 10^{14}$		$\sim 10^{12}$	
Volume resistivity, 300°C	ohm cm	2×10^9	6×10^{11}		$\sim 10^{10}$	$\sim 3 \cdot 10^9$
Volume resistivity, 500°C	ohm cm	5×10^6	4.6×10^9	$\sim 10^7$		
Dielectric constant, 1 Mc		5.3	5.5	6.6	9	5.58
Dissipation factor, 1 Mc		0.01	0.0002		0.00035	0.0015
Loss factor, 1 Mc		0.053	0.001		0.003	0.009

binder.   The B_2O_3 gives off water vapor in vacuum for a long time unless the system is baked.   Flat plates of pure gas-tight BN are now marketed which are free from oxide.   Boron nitride blackens, because of thermal dissociation, when heated to 800 to 1000°C in vacuum. The formation of free boron at the surface is not necessarily harmful.

Glass-bonded mica is also a gas-tight insulator.   It can be machined with cemented-carbide tools.   Although not as refractory as ceramics or BN, the most refractory grades can be operated at a maximum temperature of about 700°C.

REFERENCES

(1) Max Knoll, "Materials and Processes of Electron Devices," 484 pp., Springer-Verlag OHG, Berlin, 1959.
(2) Walter H. Kohl, "Materials and Techniques for Electron Tubes," 638 pp., Reinhold Publishing Corporation, New York, 1960.
(3) Werner Espe, "Materials Technology of High Vacuum Technique": vol. 1, Metals and Materials with Metallic Conduction, 916 pp.; vol. 2, Silicates, 730 pp.; vol. 3, Auxiliary Materials, 542 pp.; VEB Deutscher Verlag der Wissenschaften, Berlin, 1961.   (In German.)
(4) Tube Laboratory Manual, 2d ed., 132 pp., Massachusetts Institute of Technology, Research Laboratory of Electronics, Cambridge, Mass., 1956.
(5) Corning Glass Works, Properties of Selected Commercial Glasses, Booklet B-83.
(6) C. F. Miller and R. W. Shepard, *Vacuum*, vol. 11, p. 58, 1961.

Joining and Preparatory Treatment of Components

9

9-1   General Remarks; Reliability

Some parts of a vacuum system, such as metal bellows, windows, ceramic tubes, etc., have to be joined permanently by welding, brazing, etc. Subassemblies are formed, terminating in detachable joints. They are cleaned, heat-treated, and leak-tested and then are ready for the final assembly of the vacuum system.

What was said in Sec. 7-1 about the importance of reliability applies here as well. In fabricating these assemblies, the large amount of knowledge accumulated in the manufacture of electron tubes can be drawn upon, with one important reservation. Electron tubes are baked only once or twice, vacuum systems many times. Dissimilar joints that are acceptable in an electron tube may open up in a baked vacuum system, because of fatigue cracks. Hence testing, i.e., thermal cycling, is required. (To check for rate of oxidation, the part must be kept at elevated temperature.) Stress analysis is needed properly to scale a proved design to other sizes. To give an example: We bought some ceramic-to-metal seals from an electronic-tube manufacturer. One seal failed after 12 heat cycles and a second one after 15.

We shall limit our discussion to the special conditions encountered in vacuum work. The common techniques of brazing, welding, and glassblowing are not treated in detail. References (1) to (4) contain much useful information. Scientific glassblowing was treated by Wheeler (5).

9-2   *Vacuum Greases, Waxes, and Cements*

Formerly vacuum greases, waxes, and cements were used extensively, but their application in modern vacuum equipment is very limited. Greases for lubrication of stopcocks were mentioned in Sec. 7-2. They are also used sometimes to lubricate O rings and render them gas-tight if they fit poorly, e.g., the cemented joint of an O ring made of a piece of straight rubber. Waxes are useful in stopping leaks in temporary, ill-fitting setups; e.g., a component is put on a leak test station and a hole in the wall is plugged with a rubber stopper covered with wax. The characteristics of these waxes and greases are supplied by the manufacturers.

Cements are used to join parts, mainly in temporary setups. Thermoplastic sealing wax, picein, and De Khotinsky cement have softening points of 50 to 100°C. For proper vacuum-tight application, the clean surface must be preheated. If heated with a gas flame, the surface must be hot enough to assure freedom from condensed moisture, but it must not be so hot as to cause decomposition of the cement. Epoxy resin cements are cured by mixing with a hardener. Table 3-11 lists a combination of especially low gassing rate; but all epoxies have high permeation rates. Their expansion is substantially greater than that of metals. This can cause cracks under extreme conditions. In some special cases vacuum chambers for accelerators have been built with epoxy-metal sandwiches (see Sec. 10-2).

Silver chloride is an inorganic cement. It has a melting point of 457°C and can be baked up to about 300°C. It is very corrosive at elevated temperatures and in moist atmosphere even at room temperature. It can be used in contact with glass, silver, and platinum. It must be protected from strong light which causes photodissociation. Application in thin cross section is recommended to avoid cracks due to differential contraction during cooling. Martin (6) found that AgCl may give off appreciable amounts of HCl in vacuum before a bake and at 300°C. No Cl or AgCl was detected at any time. Despite its limitations, AgCl is used in special cases, e.g., for cementing LiF windows onto photomultiplier tubes.

9-3   *Soldering and Brazing*

Soft-solder joints containing tin and lead are not used extensively, because the joints are mechanically weak.   The author has used standard copper fittings of the type employed extensively in general plumbing, with 50 Pb, 50 Sn solder, on forevacuum lines. Many of them developed small leaks, apparently because of the vibration generated by the forepump.   Hence they were replaced by brazed joints and, sometimes, by O-ring couplings.   For soft solder the author uses liquid acid fluxes which are removed by thorough rinsing with hot water (see Sec. 9-8).   Solders are attacked by mercury.

Joints made with hard solders or brazing alloys are strong and do not soften at bakeout temperatures.   A comprehensive table of brazes and a treatment of the metallurgical aspects of brazing can be found in Ref. (2).   Although the joints are strong, braze joints should be designed in such a manner as to provide large areas of contact, as shown in Fig. 9-1.   In most cases, brazing alloys suitable for vacuum work must have a low vapor pressure at elevated temperatures.   This excludes such metals as Zn and Cd.   Table 9-1 lists some alloys of interest.   It reflects in part the experience at PPL.

The braze has to wet the metals to be joined.   Therefore these metals must alloy with at least one constituent of the braze; e.g., copper adheres poorly to tungsten unless some nickel is added.   Melting point and flow point coincide for pure metals and eutectic brazes. For other alloys the melting point is the temperature at which a liquid phase is formed.   The braze becomes pastelike, with some solid metal still in suspension.   At the flow point, only a liquid phase exists.   The flow and melting points should not be far apart.   Otherwise, in slow heating, the liquid may dissolve some metal of the joint which increases the melting point and also raises the flow point.   In thin sections, solution of the joint metal can become a problem and may require a minimum amount of braze and selection of a special brazing alloy. Most of the time, remelting requires higher temperatures, because of the solution of some joint metal.   If several brazes are to be made on one piece, brazes of progressively lower flow points are used.

If Kovar and other Ni-Fe alloys are stressed, silver brazes, e.g., the Ag-Cu eutectic, exhibit intergranular penetration and cause leaks. Brazes without Ag and higher melting points ($> 900°C$) (Cu, Ni, Au alloys) have to be used or the metal has to be nickel-plated to retard penetration.   It is said that penetration of Ag-bearing alloys can continue during baking.   Hence the first-mentioned approach appears

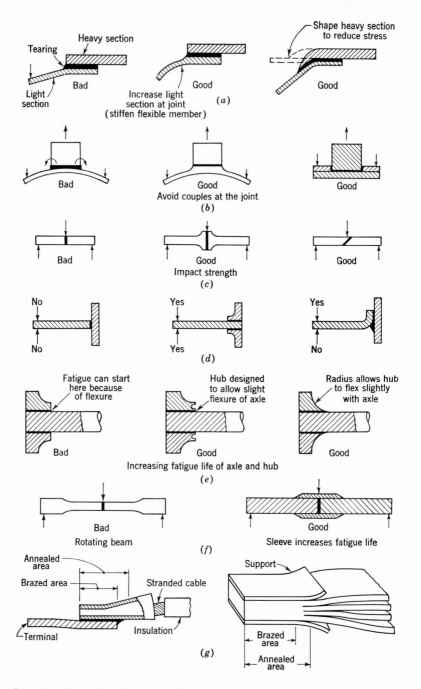

Fig. 9-1 Examples of good and bad designs of brazed joints. (From "Brazing Manual," Committee on Brazing and Soldering of American Welding Society, Reinhold Publishing Corporation, New York, 1955.)

Table 9-1   Some Brazes for Vacuum Work (partially PPL experience)

Alloy	Temperature, °C		Applications
	Melting	Flow	
Mo and Mo$_2$B	~2000	~2000	Eutectic high-temperature braze for Mo, W, Ta, Re; much higher remelting temperature; limited experience.
Pt	1769	1769	For Mo, W.
OFHC copper	1083	1083	For Fe, Kovar, Monel, Ni, etc.; does not wet reliably Mo, W; stainless steel in dry H$_2$ or vacuum.
Au	1063	1063	Mo, Kovar, Pd in H$_2$ or vacuum.
0.6 C, 3.8 B, 4 Fe, 4.5 Si, 16.5 Cr, Bal. Ni	971	1038	For Inconel, stainless steels in dry H$_2$; not attacked by Hg; high-temperature strength, oxidation-resistant.
18 Ni, 82 Au	950	950	Eutectic, high strength, wets Mo, W, Cu, Fe, Kovar, Monel, Ni, Pd, etc. Stainless steel in dry H$_2$ or vacuum, Ta in vacuum.
5 P, 15 Ag, 80 Cu	641	815	Wide melting range, not to be used at elevated temperatures, no flux required for Cu. Not for brazing in H$_2$ (danger of porosity); not for ferrous metals or Mo, W.
28 Cu, 72 Ag	779	779	Eutectic; many metals; not for Mo, W; for Kovar only when plated. Ta in vacuum at ~1000°C, stainless steel at ~1000°C in dry H$_2$ or vacuum. Pd, Ni, Cu, in H$_2$ or vacuum.
10 In, 27 Cu, 63 Ag	685	710	Low flow point, moderate strength
50 Ag, 18 Cd, 16.5 Zn, 15.5 Cu	627	635	Low flow point; narrow melting range; good general-purpose braze; not for use at elevated temperatures.

to be the safer one. Although Cu oxidizes at bakeout temperature, we have experienced no leaks in joints brazed with copper after protracted baking.

To obtain wetting, the surface must be free from oxide. If the metals are heated with a torch, a flux protects and cleans the surface. This flux has to be removed afterward by washing with hot water (see Sec. 9-4). At PPL copper tubing is brazed without flux by keeping the joint in the reducing part of a hydrogen flame. Since chromium oxide is not readily removed by many fluxes, chromium-bearing alloys must be constantly protected by the flux lest chromium oxide be formed. Some brazing alloys contain phosphorus, which acts as flux. Phosphorus has a high vapor pressure. This renders it objectionable at elevated temperatures.

But the metals are always oxidized next to the joint in torch brazing, and the flux is difficult to remove from blind holes, etc.; hence brazing in hydrogen or vacuum is the preferred method. The PPL hydrogen furnace has a tubular Inconel muffle with an adjacent water-cooled cooling chamber. The muffle is heated by passing current through it. This permits fast heating and is very convenient for laboratories with short irregular runs. Chromium-bearing alloys require very dry hydrogen to avoid formation of Cr_2O_3. The PPL uses an extra retort inside the muffle, passes the tank hydrogen over a Pd catalyst to convert O_2 to H_2O, and dries the hydrogen with liquid nitrogen. The higher the temperature, the higher is the permissible dew point of the H_2. The practical lower limit is 1000°C. Hydrogen brazing is also done in a bell jar where the parts are heated either by induction with a r-f coil or by radiation from a tungsten coil. Tantalum must not be heated in hydrogen, and copper has to be oxygen-free (see Sec. 9-8).

Metals are also brazed in vacuum. Either the oxide on the surface must be removed or the braze must penetrate it. The metal may dissolve its own surface oxide or the oxide evaporates. It is more difficult to wet alloys containing metals that form stable oxides, such as Al or Cr. Some brazing alloys contain reducing elements, e.g., Si and B; they reduce the surface oxides and facilitate wetting. The surface stays clean if the pressure is low and the temperature high enough that the rate of oxide formation is smaller than the rate of oxide removal. In the case of Al-bearing alloys, the braze may penetrate an imperfect Al_2O_3 film and spread along the oxide-metal interface. These processes were investigated by Wall and Milner (8).

Huschke (9) showed that various alloys containing Cr, Al, and Ti can be wetted by a Ni-Cr-Si brazing alloy at 10^{-3} to 10^{-1} torr pressure, depending on the alloy.   At PPL brazing is done at a pressure of 10^{-5} to 10^{-4} torr.   When the Cu-Ag eutectic is used, stainless steel must be heated to about 1000°C to obtain good wetting.   The silver evaporates noticeably at this temperature.   Therefore an atmosphere of dry hydrogen is preferred.   In vacuum the metal is sometimes first "tinned" with the Ag-Cu eutectic and then brazed at a lower temperature.   Copper and the Ni-Au eutectic can be used without excessive evaporation.   Formation of Cr_2O_3 can also be prevented by plating with Cu or Ni.

The brazing alloy is applied as wire, foil, or powder.   The powder is kept in place with a volatile binder such as acrylic resin.   When the braze melts, it must be sucked into the gap of the joint by capillary action.   This puts an upper limit on the width of the gap.   As a rule of thumb, the gap should be not more than 0.003 in.   This has to be considered when dissimilar metals are to be brazed.   In case of two telescoping tubes, the tube with the higher expansion is preferably on the outside, to put the joint under compression.   But if the diameters are very large, this has to be reversed, and the wall thickness must be small to permit bending.   In the case of a stainless-steel tube brazed to a Kovar tube with the Au-Ni eutectic, the reversal occurs at $\frac{5}{8}$-in. diameter for an initial gap of 0.0005 in.

To avoid excessive spreading of the braze and dissolving of the joint metal, fast brazing is preferred.   This is impossible in furnace brazing, and the braze is confined by coating the metal with a suitable wetting inhibitor, such as milk of magnesia or a commercial product.

New designs may require testing.   For example, eight $\frac{3}{8}$-in. Kovar tubes were brazed with Cu into $\frac{1}{2}$-in. Ni tubes.   All were leak-tight after 65 heat cycles (20 min in the furnace at 425°C, 10 min cooling at room temperature).   Six leaked after 98 cycles.   Seven $\frac{5}{16}$-in. Kovar tubes were brazed into $\frac{3}{8}$-in. Monel tubes with Au-Ni eutectic.   All were leak-tight after 160 cycles.   Though not directly comparable, indications are that the Au-Ni (a rather expensive braze) is exceptionally strong.

9-4 Welding

Welding is the joining of metals by fusion.   Among the various methods, the one most ideally suited for vacuum work is the inert-gas-shielded arc welding.   It requires a minimum setup and no flux and produces little oxidation.   The tungsten electrode is surrounded by a mantle of inert gas.   The arc is struck by touching the work with the

Table 9-2   Some Metal Combinations Joined Satisfactorily by Inert-Gas-Shielded Arc Welding (PPL)

OFHC copper to OFHC copper—helium
OFHC copper to 300 stainless steel—argon
Molybdenum to tantalum
Molybdenum to molybdenum } argon-filled box; 75% Mo—25% Re filler rod*
300 stainless steel to tantalum.   Argon-filled box*
Soft Inconel X to 300 stainless steel—argon
Inconel to copper—argon*
Inconel to Inconel—argon (Inconel A filler rod)
Platinum to 300 stainless steel—argon
Kovar to 300 stainless steel—argon
46–54% iron, balance nickel to 300 stainless steel—argon
K.R. Monel to 300 stainless steel—argon
Monel to Monel—85% argon 15% hydrogen
Copper-clad 430 stainless steel to 300 stainless steel—argon
Palladium to 300 stainless steel—argon

All welds were made with 2 percent thoriated tungsten electrode—direct current—
   electrode negative.

   * Limited experience.

tip of the electrode or by bridging the gap with a high-frequency spark. Table 9-2 gives some metal combinations joined satisfactorily in the PPL.   The refractory metals have to be welded in an enclosed gas-filled box to exclude the oxygen more completely.   The Mo-Re alloy filler rod gives a much stronger weld than plain Mo.   Otherwise Mo and W welds are very brittle, because of recrystallization.   Unless the 300 series stainless steel is low in carbon (< 0.05 percent) or contains special additions such as Nb, the chromium will combine with the carbon and leave some ferritic iron which is magnetic and subject to corrosion.   Alloys containing ferritic iron must not be welded in H_2. This would cause porosity since H_2 is more soluble in liquid iron.

Figures 9-2 and 9-3 give examples of welding of large and small cross sections.   Trapped volumes should be avoided since they may become virtual leaks that cannot be found with a leak detector. Because a smaller volume is heated in welding, compared with brazing, the work is not heated uniformly.   This can cause distortion. Complicated shapes are sometimes made more economically from formed sheet metal and tubes than from solid stock.   The parts are joined and fixed in their relative position by tack welding and then completely welded or brazed in a furnace.   The latter produces little distortion.   In baked equipment, brazed and welded assemblies are preferable to detachable joints, since the latter are more likely to develop leaks.

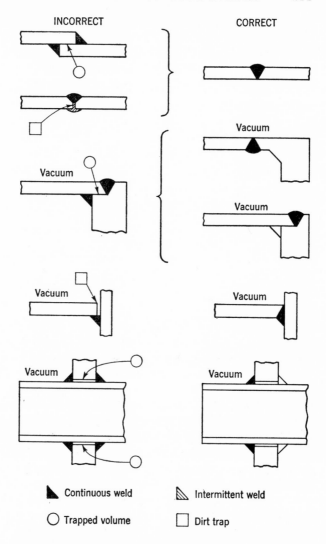

INCORRECT

CORRECT

Fig. 9-2 Examples of good and bad welding practice for heavy cross sections. [From H. Kronberger, *Proc. Inst. Mech. Engrs. (London)*, vol. 172, p. 113, 1958.]

A relatively new welding method is electron-beam welding. The joint is heated in vacuum by a high-energy (10 to 100 kV), electron beam. A weld of high penetration and narrow width is obtained in the absence of any gas. The equipment is quite expensive, but some companies perform this welding service. In special cases, e.g., active

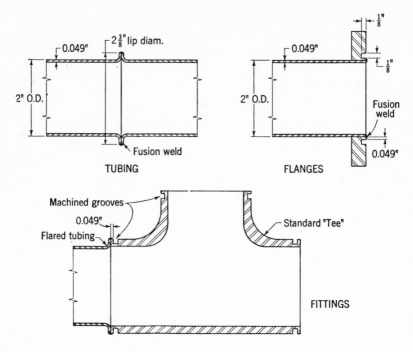

Fig. 9-3 Joint designs for welding of thin cross sections.   (From D. J. Grove, 1958 *Vacuum Symp. Trans.*, p. 9, 1959.)

metals, the method gives superior results.   Electron-beam welding has been reviewed by Wyman (12), and an electron-beam welding machine was described by Solomon (13).

    In resistance or, in particular, spot welding, the metals are clamped between two electrodes and melted at the point of contact by Joule heat.   The current flows for less than 0.1 sec.   This method is used extensively for assembly of structures mounted inside electron tubes; vacuum-tight joints are rarely made.   An example is the fabrication of a cylinder from a stainless-steel sheet by seam welding (a series of overlapping spot welds) in the manufacture of bellows. The parameters—time, pressure, and voltage—must be carefully controlled.   Spot welding is not suited to make a variety of vacuum-tight joints on a laboratory scale.

9-5   *Dissimilar Glass-to-glass Seals*

    To join glass tubes of different thermal expansion, a so-called graded seal has to be made.   It consists of several sections; each section has a slightly larger expansion than the preceding one.   The theory of tubular seals between thin-walled tubes of the same wall thickness is given in Ref. (14).   The maximum stress is 0.5 δE, where E is Young's modulus (approximately 10^7 psi for commercial glasses) and δ is the differential contraction between freezing point and room temperature.   It is independent of the tube diameter D and the wall thickness t, but the equation is valid only for thin walls, $D > 10t$. The length L of the individual sections must be large enough that the stress existing at one end is sufficiently attenuated at the other end. A very safe value is

$$L \geq 2.5(Dt)^{\frac{1}{2}} \tag{9-1}$$

See Ref. (14) for a more accurate calculation if L has to be smaller. The differences δ are listed in Table 9-3 for some Corning glasses and metals.   They must not be more than 500 ppm for each glass-to-glass seal.   Smaller differences are preferred.   Needless to say, the seals must be of high quality, of uniform and thin wall, and perpendicular to the axis.

Special glasses are available for making graded seals to quartz, which has such an exceptionally small expansion.   The author prefers the shorter "leached seal."   It has a continuous gradual change of expansion with less stress.   It is available from Corning Glass Works in sizes up to 2 in.

A special technique of joining glass tubes is the use of a solder glass.   These are glasses that have a short softening range and soften at a rather low temperature.   They are mostly applied as powders, and the joint is made in a furnace without distorting the other glasses. Solder glasses are available to match various glasses.   Also, Pyroceram cements are marketed by Corning.   They are glasslike powders with a volatile binder which, after melting, devitrify and become a ceramic of higher softening temperature.

9-6   Glass Seals to Metals and Ceramics

Glasses can be sealed to several metals, e.g., W, Mo, Fe, and special alloys.   So-called headers or terminals, i.e., a metal sleeve with a glass insert containing one or several lead-in wires, are commercially available and used extensively.

The preferred metal for tubular seals is Kovar.   This is the trade name of the Westinghouse Electric Corporation for an alloy of 29 percent Ni, 17 percent Co, 54 percent Fe, which matches the expansion of Corning 7052 glass very well.   Since the patents have

Table 9-3 Differential Contraction δ in ppm Between Freezing Point and Room Temperature

Metal / Glass code no.	1761	7070	7740	7760	1715	7720	Tungsten	7251	5420	9700	7780	9741	3320	7750	1720	7331	1723	7052	7050	Molybdenum	7040	1826	8830	7510	Kovar	7055	7056	8800	7520	7280	7340	Alumina	7530	42 Ni-Fe	46 Ni-Fe	7550
7761	0	380	50	210	230	400	630	210	260	180	470	860	400	770	640	610	740	+730	890	—	—	—	—	—	—	—	—	—	—	—	—	—	—	—	—	—
7070	380	0	290	160	130	470	290	150	100	150	50	680	60	520	300	390	680	880	500	—	—	—	—	—	—	—	—	—	—	—	—	—	—	—	—	—
7740	50	290	0	180	90	470	550	50	310	140	400	690	440	630	580	250	140	790	820	690	940	—	990	970	770	690	690	980	950	—	750	—	940	490	960	—
7760	210	160	180	0	30	230	400	220	100	140	50	630	180	550	420	390	240	680	690	700	940	—	850	800	—	910	910	—	—	—	—	—	—	—	—	—
1715	230	130	90	30	0	310	330	80	190	80	260	550	310	510	480	390	190	510	660	820	820	—	830	810	—	920	920	—	—	—	—	—	—	—	—	—
7720	400	470	230	470	310	0	120	270	220	330	90	550	130	90	180	570	240	730	520	770	690	—	670	550	860	700	700	980	980	—	—	×	830	—	×	×
Tungsten	630	290	550	400	330	120	0	360	250	410	330	550	410	550	550	140	20	620	660	520	610	—	560	420	×	490	490	470	470	650	750	×	—	×	×	—
7251	210	150	50	220	80	270	360	0	50	80	250	570	190	570	320	150	0	510	520	370	420	—	350	350	×	490	490	—	620	810	910	—	—	—	—	—
5420	260	100	310	100	190	220	250	50	0	180	200	550	150	470	290	150	60	310	250	250	350	—	250	350	—	900	900	470	620	810	—	—	—	—	—	—
9700	180	150	140	140	80	330	410	80	180	0	270	580	310	500	450	240	20	—	160	170	800	—	640	610	—	720	720	—	—	—	—	—	—	—	—	—
7780	470	50	400	50	260	90	330	250	200	270	0	550	50	430	50	180	80	330	290	290	180	—	180	180	230	240	240	620	—	—	—	—	—	—	—	—
9741	860	680	690	630	550	550	550	570	550	580	550	0	400	0	550	150	20	—	330	360	540	—	400	370	—	480	480	—	—	—	—	—	—	—	—	—
3320	400	60	440	180	310	130	410	190	150	310	50	400	0	350	250	240	20	240	180	410	620	—	440	310	890	510	510	890	—	810	—	—	650	—	—	—
7750	770	520	630	550	510	90	550	570	470	500	430	0	350	0	400	190	0	150	260	270	670	540	310	250	—	390	390	—	390	590	590	—	—	—	—	—
1720	640	300	580	420	480	180	550	320	290	450	50	550	250	400	0	240	20	200	150	150	540	350	280	250	20	380	380	390	390	730	840	800	900	640	960	—
7331	610	390	580	390	350	140	150	150	380	330	150	240	190	240	190	0	0	50	160	190	620	350	40	60	20	0	0	0	—	—	—	—	—	—	—	—
1723	740	680	140	240	190	240	170	60	240	290	20	380	0	0	240	0	0	240	50	50	510	510	150	90	270	180	180	180	530	730	840	940	940	640	960	—
7052	+730	880	790	680	510	730	620	510	240	480	660	560	560	240	320	380	240	0	200	160	190	510	40	40	20	0	0	390	530	800	800	800	900	640	960	—
7050	890	500	820	690	660	520	730	100	180	690	450	690	480	0	240	290	290	200	0	—	—	—	150	—	270	180	180	180	530	730	840	940	—	960	—	—

Table 9-3 Differential Contraction δ in ppm Between Freezing Point and Room Temperature (Continued)

Metal	Glass code no.	7550	46 Ni-Fe	42 Ni-Fe	7530	Alumina	7340	7280	7520	8800	7056	7055	Kovar	7510	8830	1826	7040	Molybdenum	7050	7052	1723	7331	1720	7750	3320	1741	7780	9700	5420	7251	Tungsten	7720	1715	7760	7740	7070	7761
Molybdenum	7040	—	×	×	—	×	—	950	710	710	80	80	×	30	10	250	20	0	160	160	190	330	290	290	570	170	580	870	700	800	×	550	+	820	+	690	+
	1826	—	—	720	900	800	680	380	710	380	10	10	×	70	40	380	0	20	190	50	270	410	360	160	600	10	640	800	750	800	610	690	770	820	940	700	+
	8830	920	680	270	580	480	380	280	80	80	300	300	320	360	350	0	380	250	510	350	540	670	620	540	850	120	960	860	790	+	990	990	830	+	+	970	+
	7510	—	270	840	910	800	680	570	370	370	50	50	70	70	0	350	10	10	150	40	310	440	400	180	640	40	590	860	790	840	420	670	830	850	990	650	+
Kovar	7055	—	—	—	990	870	760	630	450	450	120	120	140	140	70	360	70	50	90	60	280	400	370	180	610	60	520	840	740	790	390	560	810	800	970	600	980
	7056	—	—	—	—	740	630	550	320	320	0	0	130	120	30	300	10	10	180	0	390	510	480	240	720	100	620	940	850	910	490	700	920	910	+	690	+
	8800	—	—	—	+	740	630	520	320	320	0	0	130	120	30	300	0	80	180	0	390	510	480	240	720	100	620	940	850	910	490	700	920	910	+	690	+
	7520	—	—	—	+	270	260	260	0	0	320	320	30	450	370	80	380	710	530	390	+	890	+	620	+	470	970	+	+	+	980	980	+	+	+	+	+
	7280	990	—	—	0	160	80	0	10	10	520	520	260	630	570	280	580	950	730	590	+	+	+	810	+	650	+	+	+	+	+	+	+	+	+	+	+
	7340	800	530	530	310	80	0	330	290	290	630	630	260	760	680	380	680	+	840	690	+	+	+	910	+	750	+	+	+	+	+	+	+	+	+	+	+
Alumina	7530	730	×	×	0	0	300	160	270	270	740	750	×	870	800	480	800	×	940	800	+	940	+	+	+	830	+	+	+	900	+	+	+	×	+	+	+
42 Ni-Fe		530	450	0	300	300	310	550	270	270	870	860	570	990	910	580	900	+	+	900	+	490	+	620	+	490	+	+	+	570	×	×	+	450	+	+	+
46 Ni-Fe	7550	330	×	0	210	300	530	160	160	810	810	840	×	+	840	270	870	×	+	640	+	960	+	810	+	960	+	810	+	840	×	×	+	×	+	+	+
	0280	320	80	0	780	950	730	990	990	+	+	+	+	+	+	+	+	+	+	+	+	+	+	+	+	+	+	+	+	+	+	—	+	+	+	+	+
Platinum	7570	360	560	+	620	720	770	840	990	990	+	+	+	+	+	+	+	+	+	+	+	+	+	+	+	+	+	+	+	+	+	—	+	+	+	+	+

SOURCE: H. E. Hagy, Corning Glass Works, Research and Development Division, Revised 1962.
The − sign means that the material in row has the lower expansion.

215

expired, it is manufactured by several companies under various names. Kovar does not oxidize excessively at bakeout temperature. If Kovar is to be used for low-temperature work, a special batch has to be selected which has a sufficiently low transformation point. For tubular metal-to-glass seals the expansion differential δ of Table 9-3 must not be larger than 250 ppm. The following graded seal combinations are used at PPL: Kovar-7052-7050-7070-7740 and Kovar-7052-7750-3320-7720. Kovar can also be sealed to 7750 glass. Since this glass seals to tungsten, it can be used to seal a tungsten rod into a Kovar sleeve. To prepare the Kovar tubes for glassing, the ends are rounded and polished with Al_2O_3 cloth (320 grit). The tubes are then fired in wet H_2 at 1050°C for 20 min to remove all carbon which would cause bubbly seals.

If a low-expansion Kovar tube is sealed to a glass tube at one end while the other end is welded to a high-expansion stainless-steel tube, the Kovar tube must have the minimum unglassed length, calculated from Eq. (9-1), to prevent deformation of the glassed end by the thermal flexing of the welded end. In this case, Eq. (9-1) applies without any excessively large safety margin. The weld should preferably be made before glassing. If necessary, a glass seal may be immersed in water during subsequent welding or brazing to keep it cool. After such operations, the seals must be annealed and inspected for residual stress in a polariscope with a sensitive tint plate (red first order). Oldfield (15) reports that a Kovar seal develops axial stresses in the glass, resulting in eventual seal fracture when heated above 300°C for long times. We have never observed this.

Kovar is magnetic and a poor conductor of heat and electricity. A nonmagnetic seal is the "housekeeper" seal. A copper tube is thinned down ($1\frac{1}{4}°$ taper) to a feather edge (0.002-in.) and glassed on the inside and outside. The copper yields when stressed during cooling. The author does not know whether metal fatigue limits the number of heat cycles at any given temperature. Otherwise, when made properly, this is a very reliable seal. Graves (16) describes such a seal between platinum and 7740 glass.

Thin Mo foils can be sealed into quartz but metal sleeves cannot be sealed to quartz tubes. Metal sleeves can be soldered to quartz by using certain wetting techniques discussed in the next section.

Figure 9-4 shows an example of a brazed metal assembly which includes two Kovar-to-glass seals. It is a 150-amp leadthrough used in the PPL. The braze A is done last with radio frequency in 6 sec to avoid overheating of the seal. The assembly is annealed afterward.

Glass can also be sealed to ceramic tubes. Several glasses are

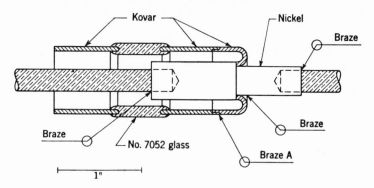

Fig. 9-4 A 150-amp leadthrough.

available in the expansion range of mullite tubes; e.g., Corning 7720 glass matches the mullite-type Triangle H5 of Morganite Inc. and 7070 seals to type MV30 of the McDanel Refractory Porcelain Company.   Seals to sapphire windows with 7280 glass were described by Anderson and Stepp (17).   Martin (18) prefers 7520 glass on account of the lower softening point.   Sapphire can also be "soldered" to 7280 with 1826 solder glass.   The 7520 can be sealed directly to 7052, and 7280 to 3320 with 7800 as an intermediate.   Sapphire windows are also reliably joined to metal sleeves by brazing.

9-7   Ceramic-to-metal Seals

There exist three main techniques for joining ceramics to metals: the ram or crunch seal, the Mo-Mn seal, and the active-metal seal. All of them require considerable investment and experience for reliable results.   The last two are used with various modifications.   To guarantee reliability, one or several samples of a new design should be tested by heat cycling.   High alumina ceramic is used in all seals.

The ram seal [Ref. (14)] is made only by RCA.   It is a purely mechanical seal.   A silver-plated Inconel X sleeve is forced over the tapered end of a ceramic tube and makes a high-pressure line contact with the corner of the ceramic where the taper meets the cylinder. The seal requires precision grinding and special tooling for the sleeve. It is rather expensive even when standard parts are used.

A typical Mo-Mn seal is made as follows: A mixture of 80 percent Mo and 20 percent Mn powder suspended in a volatile binder is sprayed onto the ceramic to a thickness of 0.001 to 0.002 in.   It is

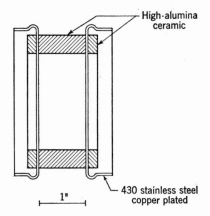

High-alumina ceramic

1"

430 stainless steel copper plated

Fig. 9-5   Washer-type ceramic-to-metal seal (active-metal type).

sintered in H_2 of 25°C dew point at about 1250 to 1500°C, depending on the softening temperature of the ceramic.   The layer is plated with copper or nickel and the metal (Kovar, copper) is brazed onto the layer in H_2.   Most companies selling ceramic-to-metal seals use the Mo-Mn process [Ref. (2)].

The active-metal process has been described by Kirchner (19). The ceramic is painted with titanium hydride, and a complete assembly, consisting of the painted ceramic, the brazing alloy, usually a foil of Ag-Cu eutectic, and the metal, is heated in a vacuum furnace.   The titanium hydride decomposes between 370 and 450°C, and the assembly is heated as rapidly as permissible to 850°C to perform the braze. The titanium renders the ceramic wettable by reduction of the aluminum oxide.   Suitable metals are Pt, 430 stainless steel (preferably copper-plated or copper-clad), Ta, Kovar, the alloys containing 42 or 46 percent Ni, balance iron (poor oxidation resistance at 400°C), and Cu if not baked.   If the metal is a sleeve around the ceramic, adequate pressure can be assured by wrapping tungsten wire (which has a lower expansion) around the sleeve at the sealing region.   This technique is also used to braze sapphire windows into metal sleeves. Figure 9-5 shows the washer-type seal which we favor because it is very strong.   At PPL it is used in sizes up to 19 in. in diameter.   The convolution makes the metal cup more flexible.   The titanium hydride process can also be applied to quartz.   The titanium renders the quartz wettable around 600°C, and good quartz seals to Invar can be made with soft solder or lead.   Braze seals to quartz are very difficult to make and are not reliable, at least when baked.

Kotowski and Muschaweck (20) measured the tensile strength of ceramic-to-ceramic seals sintered or brazed together by the Mo-Mn and Ti method, respectively, and found the same average value of 7000 psi. But these results cannot be generalized. They depend critically on all parameters such as amount of Ti, temperature of Mo-Mn sintering, etc. At PPL a bending moment of 400 ft-lb was applied to a $2\frac{3}{4}$-in.-diameter washer-type seal [see Fig. 5 of Ref. (11)], which produced a tensile stress of 3300 psi. The adjacent fusion weld opened up but the seal appeared to be undamaged.

9-8   Cleaning and Heat Treatment

These processes have been developed to a high degree of perfection by the electron-tube industry. Their cleaning methods are discussed in Refs. (3), (4), and (21). The requirements for vacuum systems are less stringent than those of sealed-off tubes containing elements such as oxide cathodes which have surfaces that can be poisoned. Cleaning is done mechanically, chemically, and electrolytically, by heat treatments (in air, H_2, or vacuum) and by ion bombardment. Mechanical cleaning does not require discussion. It may be mentioned that ultrasonic cleaning is used to dislodge dirt particles from places hard to reach, such as blind holes. This method is employed at PPL in exceptional cases only.

All parts should be degreased. Carbontetrachloride must not be used since it is very toxic. Trichlorethylene is considerably less toxic and as good a solvent. It is noninflammable. Commercial degreasers with automatic solvent purification are available. Otherwise the liquid must be changed frequently. Trichlorethylene must not be brought in contact with K, Na, Li, Ba, Sr, Ca, since highly explosive compounds are formed. Its vapor produces HCl and small amounts of phosgene at elevated temperatures (open flames, lighted cigarettes). Another effective solvent is ether (highly inflammable); acetone is less powerful.

Chemical and electrolytic cleaning is often used to remove oxide layers from surfaces. Specifications from Ref. (4) are given at the end of the chapter.

General information on plating can be found in Ref. (22), among other books. Plating is also discussed in Ref. (4). After plating, the quality of any critical plating has to be checked by a bake, preferably in vacuum. The surface must not blister.

Organic contaminants can be removed by baking in air at about 450°C or in wet hydrogen at about 900°C. Firing in H_2 reduces most surface oxides (except Cr_2O_3 and active-metal oxides) and removes some gases inside the metal, depending on the purity of the H_2. Tantalum must not be heated in H_2 since it dissolves the gas and becomes brittle. Copper must be oxygen-free. Otherwise steam forms at the grain boundaries and renders the metal brittle. So-called OFHC (oxygen-free high-conductivity) copper has to be used. Hydrogen is desorbed at 800°C.

When the metals or ceramics are fired and cooled in vacuum, gas is permanently removed since gas is not absorbed at room temperature. The effects of H_2 and vacuum firing were discussed in Sec. 3-10. Vacuum firing is necessary to degas parts that operate at elevated temperatures, such as ion sources in mass spectrometers. It is obvious that the vacuum firing is especially important in ultrahigh vacuum if high-temperature degassing in the system is impractical. The final degassing of surfaces in the system by pumping, baking, and ion bombardment is treated in Sec. 3-10.

At PPL, parts for thermonuclear machines are degreased only, unless they are badly oxidized or very dirty. They are baked overnight in a vacuum oven at about 500°C, to anneal the glass and to remove water and all other clogging substances from any leak prior to leak testing. Upon exposure to the atmosphere, CO_2 and H_2O are readsorbed. These gases are removed after assembly on the machine by a gas discharge.

SPECIFICATIONS FOR CHEMICAL AND ELECTROLYTIC CLEANING AND POLISHING [REF. (4)].

[NOTE: If fine fissures or pores (wire pressed into glass, porous ceramic) exist, it is difficult to remove the chemicals. Cleaning of these areas must be avoided.]

Electrolytic Cleaning of Tungsten and Molybdenum

The cleaning of tungsten and molybdenum can be carried out electrolytically. A step-down transformer (7.5 V, 200 W) is used; it is controlled with a variable transformer in the primary. The secondary is connected to a carbon electrode and to the work, immersed in a 20 percent potassium hydroxide solution, which can be used repeatedly.

[Since metal is removed by this method, tungsten and molybdenum filaments and heaters must not be cleaned excessively.]

1. Electrolyze as above.
2. Rinse in water.
3. Place in warm 50 percent hydrochloric acid inhibited with $\frac{1}{4}$ percent by volume of Rodine No. 50 (American Paint Co., Ambler, Pa.) for 5 min.

4. Rinse in running water to remove loose oxide.
5. Repeat steps 3 and 4 until oxide removal is complete.
6. Rinse thoroughly in water.
7. Rinse in clean methyl alcohol.
8. Dry in warm-air blast.

Electrolytic Nickel Cleaning Bath

Water	308 ml
Sulfuric acid	172 ml
Phosphoric acid	546 ml
Temperature:	60°C

Connect work as anode and use sufficient current density to cause gassing of the work. Use caution; this solution rapidly attacks and dissolves nickel.

Removal of Fluxes from Metal Parts after Soldering or Brazing

All soft-solder fluxes are more or less corrosive with time and should be carefully and thoroughly removed with appropriate solvents. The acid or chloride fluxes are removed by application of very hot water, preferably by boiling the piece in several changes. The oil or resin fluxes are removed by degreasing agents; rosin may be dissolved with methyl alcohol. The grease-paste fluxes, such as Nokorode, contain chlorides. Removal of this type of flux is accomplished by using a combination, in sequence, of degreasing agents and boiling water.

Brazing fluxes generally contain borax, boric acid, and sometimes fluorides and other compounds. These fluxes should be removed after brazing by immersing the work piece in several changes of boiling water. It may also be necessary to scrub with a wire brush or clean steel wool.

Removal of Heavy Oxide from Copper

1. Immerse piece in warm 75 percent hydrochloric acid inhibited by $\frac{3}{8}$ per cent by volume of Rodine No. 50 (American Paint Co., Ambler, Pa.).
2. Rinse thoroughly with water.
3. Dry.

Electrolytic Polishing of Copper

Orthophosphoric acid 50 percent in water.
  Anode: sheet nickel
  Large anode-to-cathode-area ratio
  Heavy current density, a-c or d-c

Electrolytic Polishing of Copper, Brass, Bronze [Ref. (22), 1949 Edition]

A. Phosphoric acid   63 percent by volume
   Water   37 percent by volume
   Current density 0.02–0.05 amp/in.^{2}
   Temperature: 20°C
   Time: 5 min
B. Phosphoric acid   58 percent by volume
   Water   42 percent by volume
   Current density: 0.5–0.7 amp/in.^{2}
   Temperature: 20°C
   Time: 10–15 min

Cleaning of Oxidized Iron

1. Place material in warm 50 percent hydrochloric acid for approximately 5 min to remove oxides. The hydrochloric acid should be inhibited with $\frac{1}{4}$ percent by volume of Rodine No. 50 (American Paint Co., Ambler, Pa.).
2. Rinse thoroughly in water.
3. Dry.

Pickling of Stainless Steel

Since the scale that forms on stainless steel is very resistant to acid, it is often advisable to pickle in two operations: the first to loosen the scale; the second for removal or for brightening the surface. If only a light scale is present, the scale-loosening treatment may be omitted. Suitable inhibitors should be added to minimize pitting of the metal.

Loosening Scale on Stainless Steel (All acids specified are concentrated).

A. Sulfuric acid   90 g/liter
   Temperature: 85°C
B. Sulfuric acid   1 liter
   Hydrochloric acid   1 liter
   Water   8 liters
   Temperature: 55–60°C

Removing Scale on Stainless Steel

Nitric acid   1 liter
Hydrofluoric acid   1.5 liters
Water   2.5 liters
   Temperature: 50–65°C

Passivation Solutions for Stainless Steel

Passivation or immunization should be employed after any pickling operation on stainless steel. [Passivation reduces oxidation during a bake in the presence of water vapor. Stainless steel also becomes passivated by exposure to the atmosphere for several weeks.] Effectiveness of this treatment may be tested by application of a copper sulfate solution, slightly acidified; no copper will be deposited on passivated surfaces.

A. Nitric acid   1 liter
    Water   4 liters
        Temperature: 50°C
        Time: 20 min
B. Nitric acid   1 liter
    Water   1 liter
        Temperature: 20°C
        Time: 1–2 hr

Electropolish for Stainless Steel (Armco Steel Corporation)

Citric acid   50–60 parts by volume
Sulfuric acid   15 parts by volume
Water, to make   100 parts
    Temperature: 85°–94°C
    Current density: 0.5–1 amp/in.^{2}
    Voltage: 6–12
    Cathode: copper or 18-8 stainless steel
(Work is made positive.)

Cleaning Solutions for Glass and Tantalum

A. Potassium dichromate   sat. sol. 35 cc
   Sulfuric acid   conc. 1 liter
B. (Preferred because of absence of alkaline salts likely to remain in crevices)
   Chromium trioxide CrO_3 (chromic) saturated solution in hot concentrated sulfuric acid
   Slowly stir the acid into the chromate or trioxide solution.

Use both solutions at 110°C. The solution should be red in color for best results. If it is muddy or greenish, the solution should be discarded.
    [Glass can also be cleaned with dilute HF which dissolves the glass surface.]

REFERENCES

(1) Max Knoll, "Materials and Processes of Electron Devices," 484 pp., Springer-Verlag OHG, Berlin, 1959.

(2) Walter H. Kohl, "Materials and Techniques for Electron Tubes," 638 pp., Reinhold Publishing Corporation, New York, 1960.

(3) Werner Espe, "Materials Technology of High Vacuum Technique": vol. 1, Metals and Materials with Metallic Conduction, 916 pp.; vol. 2, Silicates, 730 pages; vol. 3, Auxiliary Materials, 542 pp. VEB Deutscher Verlag der Wissenschaften, Berlin, 1961. (In German.)

(4) "Tube Laboratory Manual," 132 pp., 2d ed., Massachusetts Institute of Technology, Research Laboratory of Electronics, Cambridge, Mass., 1956.

(5) E. L. Wheeler, "Scientific Glass Blowing," Interscience Publishers, Inc., New York, 1958.

(6) G. Martin, *Rev. Sci. Instr.*, vol. 34, p. 707, 1963.

(7) "Brazing Manual," Committee on Brazing and Soldering of American Welding Society, Reinhold Publishing Corporation, New York, 1955.

(8) A. J. Wall and D. R. Milner, *J. Inst. Metals*, vol. 90, p. 394, 1962.

(9) E. G. Huschke, Jr., 1958 *Vacuum Symp. Trans.*, p. 50, 1959.

(10) H. Kronberger, *Proc. Inst. Mech. Engrs.* (*London*), vol. 172, p. 113, 1958.

(11) D. J. Grove, 1958 *Vacuum Symp. Trans.*, p. 9, 1959.

(12) W. L. Wyman, *Welding J.* (*N.Y.*), vol. 37, res. suppl., p. 49s, 1958.

(13) J. L. Solomon, *Welding J.* (*N.Y.*), vol. 41, p. 719, 1962.

(14) G. Lewin and R. Mark, 1958 *Vacuum Symp. Trans.*, p. 44, 1959.

(15) L. F. Oldfield, *Glastech. Ber.*, Spec. Volume, *Intern. Congr. on Glass*, p. V/16, 1959.

(16) B. B. Graves, *Rev. Sci. Instr.*, vol. 31, p. 349, 1960.

(17) R. A. Anderson and E. E. Stepp, *Rev. Sci. Instr.*, vol. 33, p. 119, 1962.

(18) F. W. Martin, Internal Report, Corning Glass Works, Corning, N.Y., 1958.

(19) K. Kirchner, 1963 *Vacuum Symp. Trans.*, p. 170, 1964.

(20) J. Kotowski and J. Muschaweck, *Vakuum Tech.*, vol. 10, p. 141, 1961.

(21) Cleaning of Electronic Device Components and Materials, *ASTM Special Tech. Publ.* 246, 1959.

(22) Metal Finishing, Metals and Plastics Publications, Inc., Westwood, N.J. (Published annually).

Vacuum Systems 10

10-1 System Requirements and Design

To design a system, the following must be known:

1. Volume and shape of vacuum chamber
2. Base pressure and pumpdown time
3. Gas desorption without operation
4. Gas desorption during operation
5. Special requirements, e.g., no oil vapor, nonmagnetic, operating temperature, instrumentation, etc.

We shall discuss items 2 and 3 in a general manner; items 4 and 5 can be illustrated only by means of examples.

The first phase is the pumpdown from atmospheric pressure to about 10^{-1} torr. The various forepumps were treated in Sec. 6-1. Typically a rotary pump is used. Its speed is approximately constant for this range. The flow in the pump line is in the viscous-flow range, and the conductance should be large enough not to throttle the speed of the forepump. The pumpdown time to 10^{-1} torr can be calculated by means of Eq. (4-7), disregarding the outgassing $(P \gg P_u)$. Outgassing has to be taken into consideration only in exceptional cases, when the pumping speed is unusually low or the surface area very large and the gassing rate high. Another requirement is that the forepump speed S_F be large enough to pump the gas load Q without increasing the forepressure P_F beyond the limit P_{FL} of the high-vacuum pump or $P_F = Q/S_F < P_{FL}$; see the example in Sec. 4-1.

The next region is the 10^{-1} to 10^{-4} torr range. Gassing begins to be noticeable. The impedance of the pipe is in the transition range and not negligible. If the high-vacuum pump is a diffusion pump, the pump functions but its speed is not constant; it increases from a low value with decreasing pressures until the rated speed is reached around 10^{-3} torr. If higher pumping speeds are required in this range, as in some metallurgical applications, an ejector pump or a Roots pump can be used. Only approximate calculations are possible for average values of conductance and pumping speed.

Gassing of surfaces was discussed in Sec. 3-10. It is caused by (1) leaks, (2) permeation, and desorption of (3) absorbed and (4) adsorbed gas. At these pressures, items 1 and 2 are negligible in a well-built system. With the possible exception of polymers, item 3 is also negligible. The initial gassing due to item 4 is the most important one. The gassing rate depends on the history of the surfaces, e.g., whether they were exposed only to dry nitrogen or to the atmosphere. Fortunately, if the system is designed to operate below 10^{-5} torr, the pumpdown time from 10^{-1} to 10^{-3} torr is usually fast enough to be of no importance.

Below 10^{-3} torr is usually the molecular-flow range. Most pumps (e.g., diffusion pumps, molecular drag pumps, condensation pumps) have constant speed. The equilibrium pressure is given by the gas load, $P = \Sigma Q/S$. Gassing rates can vary several orders of magnitude while the speed of a pumping system can be changed scarcely more than one order of magnitude, unless pumping of the system wall is substituted for a pump.

A leak as small as 10^{-9} torr liter/sec can readily be found and repaired. If $S = 10$ liters/sec, the pressure is limited to 10^{-10} torr. Such a leak may be tolerable in a system operated at 10^{-8} torr. Permeation through elastomer gaskets can be a large source of gas (see Sec. 7-3). Therefore we prefer metal gaskets for all applications where pressures below 10^{-7} torr have to be attained. Typically, a bakeout reduces the gassing rate about 10^6 times (see Table 3-11). In a smaller system with a surface area of 1000 cm² the gas load would be 10^{-11} torr liter/sec after such a bake. High pumping speed is unnecessary unless an extremely low pressure is needed. If a small portion of the system has not been baked, the pressure will be much higher. But ultrahigh vacuum is attained with diffusion pumps, despite the fact that baking up to the top vapor jet is not possible. Only the traps are baked. Baking is often cumbersome, especially with large systems. After a few days of pumping, the gassing rate of metals approaches 10^{-10} torr liter/sec cm². With an area of 1000 cm² and a pumping speed of 50 liters/sec, pressures in the 10^{-9} torr range are easily reached. Systems have been built which achieve ultrahigh vacuum without baking. The pressure in ultrahigh vacuum can be limited by imperfect pumps, e.g., because of back diffusion (diffusion pump) or reemission (ion pump).

10-2 *Examples of Vacuum Systems*

Design requirements can be met in different ways, and it is often not obvious which is the best design, a situation not uncommon in engineering. In the following we shall give instructive examples of vacuum systems to demonstrate how the information given on the preceding pages is used to arrive at solutions for a variety of vacuum problems.

Figure 10-1 shows a commercial pumping system of 2-in. manifold diameter for minimum pressures around 10^{-6} torr. A vacuum chamber (not shown) is connected to the port. For the first pump-down, valves HV, FV, and RV are all open and the whole system is evacuated by the forepump until the thermocouple gages show a pressure of about 5×10^{-2} torr. Then the diffusion pump is started. Liquid N_2 is poured into the trap when the pressure is 10^{-4} torr. To vent the vacuum chamber only, valves HV and RV are closed and the vent valve is opened. For reevacuation, the vent valve and valve FV are closed and valve RV is opened. When the pressure on thermocouple gage TC-2 has reached 5×10^{-2} torr, valve RV is closed and valves FV and HV are opened. During standby operation, valves HV and RV are closed while valve FV is open and the trap is warmed up to pump out condensed vapors and return condensed oil to the pump. The trap must not be cold when exposed to the atmosphere, in order to avoid excessive condensation of water vapor.

Systems that are not continuously guarded (and preferably even those) should have automatic safety features; in particular, all gage filaments should be shut off automatically when the pressure rises above a certain value (usually 10^{-3} torr), and the diffusion pump should likewise be shut off when the pressure on gage TC-1 approaches the limiting forevacuum pressure, when the wall of the pump becomes

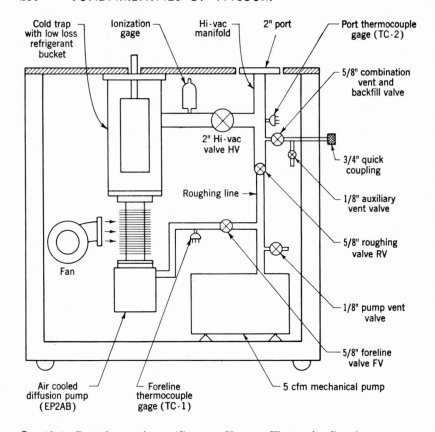

Fig. 10-1   Pumping station.   (Courtesy Vacuum Electronics Corp.)

too hot because the cooling fan or the cooling water fails, or when the forepump stops.   Such safety devices are commercially available. The forepump is mounted on vibration dampers and connected to the system through a piece of plastic or rubber hose to prevent the transfer of vibration to the pumping system.   If the gas load is small, a ballast tank can be substituted for the forepump after pumpdown to maintain the forevacuum pressure below the critical limit and the forepump is valved off and shut off.   Sometimes a trap is inserted into the fore-vacuum line to arrest forepump oil.   Its efficiency is poor in the viscous-flow range.

Similar pumping stations are often used in conjunction with a bell jar.   Many different types are marketed.   The performance of such systems, baked and unbaked, was discussed by Holland in several papers [(1), (2)].   Figure 10-2 shows the pressure as a function of

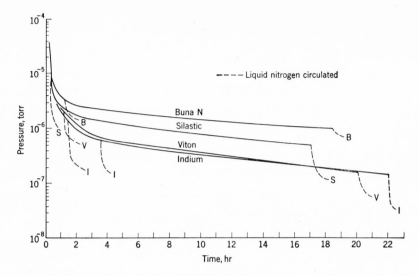

Fig. 10-2 Pumpdown characteristics of a metal bell jar with Meissner trap for various gasket materials. (From L. Holland and S. K. Bateman, 1961 *Vacuum Symp. Trans.*, p. 1201, 1962.)

pumping time for various gasket materials with and without a so-called Meissner trap. This is a liquid-nitrogen trap inside the bell jar near the base plate. The stainless steel bell jar was exhausted with an oil diffusion pump. Rivera et al. (3) published pumpdown curves for bell jars made of glass and metal, with sputter-ion pumps. Some of their curves are shown on Fig. 10-3. After 8 hr of pumping, the gassing rates of the glass bell jars were 1.4×10^{-9} and 3×10^{-9} torr liter/sec cm^2 and the rate of the stainless-steel bell jar was 1.7×10^{-9} torr liter/sec cm^2, in agreement with Table 3-11. They noticed also the beneficial effect of exposure to dry N_2 instead of the atmosphere.

Figure 10-4 is the schematic of a vacuum brazing furnace built in the PPL to braze metal ends onto a large ceramic cylinder 44 in. long and 19 in. in diameter by the titanium hydride process (4). (See Sec. 9-7.) The furnace heater is located on the axis inside the upright ceramic cylinder and the cylinder is surrounded with four heat shields. This accounts for the large surface area. The forepump evacuates to 0.5 torr in 20 min; then the trap is filled and the diffusion pump started. A pressure in the 10^{-4} torr range is reached in another 15 min. In heating up, the heat shields are gradually heated from the inside out. The gage pressure varies only slightly; it rises from 1.5×10^{-4} to 2.5×10^{-4} torr at 800°C furnace temperature. This is too high a

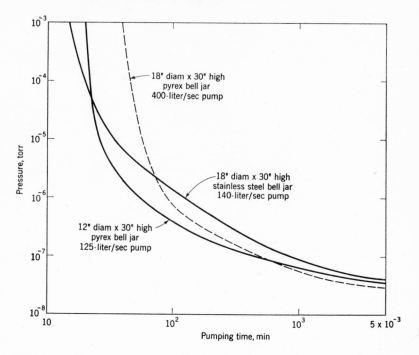

Fig. 10-3 Pumpdown characteristics of glass and metal bell jars pumped with sputter-ion pumps after preevacuation with mechanical pump. (From M. Rivera, R. Zaphiropoulos, and D. Harra, 1960 *Vacuum Symp. Trans.*, p. 206, 1961.)

pressure.   The titanium coating, which renders the ceramic wettable, oxidized and the seals leaked.

Various schemes, e.g., titanium gettering, were considered to increase the pumping speed.   Finally it was decided to add external heaters to the bell jar and bake the whole system, except the water-cooled base plate and the lower rim of the bell jar with the Neoprene gasket, at 350°C by energizing the external and internal heater simultaneously.   This temperature is below the dissociation temperature of the titanium hydride.   When raising the temperature further, the hydrogen is released around 400°C and active titanium remains.   This procedure reduced the pressure a factor of 3 and good seals were produced.   After a braze, the pressure drops to 10^{-7} torr when the furnace has cooled down.

There exists a continued interest in small glass ultrahigh-vacuum systems as initially built by Alpert (5).   These systems had glass diffusion pumps and copper traps.   A more recent version was

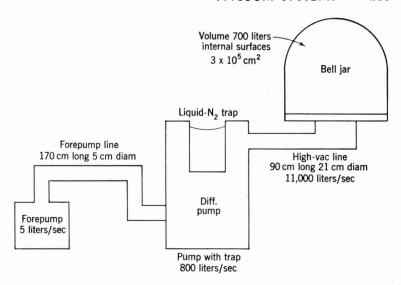

Volume 700 liters
internal surfaces
3×10^5 cm^2

Bell jar

Liquid-N$_2$ trap

Forepump line
170 cm long 5 cm diam

High-vac line
90 cm long 21 cm diam
11,000 liters/sec

Diff.
pump

Forepump
5 liters/sec

Pump with trap
800 liters/sec

Fig. 10-4   Schematic of vacuum brazing furnace.

described by Redhead et al. (6).   This system is shown in Fig. 10-5*a*
and its gas inlet and pumping section in Fig. 10-5*b*.   The basic principle of these systems is to reduce the gassing rate by baking rather than
by enhanced pumping speed.   This is the preferred approach for small
systems (5 liters) and/or pressures below 10^{-10} torr.   The parts are
mounted on a Transite-covered frame on which the oven with the
heaters is placed for baking.   The glass tubes are rendered slightly
flexible in some systems by insertion of U bends to allow differential
motion during heating.   Pyrex 7740 glass is used; it can be baked at
450°C.   The glass flask with the test gas is not baked, in order to
avoid desorption of impurities.   The system is portable and attached
to the external pumping system for initial evacuation and degassing
only.

The authors give a detailed description of the system processing.
An adsorption pump is preferably used as forepump to avoid the
danger of contamination by oil.   The high-vacuum pump is an
inverted-magnetron pump (see Sec. 6-5).   The adsorption forepump
is a brass tube filled with 150 cm^3 of Linde Molecular Sieve X13 and
immersed in liquid nitrogen.   A 2-liter volume is evacuated to
5×10^{-3} torr in 12 min.   Then the sputter-ion pump of 5 liters/sec
speed evacuates the system to a pressure in the 10^{-6} torr range and is
kept operating while the system is baked overnight.   After the bake,
internal parts that operate above bakeout temperature and/or are

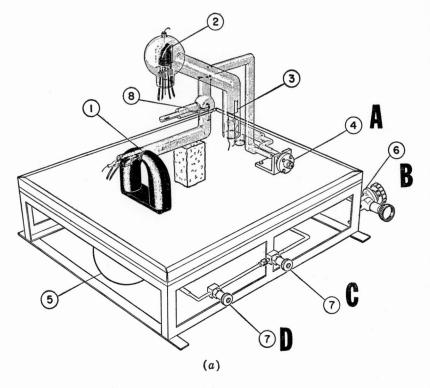

Fig. 10-5a Small glass ultrahigh-vacuum system. (1) Inverted-magnetron pump; (2) ionization gage; (3) desorption filament; (4) bakeable metal valve (valve A); (5) gas bottle; (6) Teflon seat valve (valve B); (7) gas-introduction valves (valves C and D); (8) glass valve. (From P. A. Redhead, E. V. Kornelsen, and J. P. Hobson, *Can. J. Phys.*, vol. 40, p. 1814, 1962.)

subjected to ion or electron bombardment are degassed at elevated temperature. When the pressure has dropped to its initial value, Ti is evaporated, valve A is closed, and the inverted-magnetron pump is started. With 7740 glass the ultimate vacuum is limited to 5×10^{-11} torr by He permeation. The ultimate pressure is 3×10^{-13} torr when the envelope is made of 1720 glass [Ref. (6a)]. Figure 10-6 shows a typical pressure-time curve. The pressure surge at the beginning of the bake, like gassing in general, is more pronounced in a new system that has not been baked previously. In this case, the gas load may be excessive for the sputter-ion pump and the forepump has to be used again for a while. Pumping with only a forepump is adequate during the bake.

Steinherz (7) describes larger high-vacuum systems. They are

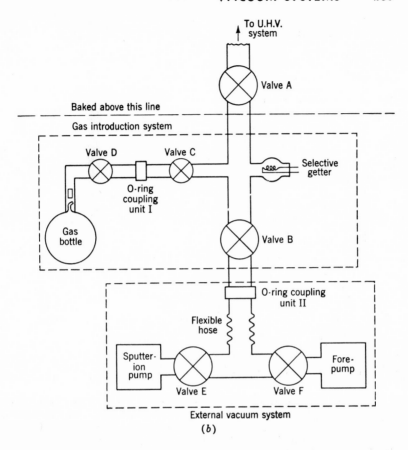

Fig. 10-5b Schematic of external pumping system for the system of Fig. 10-5a. (From P. A. Redhead, E. V. Kornelsen, and J. P. Hobson, *Can. J. Phys.*, vol. 40, p. 1814, 1962.)

three cylindrical stainless-steel chambers of 2500- to 7000-liter volume with large doors with rubber gaskets at each end, pumped with oil diffusion pumps equipped with two liquid-nitrogen traps. Typically, the pressure drops from 10^{-5} to 5×10^{-7} torr in 2 hr of pumping with the diffusion pumps. Then the traps are filled and, after 4 hr more, a pressure of 2×10^{-8} torr is reached. The pressure is 1.2×10^{-8} torr after a day. After a few hours, rubber and metal gassing are comparable. If the metal degassing is rendered negligible by a mild bake, the pressure drops into the 10^{-9} torr range. All the gassing comes from the unbaked gaskets. Further improvement is gained by refrigeration of the gaskets. As mentioned in Sec. 7-3, Shabeck (8) attained

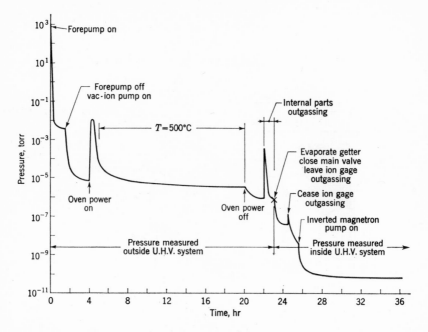

Fig. 10-6 Typical pressure-time curve during processing of a new system of the type shown in Fig. 10-5a. (From P. A. Redhead, E. V. Kornelsen, and J. P. Hobson, *Can. J. Phys.*, vol. 40, p. 1814, 1962.)

pressures in the 10^{-11} torr range by using refrigerated butyl-rubber gaskets in an otherwise baked system. The main source of gas is probably the metal adjacent to the gaskets which is not baked sufficiently. We therefore recommend bakeable metal gaskets.

The pumping speed of separate pumps is limited by the conductance of the connecting pipe. Higher pumping speeds are obtained by using part of the chamber wall as either an adsorption or a condensation pump. Adsorption pumps have limited capacity unless the sorption film is renewed. We mentioned in Sec. 6-4 the paper by Hunt et al. (9), who pumped with molybdenum films evaporated onto the chamber walls. In an 85-liter volume they had a pumping surface area of 8×10^3 cm². This gave an initial pumping speed of 10^5 liters/sec for H_2. The dependence of the pumping speed on the type of gas and the temperature has been discussed in Chap. 6.

Condensation pumping is of special interest if high gas loads are encountered in a limited space. An extreme case is an ion or plasma rocket test facility described by Keller (10). A typical test chamber is shown in Fig. 10-7. It is 16 ft long and has a diameter of 5 ft. It is

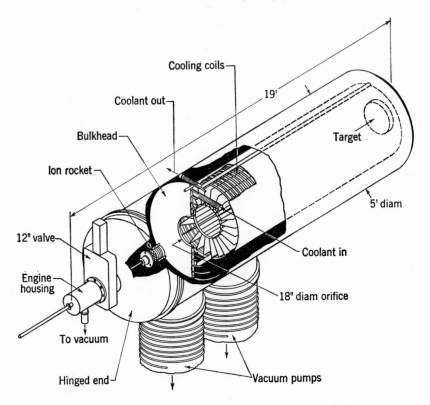

Fig. 10-7   Plasma rocket test facility.   (From T. A. Keller, 1960 *Vacuum Symp. Trans.*, p. 161, 1961.)

pumped with two 32-in. diffusion pumps which are backed by an ejector and a mechanical pump.   The rocket exhaust, e.g., Cs ions, hits a water-cooled target at the other end, is reflected, and is gradually thermalized and condensed at the cooled fins of the condenser.   The pressure must be in the low 10^{-6} torr range or less to minimize collisions of the exhaust beam with the residual gas.   Tests showed that lowering the temperature of the condenser to $-196°C$ greatly improved its performance.   A typical pressure plot is shown in Fig. 10-8. Cryopumping with liquid He is sometimes used in small ultrahigh-vacuum systems.

A difficult problem is the design of vacuum chambers for proton synchrotron accelerators.   These chambers have fairly large rectangular cross sections: 10×80 in. in Nimrod [Ref. (11)], 4×19 in. in Saturn [Ref. (12)], and 3×12 in. in the Princeton machine [Ref. (13)]. The chambers are sections of a doughnut with a radius of 80, 28, and

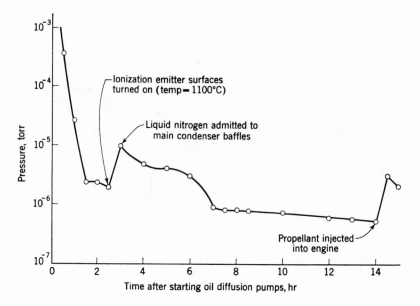

Fig. 10-8   Typical pressure-time history of test facility of Fig. 10-7 with engine in tank.   (From T. A. Keller, 1960 *Vacuum Symp. Trans.*, p. 161, 1961.)

41 ft, respectively.   The maximum pressure is around 10^{-6} torr, and the pumping speed is rather small, since only a limited number of pumping ports can be provided.   The wall must be thin to reduce the magnet gap, and it must be a poor conductor to avoid eddy currents which generate heat and distort the magnetic field.   Finally, the gassing of the wall must not increase under radiation.

The design adopted for Nimrod is a double-wall chamber made of molded sections of glass-cloth-reinforced epoxy.   The pole pieces are located inside the outer vessel.   They support the vessel and are screwed to the magnet through vacuum seals.   The wall thicknesses of the outer and inner chamber are $\frac{1}{8}$ and $\frac{1}{4}$ in.   The pressure in the outer chamber does not exceed 1 torr.   The inner vessel is lined with stainless-steel foil 0.002 in. thick to reduce gassing and avoid accumulation of charges.   In Saturn and the Princeton machine closely spaced metal laminations attached to a rigid front frame are used, as shown in Fig. 10-9.   The space between the laminations is filled with epoxy.   Saturn also has a stainless-steel liner on the inside to reduce gassing.   It consists of a sandwich of two 0.008-in.-thick stainless-steel sheets with glass-cloth-reinforced epoxy between.   The metal sections are 5 in. wide and 0.05 in. apart.   Stainless steel and exposed

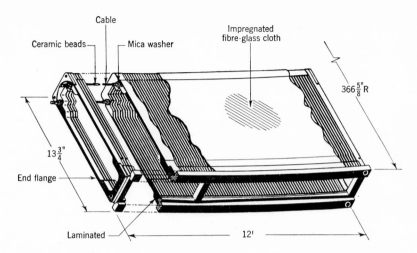

Cable

Ceramic beads

Mica washer

Impregnated
fibre-glass cloth

$366\frac{5}{8}"$R

$13\frac{3}{4}"$

End flange

Laminated

12'

Fig. 10-9 Initial design of vacuum chamber of the Princeton-Pennsylvania proton synchrotron. (From L. Seidlitz, T. Tang, D. L. Collins, and M. Szekely, 1959 *Vacuum Symp. Trans.*, p. 150, 1960.)

epoxy produce about equal gas loads since an epoxy surface has 100 times the gassing rate of stainless steel. Use of stainless-steel sheets in the Princeton accelerator also was contemplated. But the maximum permissible thickness was 0.0005 in. and the application proved to be too difficult, although the value of the liner was apparent in a few sample sections to which it had been added [Ref. (14)]. Hence a barrier to the permeation of water vapor was introduced by placing glass ribbon of 0.003 in. thickness on the outside of the chamber between layers of glass cloth and resin. In addition, the pumping speed for water was increased by attaching a reentrant $\frac{1}{4}$-in.-diameter stainless-steel tube containing liquid N_2 to the inside surface of the front frame.

Finally, let us look at another sophisticated installation, the vacuum system of the model C stellarator, a thermonuclear research machine in Princeton, N.J. Vacuum systems for thermonuclear research in general were discussed by Lewin (15), who also described an earlier version of this machine. These machines contain a high-temperature H_2 or D_2 plasma inside the vacuum space. The influx of impurities and cold gas due to wall gassing must be kept low, even under intense photon and particle bombardment emanating from the plasma. The vacuum system made of stainless steel is shown schematically in Fig. 10-10. The so-called divertor has rotational symmetry. The discharge tube has a 20-cm diameter. The volume of the tube is

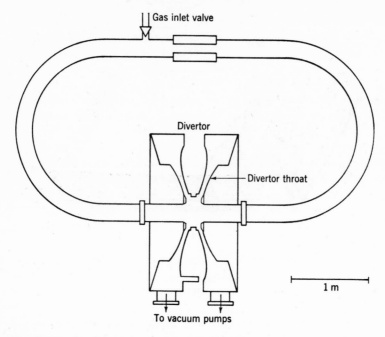

Fig. 10-10   Vacuum system of the C stellarator.   (From G. Lewin and D. Mullaney, 1963 *Vacuum Symp. Trans.*, p. 176, 1964.)

340 liters and that of the divertor 1300 liters.   Two identical sets of vacuum pumps are used.   Each aggregate has two liquid-N_2 traps and two 10-in. Hg diffusion pumps in series, with a common forepump of 100-liter/sec speed.   The pumping speed of each aggregate for H_2, the gas primarily used, is 900 liters/sec.   The pumping speed is limited by the impedance of the discharge tube.

The system is made in accordance with ultrahigh-vacuum practice and can be baked at 450°C.   Although the wall gassing is low after a bake and the base pressure is in the 10^{-10} torr range, the walls are still covered with gas and a bake is a complicated operation. Hence the tube is cleaned by a gas discharge usually in hydrogen. This discharge, as well as the main operation, must be pulsed.   Normally some of the gas released from the wall would be immediately readsorbed at the cleaned, active wall.   The amount depends on the relative sorption for H_2 and the impurities and is appreciable.   This effect is reduced by the divertor action.   Magnetic fields, necessary in such machines to confine the plasma, are arranged in such a manner as to divert the outermost layer of the plasma into the divertor.   Gas released from the wall is ionized in the outer layer of the plasma and transferred to the divertor before it penetrates deeper into the plasma. Since the conductance of the divertor throat is large, most of it streams back into the tube and only 9 percent is pumped out.   But even this is a significant amount, when discharge cleaning.   Rapid pulsing comparable to or faster than the time constant of the divertor-throat combination (0.07 sec) or d-c operation would improve the situation.

Even more important is the divertor action during the operation.   The backstreaming rate from the divertor into the tube is small enough that no appreciable influx of impurities occurs during the operational pulse of 5 msec.   It is equally important that the divertor not contain any H_2 which would back stream into the discharge tube during operation.   Therefore the gas inlet valve (see Fig. 7-16) is pulsed.   It releases a short burst of gas during the open time of 15 to 50 msec and the discharge is started before the gas has propagated into the divertor [Ref. (16)].

In a typical operation after exposure of the vacuum system to the atmosphere, the forepump pumps down to 2×10^{-2} torr in 10 min. Then the booster pumps begin to pump, and $\frac{1}{2}$ hr later the main pumps are started.   After 1 hr of operation of the main pumps the pressure is 10^{-4} torr, with a large amount of Hg vapor present despite the refrigerated baffles.   After filling of the liquid-N_2 traps, the pressure drops to 10^{-6} torr.   Then a pulsed gas discharge is run for about 6 hr usually in hydrogen.   The next morning the pressure is in the 10^{-8} torr range.   Most of the gas is H_2.   The pressure of impurities (CO, H_2O) is around 10^{-9} torr.

REFERENCES

(1) L. Holland, *Vacuum*, vol. 13, p. 173, 1963.

(2) L. Holland and S. K. Bateman, 1961 *Vacuum Symp. Trans.*, p. 1201, 1962.

(3) M. Rivera, R. Zaphiropoulos, and D. Harra, 1960 *Vacuum Symp. Trans.*, p. 206, 1961.

(4) K. Kirchner, 1963 *Vacuum Symp. Trans.*, p. 170, 1964.

(5) D. Alpert, "Encyclopedia of Physics," vol. 12, p. 658, Springer-Verlag OHG, Berlin, 1958.

(6) P. A. Redhead, E. V. Kornelsen, and J. P. Hobson, *Can. J. Phys.*, vol. 40, p. 1814, 1962.

(6a) P. A. Redhead, private communication.

(7) H. A. Steinherz, "Handbook of High Vacuum Engineering," p. 203, Reinhold Publishing Corporation, New York, 1963.

(8) J. C. L. Shabeck, Jr., 1962 *Vacuum Symp. Trans.*, p. 278, 1963.

(9) A. L. Hunt, Ch. C. Damm, and E. C. Popp, *J. Appl. Phys.*, vol. 32, p. 1937, 1961.

(10) T. A. Keller, 1960 *Vacuum Symp. Trans.*, p. 161, 1961.

(11) S. H. Cross, *Vacuum*, vol. 10, p. 86, 1960.

(12) G. Armand, R. Le Quinio, and F. Prevot, *L'Onde Elec.*, vol. 39, p. 512, 1959.

(13) L. Seidlitz, T. Tang, D. L. Collins, and M. Szekely, 1959 *Vacuum Symp. Trans.*, p. 150, 1960.

(14) N. Oser and R. Westwig, 1963 *Vacuum Symp. Trans.*, p. 72, 1964.

(15) G. Lewin, *Vide*, no. 98, p. 120, 1962.

(16) G. Lewin and D. Mullaney, 1963 *Vacuum Symp. Trans.*, p. 176, 1964.

Index